# Test Bank

to accompany

# The Art of Public Speaking

## NINTH EDITION

Stephen E. Lucas
*University of Wisconsin*

with

Amy R. Slagell
*Iowa State University*

Boston   Burr Ridge, IL   Dubuque, IA   Madison, WI   New York   San Francisco   St. Louis
Bangkok   Bogotá   Caracas   Kuala Lumpur   Lisbon   London   Madrid   Mexico City
Milan   Montreal   New Delhi   Santiago   Seoul   Singapore   Sydney   Taipei   Toronto

The McGraw·Hill Companies

## McGraw-Hill Higher Education

Test Bank to accompany
THE ART OF PUBLIC SPEAKING
Stephen E. Lucas

Published by McGraw-Hill, an imprint of The McGraw-Hill Companies, Inc., 1221 Avenue of the Americas,
New York, NY 10020. Copyright © 2007, 2004, 2001, 1998, 1995, 1992 by Stephen E. Lucas.
All rights reserved.

1 2 3 4 5 6 7 8 9 0 CUS/CUS 0 9 8 7 6 5

ISBN-13: 978-0-07-321637-9
ISBN-10:     0-07-321637-2

www.mhhe.com

# Contents

# Preface

This *Test Bank* contains 2,064 true-false, multiple-choice, short-answer, and essay questions for use in conjunction with the ninth edition of *The Art of Public Speaking*. Organized to correspond with each chapter of the textbook, the exam questions are presented in Part Two of the *Test Bank*. They are also available on CD-ROM for computerized test construction.

To provide as much flexibility as possible in constructing examinations, there is deliberate overlap among the questions. In deciding which to use, instructors should take care to avoid such oversights as a multiple-choice question that gives away the answer to a true-false or short-answer question, or an essay question that covers essentially the same ground as a true-false, short-answer, or multiple-choice question. You will also find that quite a few of the review questions at the end of each chapter in the book work well for quizzes and examinations—as do some of the Exercises for Critical Thinking in the *Instructor's Manual* if they are not otherwise assigned.

In addition, this *Test Bank* offers several special features. First, it provides two preconstructed quizzes for each chapter of *The Art of Public Speaking*. One quiz is composed of true-false questions, the other of multiple-choice questions. These quizzes can be found in Part Three of the *Test Bank*. Answers to the quizzes are in Part Four.

Second, I have constructed three complete sample final examinations based on *The Art of Public Speaking*. Presented in Part Five of the *Test Bank*, these exams are designed to illustrate different approaches to testing and evaluation. The first exam is a one-hour test composed exclusively of multiple-choice questions. The second is a two-hour exam containing a mixture of multiple-choice, short-answer, brief essay, and longer essay questions. The third is a two-hour essay involving the analysis of a speech.

Third, in keeping with my aim to provide as much assistance as possible for instructors, Part One of the *Test Bank* presents a guest essay by Anita Vangelisti of the University of Texas on test construction and assessment. Prepared exclusively to accompany *The Art of Public Speaking*, this essay discusses the functions of testing for students and instructors, the different levels of learning one can seek to assess when constructing examinations, and the strengths and weaknesses of various kinds of exam questions. It also addresses issues related to the comprehensiveness, difficulty, and length of exams.

Finally, it is important to know that the exam questions in this *Test Bank* are different from the Study Questions on the Student CD-ROM that accompanies this edition of *The Art of Public Speaking*. The Study Questions have been composed to help students review the book and prepare for exams, but they do not duplicate the questions in this Test Bank.

# Part One

# Test Construction
# and Assessment

# Test Construction and Assessment

Anita L. Vangelisti

Few teachers regard constructing and grading exams as the most enjoyable aspect of their job. Some see testing as a necessary but uninspiring part of teaching; others see it as boring, tedious, or even oppressive. Yet most are unwilling to cast aside testing. Why? Because testing serves important functions for teachers and students alike.

Teachers use tests above all as a way of gauging what students have learned in a course. Although some people may perform poorly on a given exam due to illness, personal problems, or other factors not immediately related to course content, the accumulation of test scores over a full quarter or semester usually provides a reliable index of what students have learned. In addition, tests provide information that instructors can use to improve their teaching. For example, if a test reveals that most students are having difficulty with particular aspects of the course, the instructor should think about ways she or he can present those aspects more effectively.

For students, well-constructed tests provide a stimulus for learning, an important form of feedback concerning their progress in a course, and a guide to help them refine their study habits. In an ideal world, all students would keep up with reading assignments and review their class notes on a regular basis. The reality, however, is that tests stimulate students to digest course material they might otherwise overlook. Studying for exams is one way students learn. In addition, some very important learning takes place after an exam, when students review the items they "missed." It may become clear, for instance, that a student understood the material presented in lecture and class discussion, but did not give sufficient attention to material in the textbook. Knowing this can help the student do better on subsequent exams. Students can also use test results to uncover problems in their study habits. They may discover that they need to devote more time to studying, that they need to study at a more in-depth level, that they need to write out answers to sample questions as part of their studying, or even that they need to meet with an academic counselor to review their study methods.

If exams are to function effectively for either teachers or students, however, they must be carefully constructed. Designing a good exam takes considerable time, effort, and resourcefulness. Above all, it requires a clear understanding of one's educational objectives and of the kinds of exam questions one can use to achieve those objectives. In this essay we shall focus on both of these issues. In doing so, we shall give special attention to the public speaking course and to the kinds of exam questions in the test bank to *The Art of Public Speaking*.

## Educational Objectives

One of the many challenges of constructing an exam is to design questions that reflect the full scope of the instructor's educational goals. Although most teachers want students to be able to recall important information from reading, lecture, and discussion, they typically have other instructional goals in mind as well. In public speaking courses, for instance, teachers usually want students to identify the kinds of evidence used by speakers to support their claims. But they also want students to know which kind of evidence might work best in a given situation and to be able to evaluate the quality of particular pieces of evidence in a speech.

Because instructors usually have multiple learning goals for their students, it is important to construct tests that assess multiple levels of learning. There are several taxonomies of learning in the education literature. Teachers can use these taxonomies to help ensure that the educational goals of their courses match the test questions they use to gauge what students have learned. The most widely used taxonomy for this purpose is Bloom's taxonomy of educational objectives. This taxonomy identifies six levels of learning—knowledge, comprehension, application, analysis, synthesis, and evaluation. The taxonomy is hierarchically structured so that learning at each of the lower levels must occur before learning at the higher levels is possible. In other words, if learning is to occur at the comprehension level, students must first be secure in their knowledge of the subject matter. Similarly, if learning is to occur at the analysis level, it must be preceded by learning at the knowledge, comprehension, and application levels. The following definitions and examples of test questions will help to illustrate the progressive nature of Bloom's taxonomy.

At the *knowledge* level, students are expected to recognize and recall key terms, facts, principles, and concepts. A learning objective at the knowledge level might require that students be able to identify the first step in Monroe's motivated sequence. To determine whether students have achieved this objective, the following question might be included on a test:

What is the *first* step in Monroe's motivated sequence?
  a.  action
  b.  need
  c.  visualization
  d.  satisfaction
 *e.  attention

The *comprehension* level goes one step beyond the knowledge level and requires students to explain facts and principles, to interpret information, or to compare and contrast concepts. At this level, an instructional objective might have students compare and contrast public speaking and conversation—as in the following question:

One of the major differences between public speaking and ordinary conversation is that public speaking usually requires
  a.   adapting to feedback from listeners.
 *b.   a more formal manner of delivery.
  c.   organizing ideas for effective communication.
  d.   tailoring the message to the audience.
  e.   telling a story for maximum impact.

Learning at the *application* level requires that students utilize the facts and principles they have learned. Educational objectives at this level might involve problem solving or applying a key concept to a new situation. For instance, the following question assesses students' ability to apply their knowledge about specific purpose statements to a statement they have not previously seen:

"To inform my audience about the three basic steps in preventive medicine" is an example of a(n) _____ for an informative speech.
   *a.   specific purpose
   b.    central idea
   c.    transition
   d.    general thesis
   e.    topic statement

At the *analysis* level, students must be able to understand the components of concepts, principles, or arguments. Analysis involves the ability to break down a whole into its parts and to distinguish among those parts. In a public speaking course, a multiple-choice test question at the analysis level might ask students to distinguish among the kinds of situations for persuasive speeches:

At which of the following would you be *most* likely to hear a persuasive speech on a question of fact?
   a.    a religious service
   b.    a classroom lecture
   c.    an awards ceremony
   *d.   a jury trial
   e.    a retirement banquet

The *synthesis* level involves integration and creativity in working with principles and concepts. An educational goal at this level might be for students make generalizations about the reasons for developing a limited number of main points in a speech. To test this objective, instructors might use the following question:

What is the *most* important reason for limiting the number of main points in a speech?
   a.    It is difficult to organize supporting materials if there are too many main points.
   b.    There is usually not enough time to develop more than two to five main points.
   c.    It is hard to maintain parallel wording if you have too many main points.
   d.    It is difficult to balance the time devoted to each point when there are more than five main points.
   *e.   It is hard for the audience to keep track of too many main points.

Finally, learning at the *evaluation* level suggests that students are able to assess the soundness, efficacy, logic, or universality of a given principle or concept. An objective at this level might require that students be able to assess the reliability of different sources of testimony in a speech—as in the following question:

Which of the following would probably be the most reliable source of testimony in a speech about the impact of automobile exhaust on air pollution?
- a. the president of General Motors
- b. a sociology professor at Yale University
- *c. the U.S. Environmental Protection Agency
- d. a public relations officer at Ford Motors
- e. the head of the Better Business Bureaus

Using Bloom's taxonomy in test construction does not require an equal number of questions for each of the six levels of learning. It may be, for example, that the goals of a course are best represented by the first three levels of the taxonomy. In such a situation, it would be inappropriate for instructors to use a large number of exam questions that assess learning at levels four through six. The best way to approach Bloom's taxonomy is to use it as a guide to ensure that the types of questions designed for an exam fit the teacher's instructional objectives.

## Types of Examination Questions

There are four kinds of exam questions in the test bank to *The Art of Public Speaking*—multiple-choice, true-false, short-answer, and essay. Let us look at each kind and at some factors to consider when using them in an exam.

### Multiple-Choice Questions

Multiple-choice questions require students to select one response from a set of alternatives. For instance:

Speechmaking is a form of power and therefore carries with it heavy _____ responsibilities.
- a. logical
- b. ethical
- *c. psychological
- d. emotional
- e. sociological

A common misperception among teachers and students alike is that multiple-choice questions are useful only for testing at the lower levels of Bloom's taxonomy. In fact, multiple-choice questions can also be used to assess students' ability to analyze, synthesize, and evaluate course material. Consider the following question, which requires students to synthesize concepts regarding audience analysis and apply them to a particular situation:

Ramona is preparing a persuasive speech on environmental issues to present to members of the National Wildlife Federation. The most important factor Ramona should consider when analyzing her audience is probably its
   a.   gender.
   b.   knowledge of the topic.
   c.   education.
\*d.   group membership.
   e.   ethnic background.

Even more complex is a question such as the one below, which involves a combination of levels in Bloom's taxonomy:

At the start of her informative speech, Neva placed a drawing of the major regions of Egypt on an easel to the left of the lectern so it would be easy for her classmates to see throughout the speech. Did Neva follow the guidelines for visual aids presented in your textbook?
   a.   No. Visual aids should be displayed from the right side of the lectern.
   b.   Yes. It is important to display visual aids where everyone can see them.
   c.   No. A photograph would have been a much better choice of visual aid.
   d.   Yes. Drawing a map is usually an excellent visual aid for a classroom speech.
\*e.   No. Visual aids should be displayed only while they are being discussed.

Whether simple or complex, multiple-choice questions have a number of strengths. They allow instructors to assess a wide range of learning objectives as well as a broad base of course materials. They allow for accurate, speedy grading and, when constructed well, result in highly reliable test scores.

Good multiple-choice questions, however, are difficult to construct. Because of this, instructors may be tempted to devise relatively easy items that simply test students' recall of information rather than their abilities to comprehend, analyze, or synthesize course material. Further, if a multiple-choice question is not well designed, students may misunderstand it or may easily guess the correct answer.

Teachers can take a number of precautions to avoid some of the more common difficulties associated with multiple-choice questions. First, it is crucial that the question be written in clear, familiar language. The objective is to test students' understanding of course material rather than their ability to decode a convoluted query. Second, to the extent possible, all of the potential answers should be parallel in structure and similar in length. If one of the potential answers differs dramatically from the others in structure or length, students skilled in taking multiple-choice exams may be able to use the difference in length or structure to help determine the correct response. Third, it is imperative that all of the potential answers be plausible on first reading. If one or more is patently implausible, the question may end up testing students' ability to eliminate incorrect answers rather than their ability to identify the correct one.

### True-False Questions

True-false questions require students to assess the accuracy or inaccuracy of a given statement. For instance:

T F   Under normal circumstances, the introduction should comprise about 10-20 percent of a speech.

Like multiple-choice questions, true-false questions provide highly reliable test scores as well as efficient, accurate scoring. Moreover, because of their brevity, they can be used to test a broad base of course material in a short period of time. True-false questions are usually employed to gauge students' recall of information, but they can be designed to assess learning at the upper levels of Bloom's taxonomy—as in the following questions:

T F   Research indicates that evidence is usually more persuasive when it is stated in general rather than specific terms.

T F   If you were giving a speech with the specific purpose "To inform my audience of the major geographical regions of Mexico," the most effective organizational pattern for arranging your main points would probably be chronological order.

T F   Whenever you use a hypothetical example in a speech, it is usually a good idea to follow it with statistics or testimony to show that the example is not unrealistic.

The major limitation of true-false questions, of course, is that students who have not studied for an exam have a fifty-fifty chance of guessing the correct answer. As a consequence, true-false questions are less effective than multiple-choice questions in discriminating between students who have a firm grasp of the subject and those who do not.

The ability of true-false items to measure the knowledge and understanding of students can be enhanced if teachers follow a few basic suggestions. First, it is important that true-false questions be written as simply as possible. Overly complex items can be ambiguous and confusing to students. Second, extreme terms such as "always" and "never" should be avoided except in the rare instances when something is invariably true or false. Third, instructors should avoid negatively worded statements when constructing true-false questions. Consider, for example, the following question:

T F   Graphs are not an effective way to simplify and clarify statistics.

This question is potentially confusing. By forcing students to think in terms of a double negative, it tests their ability to disentangle word puzzles more than it tests their knowledge of course content. A more effective question would be:

T F   Graphs are an effective way to simplify and clarify statistics.

Contrary to popular wisdom, it is not necessary to have an equal number of true and false items when constructing a true-false exam. Because students are more likely to respond "True" when guessing at an answer, questions with "False" answers do a better job of discriminating between students who genuinely understand the material and those who do not. Many experts in test construction recommend having a slightly larger number of false items than true items when constructing true-false exams. A good ratio to shoot for is 60 percent false items and 40 percent true.

## Short-Answer Questions

Short-answer questions can be simple or complex. *Simple* short-answer questions require students to respond to a question or statement by filling in a blank with the appropriate word or phrase. For instance:

The _____connotative_____ meaning of a word includes all of the feelings and associations the word touches off in different people.

Or:

The following set of main points is arranged in _____topical_____ order.
   I.     The first major type of environmental pollution is land pollution.
   II.    The second major type of environmental pollution is air pollution.
   III.   The third major type of environmental pollution is water pollution.

Simple short-answer questions such as these test students at the knowledge and comprehension levels of Bloom's taxonomy. *Complex* short-answer questions are more elaborate and can be used to assess students at the application level and beyond. For example:

Supply the general purpose, specific purpose, and main points for a speech with the following central idea.

General Purpose:     To inform

Specific Purpose:     To inform my audience of the three major causes of decaying bridges in the United States.

Central Idea:     The three major causes of decaying bridges in the United States are overloading, weather, and neglect.

Main Points:     I.    The first major cause of deteriorating bridges in the United States is overloading.
     II.   The second major cause of deteriorating bridges in the United States is weather.
     III.   The third major cause of deteriorating bridges in the United States is neglect.

Some teachers favor short-answer questions over multiple-choice and true-false questions because they reduce the likelihood that students will be able to guess the correct answer. Creating effective short-answer questions, however, is a challenge for even the most experienced teachers. Simple short-answer questions should be phrased so there is one, and only one, correct answer. They should also be written so as to reduce the chances of students guessing the correct answer. Instructors should make sure that all blanks for a given question are uniform in length and that the question does not contain any grammatical clues such as the word "a" before a blank when the answer begins with a consonant, or the word "an" when the answer begins with a vowel. To avoid this situation, the words "a" or "an" should be replaced with "a(n)."

Although complex short-answer questions often allow students greater latitude in wording their answers than do simple short-answer questions, they also need to be constructed carefully so as to elicit the appropriate response without either confusing students or providing undue hints about the answer. Moreover, when grading complex short-answer questions, instructors must decide how they will assess answers that are similar to, but not exactly the same as, the ideal response.

## Essay Questions

Essay questions require students to formulate, organize, and compose their own, original responses. Some essay questions ask for brief answers; others call for extended analyses. Whether brief or extended, essay questions allow instructors to test a wide range of skills and knowledge. Here, for example, is an essay question geared to the knowledge and comprehension levels of Bloom's taxonomy:

> List and explain the four objectives of a speech introduction discussed in your textbook.

In contrast, the following question goes well beyond the knowledge and comprehension levels to assess students' skills of analysis, synthesis, and evaluation:

> What are the requirements of a good speech introduction? Evaluate the following complete introduction to a classroom speech in light of those requirements. Be specific in your answer.

> > Remember the opening scene in *Raiders of the Lost Ark*? Indiana Jones enters an ancient cave, hidden deep within the jungle. After facing deadly traps of all kinds and spiders as big as your fist, he emerges from the cave with a solid gold idol of a human head.

> > Last year a golden head similar to that one was actually found in South America. Of course, there were no traps, no spiders, and certainly no Indiana Jones. But to its discoverers, this find was more exciting than any movie because this golden head was no film prop. It was the genuine article.

> This object of pure gold was only one of many treasures found during last year's archaeological excavation of an ancient tomb of the long-vanished Moche civilization of ancient Peru. Today I would like to tell you what is known about the history of the Moche civilization. Then I want to explain how recent excavations have made the Moche a hot topic for today's anthropologists.

To the delight of many teachers, essay questions can be quick and easy to construct. On the other hand, grading essay questions can be very time consuming. Whatever time is saved in constructing essay questions is often lost in reading and assessing the answers. Moreover, the open-ended nature of many essay questions can create problems for instructors and students alike. Instructors worry about whether they will be able to provide consistent, reliable evaluations, while students worry about whether they will be able to generate the "right" answer.

Teachers can take several steps to reduce these concerns. First, the task required by an essay question should be made as clear and explicit as possible. For instance, rather than asking students to "describe" several concepts, teachers can require students to "identify, define, and provide examples of" those concepts. Similarly, instead of having students "discuss" an issue, instructors can ask them to "evaluate the issue based on both its strengths and its weaknesses." Second, the number of points or the percentage of the total test grade allotted to each essay question should be clearly indicated. This allows students to estimate how much time they should devote to each essay relative to other questions on the exam.

Third, it is best to give students a limited choice of essay questions to answer. If, for example, students are asked to respond to three out of seven questions (rather than, say, three out of four), they may spend an inordinate amount of time reading each question and deciding which ones to select. Finally, it is imperative that teachers write out their criteria for grading and/or an optimal response to each essay question before they begin to read the students' answers. Failure to do so will produce inconsistent grading and substantially reduce the reliability of the exam.

## Other Issues to Consider

In addition to designing questions, there are several other issues teachers must face when they prepare examinations. These issues include the material that should be covered on the exam, the length of the exam, the kind and amount of advance information students should receive about the exam, and the appropriate level of difficulty of the exam. Let us look at each of these in turn.

### *Exam Content*

When selecting what to include on an exam, instructors should be guided by one fundamental principle—test what you teach. This does not mean material from the textbook should be included on the exam only if it is explicitly treated in lecture or discussion. Students can legitimately be held responsible for any assigned reading or exercise—whether or not it is discussed in class—as long as they are informed in advance that it will be covered on the exam.

In fact, students are often frustrated by exams that do not deal fairly comprehensively with the assigned material. For example, if an instructor, without forewarning, includes several questions from one chapter of the textbook and no questions from another chapter, students who have studied all of the required chapters may feel as if they wasted part of their study time. In addition, a test that neglects a substantial portion of the course content is also likely to slight some of the teacher's instructional goals.

### Length of Exams

Unless the goals of a course include teaching students how to deal with intense time pressure, students should have adequate time to complete examinations. If even one-third of the students in a class run out of time to finish an exam, the exam is probably too long. As a general rule, teachers should allow one minute for each multiple-choice question, five to ten minutes for a half-page essay, and ten to fifteen minutes for a full-page essay. One note of caution: When calculating the length of an exam, be sure to allow sufficient time for explaining any instructions and for distributing test booklets, score sheets, and the like.

### Reviewing for Exams

Many novice teachers worry that their exams will be too easy if students receive a great deal of information about the test beforehand. On the other hand, experienced instructors often note that regardless of how much information they provide about the test, some students don't take advantage of that information. As a general rule, instructors should let students know the topics that will be covered on the test and the kinds of questions that will be asked (essay, multiple-choice, etc.).

Many teachers give students a review sheet roughly one week before the test. Even if the review sheet consists only of a general topic outline of the class lectures, it can help students organize and synthesize the material they need to study. Another way to help students prepare for an exam is to set aside class time the session before the exam to answer questions about the course material. It is also helpful to distribute a few sample questions that clarify the format of the exam and the kinds of materials it will cover.

### Difficulty of Exams

The difficulty of an exam should be commensurate with the objectives of the course. If the course objectives involve only the first three levels of Bloom's taxonomy (knowledge, comprehension, application), then exam questions should not go beyond these three levels. On the other hand, if one of the course objectives is to encourage students to process material at higher levels of the taxonomy (analysis, synthesis, evaluation), then that objective should be reflected in the test questions.

Exams should be challenging but not unreasonable. They should distinguish between students who know the course material inside and out, those who "crammed" the night before the exam, and those who never cracked the textbook. If the test questions are well-constructed and truly reflect what was taught in the course, most students will acknowledge that the test provided a fair measurement of course material.

## References

Bloom, B. S., Engelhart, M. D., Furst, E. J., Hill, W. H., and Krathwohl, D. R. *Taxonomy of Educational Objectives: The Classification of Educational Goals*. New York: David McKay, 1956.

Goyer, R. S. "The Construction of the 'Objective' Examination in Speech." *Southern Speech Journal*, 28 (1962), 27-35.

Nunnally, J. C. *Educational Measurement and Evaluation*, 2nd ed. New York: McGraw-Hill, 1972.

Ory, J. C., and Ryan, K. E. *Tips for Improving Testing and Grading*. Newbury Park, CA: Sage, 1993.

Rubin, R. B. "Evaluating the Product." In J. A. Daly, G. W. Friedrich, and A. L. Vangelisti (eds.), *Teaching Communication: Theory, Research, and Methods*. Hillsdale, NJ: Lawrence Erlbaum, 1990, pp. 379-401.

# Part Two

# Chapter-by-Chapter
# Test Bank for
# *The Art of Public Speaking*

# Chapter 1 Speaking in Public

**True-False Questions**

1. <u>T</u> F   The teaching and study of public speaking began more than 4,000 years ago.

2. T <u>F</u>   Public speaking requires the same method of delivery as ordinary conversation.

3. <u>T</u> F   Public speaking usually requires more formal language than everyday conversation.

4. <u>T</u> F   Public speaking is more highly structured than everyday conversation.

5. <u>T</u> F   When you adjust to the situation of a public speech, you are doing on a larger scale what you do everyday in conversation.

6. T <u>F</u>   As a speaker, you can usually assume that an audience will be interested in what you have to say.

7. T <u>F</u>   Fortunately, stage fright only affects inexperienced speakers.

8. <u>T</u> F   Thinking positively about your ability to give a speech is one way to control your anxiety about speaking.

9. <u>T</u> F   Experts believe that being fully prepared for a speech can reduce stage fright by up to 75 percent.

10. <u>T</u> F   Research has shown that for most speakers anxiety decreases significantly after the first 30 to 60 seconds of a speech.

11. T <u>F</u>   Using the power of visualization to control stage fright means that you should approach your speech as a performance in which the audience is looking for perfection.

12. <u>T</u> F   Most successful speakers are nervous before taking the floor.

13.  T  <u>F</u>     Listeners usually realize how tense a speaker is.

14.  <u>T</u>  F     Some nervousness before you speak is usually beneficial.

15.  <u>T</u>  F     For most beginning speakers the biggest part of stage fright is fear of the unknown.

16.  <u>T</u>  F     As your textbook explains, most of the nervousness public speakers feel internally is not visible to their listeners.

17.  T  <u>F</u>     It is usually a bad idea to make eye contact with individual members of your audience.

18.  <u>T</u>  F     In many aspects of public speaking you will employ the skills of critical thinking.

19.  <u>T</u>  F     Organizing ideas for presentation in a speech is an important aspect of critical thinking.

20.  T  <u>F</u>     Critical thinking is a way of thinking negatively about everything you hear in a speech.

21.  T  <u>F</u>     Practicing speech delivery is one of the most important ways in which public speaking helps develop your skills as a critical thinker.

22.  T  <u>F</u>     The channel is the room in which speech communication takes place.

23.  <u>T</u>  F     The channel is the means by which a message is communicated.

24.  <u>T</u>  F     Your goal in public speaking is to have your intended message be the message that is actually communicated.

25.  <u>T</u>  F     A speaker's frame of reference and a listener's frame of reference will never be exactly the same.

26.  T  <u>F</u>     Most of the time the listener's frame of reference is identical with the speaker's frame of reference.

27.  <u>T</u>  F     Most public speaking situations involve two-way communication.

28.  T  <u>F</u>     When you give a speech to your classmates, you are engaged in one-way communication.

29.  <u>T</u>  F     The nonverbal messages that listeners send back to speakers are called feedback.

30.  <u>T</u>  F     Interference is anything that impedes the communication of a message.

31.  T <u>F</u>    As your textbook explains, the speaker's message consists only of what the speaker says with language.

32.  T <u>F</u>    Because most people share the same frame of reference, the meaning of a message is usually the same to a listener as to a speaker.

33.  <u>T</u> F    Interference can come from either inside or outside your audience.

34.  <u>T</u> F    Speechmaking becomes more complex as cultural diversity increases.

35.  T <u>F</u>    Although language changes from culture to culture, the meaning of nonverbal signals is consistent across cultures.

36.  T <u>F</u>    Ethnocentrism is an advantage to speakers who seek to understand the values, beliefs, and customs of audiences from different cultures.

37.  <u>T</u> F    Ethnocentrism often leads to prejudice and hostility toward people of different racial, ethnic, and cultural backgrounds.

38.  <u>T</u> F    Public speakers who seek to avoid being ethnocentric need to show respect for the cultures of the people they address.

39.  T <u>F</u>    Avoiding ethnocentrism means that you must agree with the values and practices of all groups and cultures.

40.  <u>T</u> F    Ethnocentrism needs to be avoided when you are in the role of listener as well as when you are in the role of speaker.

41.  T <u>F</u>    Ethnocentrism is unique to western cultures such as those in the United States and Europe.

42.  <u>T</u> F    Ethnocentrism is a part of every culture.

43.  <u>T</u> F    Ethnocentrism is the belief that one's own group or culture is superior to all other groups or cultures.

## Multiple Choice Questions *(Students are to indicate the <u>best</u> answer for each question by circling the correct letter.)*

44.    When your textbook describes public speaking as a form of empowerment, it means that public speaking is

    a.    a way to manipulate people.
\*b.    a way to make a difference in something we care about.
    c.    a way to make everyone see things through our frame of reference.
    d.    a way to demonstrate how clever we are.
    e.    a way to support ethnocentrism.

45.    How much time does the average adult spend in conversation?

    a.    about 50 percent of waking hours
    b.    about 10 percent of waking hours
    c.    about 20 percent of waking hours
\*d.    about 30 percent of waking hours
    e.    about 40 percent of waking hours

46.    Many of the skills used in public speaking are the same as those used in everyday conversation. These skills include

    a.    organizing your thoughts logically.
    b.    tailoring your message to your audience.
    c.    adapting to listener feedback.
\*d.    all of the above.
    e.    b and c only.

47.    When you experience stage fright, your body is producing extra _____, a hormone that is released into the bloodstream in response to physical or mental stress.

\*a.    adrenaline
    b.    serotonin
    c.    potassium
    d.    glauconite
    e.    cortisone

48.    According to your textbook, rather than trying to eliminate every trace of stage fright, you should aim at transforming it into

    a.    general anxiety.
    b.    visualized adrenaline.
    c.    professional stage fright.
\*d.    positive nervousness.
    e.    confident apprehension.

49.    Which of the following strategies is *least* likely to help you deal with nervousness in your speeches?

    a.    thinking positively
\*b.    concentrating on your stage fright
    c.    working especially hard on your introduction
    d.    making eye contact with members of your audience
    e.    using visual aids

50.    Heather was in the midst of an excellent speech on campus history when she made a minor mistake by giving the wrong date for the opening of a campus building. She suddenly stopped speaking and said, "Oh, I messed up." She then finished her speech, but all she could think about afterward was her mistake. What is the major piece of advice from your textbook that Heather needs to be reminded about?

    *a.    There is no such thing as a perfect speech.
    b.    You should work especially hard on your introduction.
    c.    Audiences usually can't tell how nervous a speaker is.
    d.    You should take slow, deep breaths before you speak.
    e.    It is natural for public speakers to be nervous.

51.    Which of the following does your textbook recommend as a way to deal with nervousness in your speeches?

    a.    Concentrate on thinking about your stage fright.
    b.    Work especially hard on your conclusion.
    c.    Avoid making eye contact with your audience.
    d.    Try to generate extra adrenaline as you speak.
    *e.    Think of your speech as an act of communication.

52.    Research has shown that the anxiety level of most speakers drops off significantly

    a.    before they rise to speak.
    b.    as soon as they begin to speak.
    *c.    when they are 30 to 60 seconds into the speech.
    d.    after they reach the middle of the speech.
    e.    none of the above.

53.    One way to build confidence as a speaker is to create a vivid mental blueprint in which you see yourself succeeding in your speech. According to your textbook, this process is called

    a.    representation.
    b.    imagistic practice.
    c.    anticipatory rehearsal.
    d.    foreshadowing.
    *e.    visualization.

54.    Which of the following does your textbook recommend as a way to deal with nervousness in your speeches?

    a.    Visualize the worst things that could happen.
    *b.    Turn negative thoughts into positive thoughts.
    c.    Avoid making direct eye contact with the audience.
    d.    Stay up late the night before to finish preparing.
    e.    Generate extra adrenaline as you speak.

55.    Which of the following does your textbook recommend as a way of dealing with nervousness in your speeches?

   a.    Remember that your nervousness is not usually visible to your audience.
   b.    Concentrate on communicating with the audience rather than on your nerves.
   c.    As you rehearse, visualize yourself giving a successful speech.
  *d.    all of the above
   e.    b and c only

56.    Which of the following does your textbook recommend as a way to deal with nervousness in your speeches?

   a.    Tell your audience how nervous you are.
   b.    Avoid making eye contact with the audience.
   c.    Focus on achieving perfection in your speech.
  *d.    Visualize yourself giving a successful speech.
   e.    Memorize your conclusion word for word.

57.    According to your textbook, when you employ the power of visualization as a method of controlling stage fright, you should

   a.    decrease the time necessary for preparing your speech.
   b.    keep your mental pictures from becoming too vivid.
  *c.    focus on the positive aspects of your speech.
   d.    all of the above.
   e.    a and b only.

58.    Dealing with such matters as the logical relationships among ideas, the soundness of evidence, and the differences between fact and opinion are all part of what your textbook calls

   a.    deduction.
  *b.    critical thinking.
   c.    rational communication.
   d.    oral deliberation.
   e.    induction.

59.    As you listen to a speech about campus crime, you relate the speaker's ideas to your own knowledge, goals, and experience. According to your textbook, you are filtering the speech through your own

   a.    psychological screen.
   b.    cognitive field.
  *c.    frame of reference.
   d.    social perspective.
   e.    personal vision.

60.    Which of the following aspects of public speaking is *least* likely to help strengthen your skills as a critical thinker?

    a.    researching your speech
    b.    outlining and organizing your speech
    c.    testing the logic of your arguments
 *d.    practicing the delivery of your speech
    e.    assessing the validity of your evidence

61.    Everything a speaker says is filtered through a listener's

 *a.    frame of reference.
    b.    credibility.
    c.    feedback.
    d.    personal screen.
    e.    psychological field.

62.    According to your textbook, the knowledge, experience, goals, values, and attitudes through which each listener filters a message is called the listener's

    a.    personal screen.
    b.    sphere of values.
    c.    attitudinal core.
 *d.    frame of reference.
    e.    psychological field.

63.    As you present your speech, you notice that many of your listeners have interested looks on their faces and are nodding their heads in agreement with your ideas. According to your textbook, these reactions by your listeners are called

    a.    interference.
    b.    cognitive cues.
 *c.    feedback.
    d.    audience cues.
    e.    indicators.

64.    According to your textbook, a listener anxious about an upcoming exam, worried about a recent argument with a friend, or distracted by cold air in the classroom would be experiencing

 *a.    interference.
    b.    situational cues.
    c.    communication apprehension.
    d.    psychological dissonance.
    e.    feedback.

65.     Concern by a listener about an upcoming job interview, the lack of air conditioning, or a mosquito bite are all examples of _____ in the speech communication process.

     a.    feedback
     b.    avoidance
     c.    blockage
  *d.    interference
     e.    divergence

66.     Whatever a speaker communicates to someone else is termed the

     a.    channel.
     b.    code.
     c.    feedback.
  *d.    message.
     e.    source.

67.     What, according to your textbook, is the term for anything that impedes the communication of a message?

     a.    divergence
     b.    blockage
     c.    intrusion
     d.    avoidance
  *e.    interference

68.     Someone coughing in the audience or walking in late during a presentation are examples of what element in the speech communication process?

     a.    channel
     b.    message
     c.    feedback
  *d.    interference
     e.    disturbance

69.     The means by which a message is communicated is termed the

  *a.    channel.
     b.    stimulus.
     c.    occasion.
     d.    catalyst.
     e.    setting.

70.     _____ lets you know how your message is being received.

     a.    Vocal variety
     b.    Credibility
  *c.    Feedback
     d.    Interference
     e.    Audience adaptation

71.    As Benita approached the podium, loud voices from the hallway filled the room. Before beginning her speech, she asked someone in the back of the room to close the door. In this case, Benita was dealing with

    a.    stage fright.
  *b.    interference.
    c.    nonverbal communication.
    d.    audience attitudes.
    e.    feedback.

72.    In the midst of a speech about volcanoes, a speaker notices quizzical expressions on the faces of her listeners. In response, she says, "Let me explain that point again to make sure it's clear." When this happens, the speaker is

    a.    building her credibility.
  *b.    adapting to feedback.
    c.    compensating for the situation.
    d.    interpreting the audience's frame of reference.
    e.    adjusting the channel.

73.    Mary listened to the campus president speak on the radio at the same time that Jamal was part of the audience in the hall where the president was speaking. Later, Mary said she thought the president's words stated clearly that he opposed an increase in tuition. But Jamal said that the way the president avoided looking at students when he talked about tuition made it seem the president actually supported an increase in tuition. The difference in the messages Mary and Jamal received *most likely* resulted from the fact that

    a.    Jamal is a better listener than Mary.
    b.    Mary and Jamal both experienced feedback.
  *c.    Mary and Jamal received the message through different channels.
    d.    Mary and Jamal are majoring in different subjects.
    e.    Mary is a better listener than Jamal.

74.    As Christopher delivered his speech, he noticed that some members of his audience looked confused as he explained one of his main points. As a result, he slowed down and explained the point again. In this case, Christopher was

    a.    dealing with external interference.
    b.    adjusting the channel of communication.
    c.    interpreting the audience's frame of reference.
    d.    compensating for the situation.
  *e.    adapting to audience feedback.

75.     The tendency to see the beliefs, values, and customs of one's own culture or group as "right" or "natural" is called

    a.  ethnicity.
    b.  egocentrism.
 *c.  ethnocentrism.
    d.  exclusivity.
    e.  essentialism.

76.     According to your textbook, the belief that one's own group or culture is superior to all other groups or cultures is termed

    a.  egocentrism.
    b.  ethnicity.
    c.  ecumenism.
 *d.  ethnocentrism.
    e.  exclusivity.

77.     Renée is a U.S. college student who was asked to speak at an end-of-the-year banquet sponsored by the International Student Association. When Renee suggested in her speech that all students should behave like people in the United States, she was reflecting

    a.  effective audience analysis.
    b.  a sensitivity to cultural diversity.
    c.  the environmental dictates of the situation.
 *d.  an ethnocentric point of view.
    e.  her listeners' frame of reference.

78.     Public speakers who seek to communicate with listeners from cultures other than their own need to take special care to avoid _____ in their speeches.

 *a.  ethnocentrism
    b.  vocalized pauses
    c.  personal statements
    d.  visual aids
    e.  gestures

79.     Sridhar is from India and has decided to give his informative speech on Indian marriage customs. Because he will be getting married back home the next summer, he is very excited about the topic. He is concerned, however, that his classmates, all of whom are from the United States, may think he is saying that marriage traditions in India are better than those in the United States. Sridhar's concern indicates that he is sensitive to the problem of

    a.  egocentrism.
    b.  ethical relativism.
 *c.  ethnocentrism.
    d.  all of the above.
    e.  a and b only.

## Short Answer Questions

80.   As discussed in your textbook, conversation and public speaking share at least four similarities, including:

    a.   _____ organizing one's thoughts logically _____

    b.   _____ tailoring a message to one's audience _____

    c.   _____ telling a story for maximum impact _____

    d.   _____ adapting to listener feedback _____

81.   What are the three primary differences discussed in your textbook between public speaking and conversation?

    a.   _____ Public speaking is more highly structured. _____

    b.   _____ Public speaking requires more formal language. _____

    c.   _____ Public speaking requires a different manner of delivery. _____

82.   When you experience stage fright, your body is producing extra ____ adrenaline ____, a hormone that is released into the bloodstream in response to physical or mental stress.

83.   Mental imaging in which a speaker vividly pictures himself or herself giving a successful presentation is called _____ visualization _____.

84.   List five measures you can take to help control your nervousness when giving a speech.

    a.   _____

    b.   _____

    c.   _____

    d.   _____

    e.   _____

Major methods of controlling stage fright mentioned in the chapter are:

Acquire speaking experience.
Prepare thoroughly for every speech.
Think positively about your speech.
Use the power of visualization.
Know that your nervousness is not visible to the audience.
Don't expect perfection.

Other methods mentioned in the chapter are:

Be at your best physically and mentally.
Quietly flex and relax your muscles while waiting to speak.
Take a couple of deep breaths before starting to speak.
Work especially hard on your introduction.
Make eye contact with members of the audience.
Concentrate on communicating with the audience.
Use visual aids.

85.    The _____situation_____ is the time and place in which speech communication takes place.

86.    Because a listener's _____frame of reference_____ can never be exactly the same as a speaker's, the meaning of a message will never be exactly the same to a listener as to a speaker.

87.    The messages sent by listeners to a speaker are called _____feedback_____.

88.    Concern by a listener about lawn mower noise outside the room, an upcoming test, or a sick relative are all examples of _____interference_____.

89.    _____Feedback_____ lets you know how your message is being received by your audience.

90.    The _____channel_____ is the means by which a message is communicated.

91.    The belief that one's own group or culture is superior to all other groups or cultures is termed _____ethnocentrism_____.

## Essay Questions

92.    Explain two ways in which public speaking and conversation differ, and two ways in which they are similar.

93.    Briefly explain the four skills you use in everyday conversation that are also among the skills required for effective public speaking.

94.    In a brief essay, identify and discuss six methods a public speaker can use to help control stage fright.

95.    Explain the following statement: "Because a listener's frame of reference can never be the same as a speaker's, the meaning of a message will never be exactly the same to a listener as to a speaker."

96.    Explain the difference between one-way communication and two-way communication.

97.    Identify and briefly explain the seven elements of the speech communication process. Include in your answer a sketch of the complete speech communication model presented in the textbook. Be sure to label each part of the model.

98.    Briefly discuss the impact of cultural diversity on the speechmaking process.

99.    What is ethnocentrism? Why does it often pose a barrier to speakers who are addressing audiences of different racial, cultural, or ethnic background from the speaker? Identify two steps a speaker can take to avoid ethnocentrism in her or his speech.

_____

# Chapter 2 Ethics and Public Speaking

## True-False Questions

1. T <u>F</u> The aim of a speaker is to accomplish his or her goals by any means necessary.

2. <u>T</u> F Ethics is the branch of philosophy that deals with issues of right and wrong in human affairs.

3. <u>T</u> F Ethical issues can arise at every stage of the speechmaking process.

4. T <u>F</u> The ethical obligation of a speaker to be fully prepared increases as the size of the audience increases.

5. T <u>F</u> A public speaker need only be concerned about ethics in the conclusion of a speech.

6. <u>T</u> F The first responsibility of a speaker is to make sure her or his goal is ethically sound.

7. T <u>F</u> A speaker's ethical obligations decrease as the size of the audience decreases.

8. T <u>F</u> As the Roman rhetorician Quintilian noted 2,000 years ago, the ideal of commendable speechmaking is to persuade the audience by any means necessary.

9. T <u>F</u> Because persuasion is such a complex process, juggling statistics and quoting out of context to maximize your persuasive effect are ethically acceptable in speeches to persuade.

10. <u>T</u> F Ethical decisions need to be justified against a set of standards or criteria.

11.  T <u>F</u>    As your textbook explains, ethical decisions are essentially a matter of personal whim or opinion.

12.  <u>T</u> F    One of the best ways to avoid falling into the trap of plagiarism is to start work on your speeches well before they are due.

13.  T <u>F</u>    It is true, as the old adage says, that "sticks and stones can break my bones, but words can never hurt me."

14.  T <u>F</u>    As your textbook explains, the ethical obligation of a speaker to avoid name-calling and other forms of abusive language is essentially a matter of political correctness.

15.  T <u>F</u>    Avoiding sexist, racist, and other kinds of abusive language is important primarily as a matter of political correctness.

16.  <u>T</u> F    Public speakers need to take their ethical responsibilities as seriously as their strategic objectives.

17.  <u>T</u> F    Sound ethical decisions involve weighing a potential course of action against a set of ethical standards or guidelines.

18.  T <u>F</u>    Because the aim of speechmaking is to secure a desired response from listeners, speakers need to give their strategic objectives priority over their ethical obligations.

19.  T <u>F</u>    If something is legal, it is also ethical.

20.  T <u>F</u>    Unlike writers, public speakers can present other people's ideas as their own without being guilty of plagiarism.

21.  T <u>F</u>    Global plagiarism occurs when a speaker takes material from several different sources and presents it as his or her own.

22.  <u>T</u> F    Taking someone's entire speech and passing it off as your own is a form of unethical behavior called global plagiarism.

23.  <u>T</u> F    It is necessary for a public speaker to identify his or her source whether the speaker is paraphrasing or quoting verbatim.

24.  T <u>F</u>    It is only necessary to identify your source in a speech when you are quoting directly, rather than paraphrasing.

25.  <u>T</u> F    Whenever you quote someone directly in a speech, you must attribute the words to that person.

26.  <u>T</u> F    Incremental plagiarism occurs when a speaker uses quotations or paraphrases without citing the sources of the statements.

27.  T̲ F    Just as you need to give credit to the authors of print books and articles that you quote or paraphrase in your speech, so you need to give credit to the authors of Internet documents.

28.  T F̲    When citing an Internet document in a speech, it is usually sufficient to introduce it by saying, "As I found on the Web."

29.  T̲ F    Just as public speakers have ethical responsibilities, so too do the people who listen to a speech.

30.  T F̲    As a matter of ethics, audience members should listen attentively to and agree with everything a speaker says.

31.  T F̲    The ethical obligation of an audience to listen to a speaker courteously and attentively is less important in speech class than for speeches outside the classroom.

32.  T F̲    All statements made by a public speaker are protected under the free speech clause of the First Amendment to the U.S. Constitution.

33.  T̲ F    It is possible to disagree entirely with a speaker's ideas but still support the speaker's right to express those ideas.

34.  T̲ F    No matter how well intentioned they may be, efforts to protect society by restricting free speech usually end up repressing minority viewpoints and unpopular opinions.

## Multiple Choice Questions *(Students are to indicate the best answer for each question by circling the correct letter.)*

35.  Speechmaking is a form of power and therefore carries with it heavy _____ responsibilities.

   a.  logical
   *b. ethical
   c.  psychological
   d.  emotional
   e.  sociological

36.  Because speechmaking is a form of power, we must always be sure to speak

   a.  concisely.
   b.  persuasively.
   *c. ethically.
   d.  forcefully.
   e.  consistently.

37.    According to your textbook, the branch of philosophy that deals with human issues of right and wrong is termed

    a.    morality.
    b.    rationalism.
 *c.    ethics.
    d.    legality.
    e.    existentialism.

38.    As a public speaker, you face ethical issues when

    a.    selecting the topic for your speech.
    b.    researching your speech.
    c.    organizing your speech.
    d.    a and b.
 *e.    all of the above.

39.    In public speaking, sound ethical decisions involve weighing a potential course of action against

    a.    the frame of reference of the audience.
 *b.    a set of ethical guidelines or standards.
    c.    the speaker's strategic objectives.
    d.    a socially accepted code of legal rules.
    e.    the personal opinions of the speaker.

40.    In public speaking, sound ethical decisions involve weighing a potential course of action against

    a.    the persuasive goals of the speaker.
    b.    an interpretation of the U.S. Constitution.
    c.    the frame of reference of the audience.
 *d.    a set of ethical guidelines or standards.
    e.    the majority views of public opinion.

41.    All of the following are presented in your textbook as guidelines for ethical speechmaking *except*

    a.    be honest in what you say.
    b.    avoid name calling and other forms of abusive language.
    c.    be fully prepared for each speech.
    d.    make sure your goals are ethically sound.
 *e.    explain your credibility on the speech topic.

42.    All of the following are presented in your textbook as guidelines for ethical speechmaking *except*

 *a.    explain your motives for speaking to the audience.
    b.    put your ethical principles into practice.
    c.    avoid name-calling and other forms of abusive language.
    d.    make sure your goals are ethically sound.
    e.    be fully prepared for each speech.

43.  Which of the following are included in your textbook as guidelines for ethical speechmaking?

a.  Make sure your goals are ethically sound, stay within your time limits, and practice your speech delivery.
*b.  Be honest in what you say, be fully prepared for each speech, and make sure your goals are ethically sound.
c.  Avoid global plagiarism, use quotations rather than paraphrases, and put your ethical principals into practice.
d.  Be fully prepared for each speech, avoid name-calling, and stay within your time limits.
e.  Establish your credibility, be honest in what you say, and put your ethical principles into practice.

44.  All of the following are presented in your textbook as guidelines for ethical speechmaking *except*

a.  be fully prepared for each speech.
b.  make sure your goals are ethically sound.
c.  avoid name-calling and other forms of abusive language.
*d.  respect your listeners' frame of reference.
e.  put your ethical principles into practice.

45.  Which of the following is presented in your textbook as a guideline for ethical speechmaking?

*a.  Be fully prepared for each speech.
b.  Explain your credibility in the introduction.
c.  Present your main points in nontechnical language.
d.  Use visual aids to clarify statistical trends.
e.  Be alert to feedback from the audience.

46.  As explained in your textbook, public speakers have an ethical obligation to avoid name-calling and other forms of abusive language because such language

a.  demeans the dignity of the groups or individuals being attacked.
b.  violates current standards of political correctness on college campuses.
c.  undermines the right of all groups in the U.S. to express their ideas.
d.  all of the above.
*e.  a and c only.

47.  As explained in your textbook, public speakers have an ethical obligation to avoid name-calling and other forms of abusive language because such language

a.  is forbidden by the first amendment to the U.S. Constitution.
b.  violates current standards of political correctness on college campuses.
c.  changes meaning based on the frame of reference of the audience.
d.  is used by speakers who are not fully prepared for their presentations.
*e.  demeans the personal dignity of the groups or individuals being attacked.

48.   For his informative speech, Douglas told his classmates how to get free food at a drive-through restaurant. Rather than focusing on legitimate deals, such as student discounts or coupons, Douglas talked about ways to trick employees into believing you had already paid for food when you had not. His instructor gave the speech a poor grade because it violated the ethical criteria for public speaking presented in your textbook. The *major* guideline Douglas violated was:

   a.   Be fully prepared for each speech.
  *b.   Make sure your goals are ethically sound.
   c.   Avoid name-calling and other forms of abusive language.
   d.   Adapt to your audience's frame of reference.
   e.   Avoid plagiarism.

49.   Having spent two years working in a television newsroom, Madison decided to give her informative speech on that topic. Because she knew a lot about it and was comfortable speaking to an audience, she didn't spend much time preparing. As a result, her speech was poorly organized, ran overtime, and did not have a clear message. Which guideline for ethical public speaking discussed in your textbook did Madison fail to live up to?

  *a.   Be fully prepared for each speech.
   b.   Make sure your goals are ethically sound.
   c.   Avoid name-calling and other forms of abusive language.
   d.   Be honest in what you say.
   e.   Avoid plagiarism.

50.   According to your textbook, global plagiarism occurs when a person

   a.   bases his or her speech completely on foreign sources.
   b.   fails to cite sources throughout the body of the speech.
  *c.   takes a speech entirely from one source and passes it off as her or his own.
   d.   uses two or three sources and blends the information into a unified whole.
   e.   bases the speech entirely on his or her personal experience.

51.   Emil began his research early and found some excellent sources for his informative speech. He cut and pasted passages from several Web sites into a file in his word processor. When he started putting his speech together, he used some complete sentences from the cut-and-pasted materials, paraphrases from other passages, and several original ideas of his own. Unfortunately, Emil forgot to record his sources in his research notes, so he didn't cite any of the sources in his speech. Which of the following statements *best* describes Emil's situation?

   a.   Emil is guilty of global plagiarism.
   b.   Emil is ethical because he used many of his own ideas.
   c.   Emil is ethical because he started his research early and found good materials.
   d.   Emil is ethical because he meant to take better notes about his sources.
  *e.   Emil is guilty of incremental plagiarism.

52.   Tanya went to the beach instead of staying in town and working on her speech. When she realized how soon the speech was due, she asked a friend who had already taken public speaking to loan her an old outline, which she used verbatim for her class speech. Which of the following statements best describes Tanya's actions?

    a.   Tanya should have planned better, but she isn't guilty of plagiarism.
 *b.   Tanya is guilty of global plagiarism.
    c.   Tanya is guilty of patchwork plagiarism.
    d.   Tanya is ethical if she cites the friend whose speech she used.
    e.   Tanya is guilty of incremental plagiarism.

53.   Jerome found several excellent sources for his informative speech. He pulled key information from them, blended those ideas into his own perspective, and cited his sources when he presented the speech. Which of the following statements *best* describes this situation?

 *a.   Jerome is ethical because he cited his sources and used them to develop his own slant on the topic.
    b.   Jerome is guilty of incremental plagiarism because he used quotations and paraphrases from other people in his speech.
    c.   Jerome is ethical because he did not copy his speech from a single source.
    d.   Jerome is guilty of patchwork plagiarism because he used ideas from several different sources in his speech.
    e.   Jerome is guilty of global plagiarism because he did not develop his speech entirely from his own knowledge and experience.

54.   Ryan Tompkins located three excellent sources for his persuasive speech. He copied long sections from each source word for word, strung them together with a few transitions, and mentioned the sources of his information in passing. Which of the following statements *best* describes Ryan's situation?

    a.   Ryan is ethical because he did research for his speech.
    b.   Ryan is guilty of global plagiarism.
 *c.   Ryan is guilty of patchwork plagiarism.
    d.   Ryan is ethical because he mentioned the sources of his information.
    e.   Ryan is guilty of incremental plagiarism.

55.   According to your textbook, _____ plagiarism occurs when a speaker copies word for word from two or three sources.

    a.   global
    b.   incremental
 *c.   patchwork
    d.   scientific
    e.   valid

56.    As your textbook explains, a speaker who assembles a speech by copying word for
       word from two or three sources is committing what kind of plagiarism?

       a.    global
       b.    incremental
       c.    scientific
     *d.    patchwork
       e.    credible

57.    According to your textbook, _____ plagiarism occurs when the speech
       as a whole is ethical but the speaker fails to give credit for particular quotations and
       paraphrases.

       a.    incidental
       b.    informative
       c.    inferential
       d.    invalid
     *e.    incremental

58.    According to your textbook, _____ plagiarism occurs when the speech
       as a whole is ethical but the speaker fails to give credit for particular quotations and
       paraphrases.

     *a.    incremental
       b.    patchwork
       c.    accidental
       d.    incidental
       e.    global

59.    Which of the following is recommended by your textbook as a way to avoid
       plagiarism?

       a.    Avoid using direct quotations from other people in your speech.
       b.    Try to use as few sources as possible in researching your speech.
       c.    Avoid citing quotations and paraphrases in your speech.
     *d.    Get an early start on researching and preparing your speech.
       e.    Make sure you include information from the library in your speech.

60.    Which of the following does your textbook recommend as a way to steer clear of
       incremental plagiarism?

       a.    Avoid using direct quotations from other people in your speech.
       b.    Only use your original ideas so there is no risk of plagiarism.
       c.    Avoid citing sources that might make someone suspect plagiarism.
     *d.    Cite the sources of all quotations and paraphrases in your speech.
       e.    Avoid paraphrasing information from other people in your speech.

61.    The three kinds of plagiarism discussed in your textbook are

    a.    valid plagiarism, incremental plagiarism, and necessary plagiarism.
    b.    patchwork plagiarism, speech plagiarism, and global plagiarism.
    c.    literary plagiarism, scientific plagiarism, and speech plagiarism.
    d.    idea plagiarism, quotation plagiarism, and paraphrase plagiarism.
 *e.    global plagiarism, patchwork plagiarism, and incremental plagiarism.

62.    The three guidelines for ethical listening discussed in your textbook are

    a.    listen attentively, take accurate notes, and avoid prejudging the speaker.
    b.    support free speech, avoid name-calling, and listen attentively.
 *c.    listen attentively, avoid prejudging the speaker, and support free speech.
    d.    take accurate notes, support free speech, and avoid name-calling.
    e.    avoid stereotyping the speaker, support free speech, and take accurate notes.

63.    According to your textbook, the ethical obligations of listeners in a public speaking
    situation include

    a.    maintaining the free and open expression of ideas.
    b.    judging the speaker on the basis of her or his prestige.
    c.    being courteous and attentive during the speech.
    d.    all of the above.
 *e.    a and c only.

64.    According to your textbook, the guidelines for ethical listening in a public speaking
    situation include

 *a.    maintaining the free and open expression of ideas.
    b.    judging the speaker on the basis of her or his prestige.
    c.    taking accurate notes of what the speaker says.
    d.    all of the above.
    e.    a and c only.

65.    In his persuasive speech, Jeremy argued that the category "sexual orientation"
    should be added to his state's civil rights law. Most of Jeremy's classmates listened
    carefully to his argument. Some were persuaded, while others continued to believe
    that the current system was justified. Two audience members disagreed so strongly
    with Jeremy that instead of listening, they wrote notes back and forth to each other
    throughout the speech. Which of the following statements *best* describes the issues
    of ethical listening involved in this situation?

    a.    Everyone in the class was an ethical listener because no one interrupted Jeremy
       or prevented him from speaking.
    b.    The people who listened carefully to Jeremy's arguments were ethical listeners,
       regardless of whether they were persuaded.
    c.    The two classmates who refused to listen to Jeremy's speech and wrote notes
       back and forth violated the guidelines for ethical listening.
    d.    All of the above.
 *e.    b and c only.

66.    According to your textbook, the ethical obligations of listeners include

    a.    judging the speaker on the basis of his or her delivery.
    b.    listening to the speaker courteously and attentively.
    c.    maintaining the free and open expression of ideas.
    d.    all of the above.
*e.    b and c only.

67.    When Susan attended the first discussion section for her math class and heard her instructor begin speaking with an unfamiliar accent, she immediately decided, "I won't learn anything from this teacher." Susan failed to uphold which guideline for ethical listening?

    a.    Listen attentively.
*b.    Avoid prejudging the speaker.
    c.    Take accurate notes.
    d.    Support free speech.
    e.    Avoid name-calling.

## Short Answer Questions

68.    _____Ethics_____ is the branch of philosophy that deals with issues of right and wrong in human affairs.

69.    According to the ancient Roman rhetorician Quintilian, the ideal of ethical speech-making is the _____good_____ person speaking _____well_____.

70.    The five guidelines in your textbook for ethical public speaking are:

    a.    _____Make sure your goals are ethically sound._____
    b.    _____Be fully prepared for each speech._____
    c.    _____Be honest in what you say._____
    d.    _____Avoid name-calling and abusive language._____
    e.    _____Put ethical principles into practice._____

71.    Representing someone else's information in a speech or paper as though it were your own is called _____plagiarism_____.

72.    The three types of plagiarism discussed in your text are _____global plagiarism,_____ _____patchwork plagiarism,_____ and _____incremental plagiarism_____.

73.    _____Global_____ plagiarism occurs when a speaker steals a speech entirely from another source and passes it off as his or her own.

74.    The three guidelines presented in your textbook for ethical listening are:

a.    _____Be courteous and attentive._____

b.    _____Avoid prejudging the speaker._____

c.    _____Maintain the free and open expression of ideas._____

## Essay Questions

75.    Briefly explain the following statement: "Public speaking is a form of power and therefore carries with it heavy ethical responsibilities."

76.    Identify and discuss four of the basic guidelines presented in your textbook for ethical speechmaking.

77.    Briefly discuss the ethical importance of avoiding sexist, racist, and other forms of abusive language in a public speech.

78.    Explain two reasons why it is important from an ethical standpoint for a public speaker to be fully prepared for each speech.

79.    What are the three types of plagiarism discussed in your textbook? Give a hypothetical example of each type.

80.    Explain the following statement: "Speechmaking is a two-way street. Just as public speakers have ethical responsibilities, so too do listeners."

81.    Identify and explain the three guidelines for ethical listening discussed in your textbook.

82.    Explain the following statement: "It is important to keep in mind that ensuring a person's freedom to express her or his ideas does not imply agreement with those ideas. You can disagree entirely with the message but still support the speaker's right to express it."

———————————————————

# Chapter 3 Listening

## True-False Questions

1. <u>T</u> F    People need effective listening skills in almost all occupations.

2. <u>T</u> F    Research indicates that even when we listen carefully, we understand and retain only about half of what we hear.

3. T F    People spend more time listening than in any other communicative activity.

4. T <u>F</u>    Hearing and listening are identical.

5. T <u>F</u>    It is impossible to listen too hard.

6. <u>T</u> F    The aim of active listening is to set aside one's own frame of reference and, as far as possible, to listen from within the speaker's frame of reference.

7. T <u>F</u>    As your textbook explains, focusing on a speaker's delivery and personal appearance is an excellent way to strengthen your listening skills.

8. <u>T</u> F    One of the major obstacles to listening effectively is that the brain can process many more words than can be spoken in a minute.

9. T <u>F</u>    According to your textbook, a skilled therapist listening to a patient is an example of appreciative listening.

10. T <u>F</u>    Appreciative listening is closely tied to critical thinking.

11. T <u>F</u>    Listening is a passive process, while critical thinking is an active process.

12. <u>T</u> F    Listening to provide emotional support for someone is called empathic listening.

13. T <u>F</u>    According to your textbook, listening to understand a classroom lecture is an example of appreciative listening.

14.  <u>T</u>  F    According to your textbook, listening to understand a classroom lecture is an example of comprehensive listening.

15.  T  <u>F</u>    When you listen to someone give a sales presentation, and you need to decide whether you will buy the item, you are engaged in comprehensive listening.

16.  <u>T</u>  F    You can improve your own speeches by listening carefully to the speeches of other people.

17.  <u>T</u>  F    Listening to evaluate a message for purposes of accepting or rejecting it is known as critical listening.

18.  <u>T</u>  F    When you listen to the campaign speech of a political candidate for the purpose of accepting or rejecting the speaker's message, you are engaged in critical listening.

19.  T  <u>F</u>    When listening critically for evidence, you should consider primarily how the evidence relates to your personal frame of reference.

20.  T  <u>F</u>    When you listen to the campaign speech of a political candidate for the purpose of accepting or rejecting the speaker's message, you are engaged in empathic listening.

21.  <u>T</u>  F    Critical listening involves listening to evaluate a message for purposes of accepting it or rejecting it.

22.  <u>T</u>  F    Active listeners give their undivided attention to the speaker in a genuine effort to understand her or his point of view.

23.  <u>T</u>  F    One of the major barriers to effective communication is that the brain can process words much faster than a speaker can talk.

24.  T  <u>F</u>    Usually it is easy to block out physical and mental distractions when listening to a speaker.

25.  T  <u>F</u>    When you listen to a speech, it is usually a good idea to try to remember everything the speaker says.

26.  T  <u>F</u>    Concentrating on details is an excellent way to become a better listener.

27.  <u>T</u>  F    Jumping to conclusions can be a barrier to effective listening even when a speaker and a listener know each other very well.

28.  <u>T</u>  F    According to your textbook, reviewing mentally what a speaker has said is a good way to avoid becoming distracted in a speech.

29.  T  <u>F</u>    If you disagree with a speaker, you have nothing to gain by listening carefully.

30.   <u>T</u>  F    According to your textbook, when focusing your listening, you should concentrate on a speaker's main points, evidence, and technique.

31.   T  <u>F</u>    Note taking is usually a barrier to effective listening.

32.   <u>T</u>  F    Taking notes on a speaker's key points and supporting material will help improve your listening ability and retention.


**Multiple Choice Questions** *(Students are to indicate the <u>best</u> answer for each question by circling the correct letter.)*

33.   People spend more time _____ than in any other communication activity.

    a.   speaking
    b.   writing
    c.   reading
  *d.   listening
    e.   discussing

34.   Even when we are listening carefully, we usually grasp only about _____ percent of what we hear.

    a.   20
    b.   30
    c.   40
  *d.   50
    e.   60

35.   When business managers are asked to list the communication skills most crucial to their job, they usually rank _____ number one.

    a.   conversation
    b.   critical thinking
  *c.   listening
    d.   public speaking
    e.   writing

36.   Sarah is listening to her roommate to provide emotional support in a time of distress. According to your textbook, Sarah is engaged in _____ listening.

    a.   critical
    b.   appreciative
  *c.   empathic
    d.   personal
    e.   comprehensive

37.    Nuzhat is listening to provide emotional support to her friend Sousan, who is talking about the health of her aging parents. According to your textbook, Nuzhat is engaged in _____ listening.

    a.    critical
    b.    appreciative
   *c.    empathic
    d.    intimate
    e.    comprehensive

38.    Fletcher is listening for pleasure as a friend discusses her trip to Australia. According to your textbook, Fletcher is engaged in _____ listening.

   *a.    appreciative
    b.    receptive
    c.    personal
    d.    comprehensive
    e.    empathic

39.    According to your textbook, when you listen to evaluate a speaker's message for purposes of accepting it or rejecting it, what kind of listening is involved?

   *a.    critical
    b.    reflective
    c.    evaluative
    d.    empathic
    e.    comprehensive

40.    Lance is enjoying Chris Rock's stand-up comedy routine at the Civic Center. According to your textbook, Lance is engaged in _____ listening.

    a.    critical
   *b.    appreciative
    c.    comprehensive
    d.    empathic
    e.    intimate

41.    Natasha and Ramone are listening to a realtor who is encouraging them to buy a house they looked at earlier in the day. As they listen, they are trying to decide whether or not to purchase the house. According to your textbook, Natahsa and Ramone are engaged in _____ listening.

   *a.    critical
    b.    appreciative
    c.    comprehensive
    d.    empathic
    e.    intimate

42.    Tara's campus organization has invited several travel agents to speak to the group about their best deals on trips for spring break. As Tara listens, she is deciding which travel package is the best one for her. During the presentations, she is engaged in which form of listening?

   *a.    critical
    b.    appreciative
    c.    comprehensive
    d.    empathic
    e.    intimate

43.    Brian's fraternity is deciding whether to become alcohol free. On the evening of the vote, speakers present arguments on both sides of the issue. Because Brian has to decide whether to accept or reject the proposed policy, he is engaged in _____ listening.

    a.    emphatic
    b.    appreciative
    c.    comprehensive
   *d.    critical
    e.    intimate

44.    Kristen is listening to a political candidate's speech for purposes of deciding whether to accept or reject the speaker's message. According to your textbook, Kristen is engaged in _____ listening.

    a.    comprehensive
    b.    judgmental
   *c.    critical
    d.    empathic
    e.    conclusive

45.    Devon Williams, president of the Minority Student Organization, is listening to the Dean of Students present her plan for a new multicultural center so he can decide whether or not to support the plan. According to your textbook, Devon is engaged in _____ listening.

    a.    reflective
    b.    personal
    c.    empathic
   *d.    critical
    e.    receptive

46.    Sun-Wan is listening to a classroom lecture to understand the message of the speaker. According to your textbook, Sun-Wan is engaged in _____ listening.

   *a.    comprehensive
    b.    judgmental
    c.    critical
    d.    empathic
    e.    appreciative

47.    A new class registration system has been established on campus. Tonight, a representative from the Registrar's office will speak about how to use the new system. You will be listening to the speaker in hopes of understanding the steps involved in registering for classes next semester. As explained in your textbook, you will be engaged in _____ listening.

    a.    intimate
    b.    critical
    c.    empathic
*d.    comprehensive
    e.    appreciative

48.    Giving excessive attention to the details of a speech is an example of

*a.    listening too hard.
    b.    giving in to distractions.
    c.    listening for technique.
    d.    jumping to conclusions.
    e.    focusing on delivery.

49.    Brad Falk is listening to a speaker explain how a new computer program works so Brad can use it in his business. According to your textbook, Brad is engaged in _____ listening.

    a.    passive
    b.    appreciative
    c.    active
*d.    comprehensive
    e.    empathic

50.    Which of the following is one of the four major causes of poor listening discussed in your textbook?

*a.    focusing on a speaker's appearance or delivery
    b.    taking key-word notes during a speech
    c.    suspending judgment about a speaker's ideas
    d.    concentrating on a speaker's evidence and reasoning
    e.    listening empathically rather than critically

51.    Which of the following is included among the four major causes of poor listening discussed in your textbook?

    a.    trying to remember everything the speaker says
    b.    jumping to conclusions about the speaker's ideas
    c.    taking written notes while the speech is in progress
    d.    all of the above
*e.    a and b only

52.     Margaret is passionately committed to animal rights. At an evening lecture required
        for her biology class, she learned that the title of the speaker's talk was "The
        Importance of Animal Experimentation to Medical Advances." Offended and sure
        that the speaker had nothing ethical or interesting to say, Margaret paid no attention
        at all during the lecture. According to your textbook, the *primary* cause of
        Margaret's poor listening was

        a.   poor concentration.
        b.   focusing on the speaker's topic.
        c.   being distracted by external interference.
     *d.   jumping to conclusions.
        e.   spare "brain time."

53.     Ted is listening to the introduction of Janine's speech when he thinks to himself,
        "Man, this is really going to be boring." What aspect of poor listening identified in
        your textbook is Ted exhibiting in this example?

        a.   listening too hard
     *b.   jumping to conclusions
        c.   rejecting the speaker's frame of reference
        d.   giving in to distractions
        e.   not listening comprehensively

54.     Matt's political science professor announces that next week there will be a guest
        lecture by peace activist Rachel Phelps entitled "The History of War, the Prospects
        for Peace." Matt decides to skip class that day, saying to himself, "What can a
        peace activist possibly tell me about war?" What aspect of poor listening identified
        in your textbook is Matt exhibiting in this example?

        a.   failing to concentrate
     *b.   jumping to conclusions
        c.   rejecting the speaker's frame of reference
        d.   giving in to distractions
        e.   suspending judgment

55.     What does your textbook say is the *first* step to improving your listening skills?

        a.   resist distractions during a speech
        b.   focus on the speaker's message
     *c.   take listening seriously
        d.   suspend judgment until the end of the speech
        e.   learn to empathize with the speaker

56.     Although most people speak at a rate of 125 to 150 words a minute, the brain can
        process words at a rate of

        a.   100 to 200 words a minute.
        b.   200 to 400 words a minute.
     *c.   400 to 800 words a minute.
        d.   600 to 900 words a minute.
        e.   1000 to 1200 words a minute.

57.    According to your textbook, skilled listeners do not try to absorb a speaker's every word. Rather, they focus on three major aspects of a speech. Those aspects include

    a.    main points.
    b.    evidence.
    c.    technique.
\*d.    all of the above.
    e.    a and b only.

58.    When listening for a speaker's evidence, you should keep an ear out for its

    a.    sufficiency.
    b.    accuracy.
    c.    objectivity.
    d.    relevance.
\*e.    all of the above.

59.    According to your textbook, one way to focus your listening is to

    a.    concentrate on what the speaker is wearing.
    b.    try to remember every word the speaker utters.
    c.    engage in mental arguments with the speaker.
    d.    pay attention to feedback from other listeners.
\*e.    listen for the speaker's main points.

60.    Your textbook recommends _____ as the most effective method of note taking for listening to a speech.

    a.    writing down a speaker's most interesting ideas
    b.    making a full-sentence outline
    c.    using the Harvard listening system
    d.    trying to write down everything a speaker says
\*e.    creating a key-word outline

61.    Which of the following is recommended by your textbook as a way to improve your listening?

    a.    Try to remember everything the speaker says.
    b.    Pay close attention to feedback from other listeners.
    c.    Concentrate solely on the speaker's gestures and eye contact.
\*d.    Suspend judgment until you hear all the speaker has to say.
    e.    Do not take written notes as the speech is in progress.

62.    Andrew went to hear a speech by a community leader he very much admired. He took a notebook and pen and, during the speech, wrote down everything he could from the speech. When he got home later, he reviewed his notes and could barely make sense out of them. What went wrong?

    a.    Andrew should have simply listened to the speech rather than taking notes.
    b.    Andrew should have taken notes by making a full-sentence outline of the speech.
    c.    Andrew should have paid more attention to the speaker's delivery rather than focusing on the words of the speech.
    d.    Andrew should have resisted distractions and concentrated more effectively on the speech.
   *e.    Andrew should have made a key-word outline of the speech instead of trying to write down everything.

## Short Answer Questions

63.    Even when we think we are listening carefully, we usually grasp only about ____50____ percent of a speaker's message.

64.    People spend more time ____listening____ than in any other communication activity.

65.    According to your textbook, listening to evaluate a message for purposes of accepting it or rejecting it is known as ____critical____ listening.

66.    According to your textbook, when you listen primarily for pleasure or enjoyment, you are engaged in ____appreciative____ listening.

67.    According to your textbook, when you listen to provide emotional support for the speaker, you are engaged in ____empathic____ listening.

68.    According to your textbook, when you listen primarily to understand the message of a speaker (for example, taking notes in a classroom lecture), you are engaged in ____comprehensive____ listening.

69.    Although we speak at a rate of 125 to 150 words a minute, the brain can process information at a rate of ____400____ to ____800____ words a minute.

70. List the four causes of poor listening discussed in your textbook.

    a.    <u>not concentrating</u>

    b.    <u>listening too hard</u>

    c.    <u>jumping to conclusions</u>

    d.    <u>focusing on delivery and personal appearance</u>

71. Your textbook gives seven suggestions for becoming a better listener. List five of them.

    a. _____

    b. _____

    c. _____

    d. _____

    e. _____

Possible answers include:

Take listening seriously.
Be an active listener.
Resist distractions.
Don't be diverted by appearance or delivery.
Suspend judgment.
Focus your listening.
Develop note-taking skills.

72. When focusing your listening, you should listen for <u>main points</u>, <u>evidence</u>, and <u>technique</u>.

73. List at least three qualities you should listen for in a speaker's evidence.

    a. _____

    b. _____

    c. _____

Possible answers include:

sufficiency
accuracy
objectivity
relevance

## Essay Questions

74.    What is the difference between hearing and listening?

75.    Why are your own listening skills important to you as a public speaker?

76.    Identify and briefly explain each of the four types of listening discussed in your textbook.

77.    What is meant by "spare brain time"? Explain how it affects the listening process.

78.    Identify and explain the four causes of poor listening discussed in your text.

79.    What is meant by "listening too hard"? How does it affect the listening process?

80.    Imagine that you are listening to a speech about hurricanes. Explain how a keyword outline method of note taking might enhance your listening and recall of the speech.

81.    Identify and explain five of the methods discussed in your textbook for becoming a better listener.

_____

# Chapter 4

# Selecting a Topic and a Purpose

## True-False Questions

1. <u>T</u> F     The first step in speechmaking is choosing a topic for your speech.

2. T <u>F</u>     It is usually a poor idea to choose a speech topic that requires research.

3. T <u>F</u>     You should usually avoid drawing on your personal knowledge or experience when choosing a speech topic.

4. T <u>F</u>     After choosing a topic, the next step in speech preparation is determining your central idea.

5. T <u>F</u>     Once you choose the central idea of your speech, the next step is to formulate your general purpose.

6. <u>T</u> F     After choosing a topic, the next step in speech preparation is determining your general purpose.

7. T <u>F</u>     After choosing a topic, the next step in speech preparation is determining your specific purpose.

8. <u>T</u> F     Most often, your general purpose as a speaker is to inform or to persuade.

9. T <u>F</u>     Most often, a speaker's general purpose will fall into one of two categories—to inform or to demonstrate.

10. T <u>F</u>     The difference between informing and persuading is like the difference between explaining and entertaining.

11. T <u>F</u>     When your general purpose is to persuade, you act as a teacher or lecturer.

12.  T F    The difference between informing and persuading is like the difference between teaching and advocating.

13.  T F    When your general purpose is to inform, you act as an advocate or an opponent.

14.  T F    The specific purpose statement should focus on one aspect of a topic and be expressed in a single infinitive phrase.

15.  T F    The specific purpose statement indicates precisely what the speaker hopes to accomplish in a speech.

16.  T F    "To inform my audience about terrorism" is an example of a well-worded specific purpose statement for a speech.

17.  T F    "What can we learn about ourselves from our dreams?" is an example of a well-worded specific purpose statement for a speech.

18.  T F    The specific purpose of a speech usually "sums up" the main points to be developed in the body of the speech.

19.  T F    It is important to keep your audience in mind as you formulate the specific purpose for your speech.

20.  T F    "Conducting regular car maintenance" is an example of an effective specific purpose statement for a speech.

21.  T F    "To inform my audience about golf" is an example of an effective specific purpose statement for a speech.

22.  T F    "To inform my audience about the origins of martial arts and how to perform yoga" is an example of an effective specific purpose statement for an informative speech.

23.  T F    "To inform my audience of the major steps in responding to a medical emergency" is an example of an effective specific purpose statement for an informative speech.

24.  T F    "To inform my audience about depression" is an example of an effective specific purpose statement for a speech.

25.  T F    The specific purpose statement should usually be phrased as a question.

26.  T F    It is acceptable for a specific purpose statement to include two or more unrelated ideas.

27.  T F    "To inform my audience about the current status of tennis as an international sport" is an example of an effective specific purpose statement for a speech.

28.  T <u>F</u>    "Learning water safety guidelines" is an example of an effective specific purpose statement for a speech.

29.  T <u>F</u>    The following is an example of an effective specific purpose statement for a speech: "The three major elements of the architectural style of Frank Lloyd Wright are low-pitched roofs, functional designs, and lines that blend into the landscape."

30.  T <u>F</u>    "To inform my audience how to build a birdhouse and about the migratory patterns of birds" is an example of an effective specific purpose statement for a speech.

31.  <u>T</u> F    "To inform my audience about the causes and effects of lead poisoning in children" is an example of an effective specific purpose statement for a speech.

32.  <u>T</u> F    "To persuade my audience that our school should provide more on-campus parking for students" is an example of a well-worded specific purpose statement for a speech.

33.  <u>T</u> F    The central idea reveals more about the content of a speech than does the specific purpose.

34.  T <u>F</u>    The specific purpose reveals more about the content of a speech than does the central idea.

35.  <u>T</u> F    The central idea should encapsulate or sum up the main points to be developed in the body of the speech.

36.  <u>T</u> F    The central idea of a speech should be expressed as a full sentence.

37.  <u>T</u> F    The central idea of a speech often emerges after you have done your research and have decided on the main points of the speech.

38.  <u>T</u> F    The following is an example of a well-worded central idea for a speech: "A diet that encourages eating only foods high in fat and protein has major advantages as well as serious risks."

39.  T <u>F</u>    "To persuade my audience that the federal government should institute a national sales tax to help pay for social programs" is an example of an effective central idea for a speech.

40.  <u>T</u> F    "The three most distinctive traits of Chow Chows are their black tongues, their thick coats, and their manes" is an example of a well-worded central idea for a speech.

41.  <u>T</u> F    The central idea is usually determined after the bulk of the research for a speech is completed.

42.  T <u>F</u>    "The three major expenses for people traveling abroad are transportation, food, and lodging" is an example of an effective specific purpose statement for a speech.

43.  <u>T</u> F    "The three major expenses for people traveling abroad are transportation, food, and lodging" is an example of a well-worded central idea for a speech.

44.  <u>T</u> F    "The major responsibilities of an athletic trainer are preventing, diagnosing, and treating injuries" is an example of a well-worded central idea for a speech.

45.  T <u>F</u>    "The major responsibilities of an athletic trainer are preventing, diagnosing, and treating injuries" is an example of a well-worded specific purpose statement for a speech.

46.  T <u>F</u>    The following is an example of a well-worded central idea for a speech to inform: "To tell my audience why they should support Jackson Smith for mayor."

47.  <u>T</u> F    The following is an effective central idea for a speech to persuade: "You should vote a $10 increase in student fees to pay for a new intramural athletic facility because such a facility is necessary and practical."

## Multiple Choice Questions *(Students are to indicate the <u>best</u> answer for each question by circling the correct letter.)*

48.  According to your textbook, brainstorming is especially helpful when you are having trouble

  *a.  choosing a speech topic.
   b.  determining the general purpose.
   c.  determining the specific purpose.
   d.  phrasing the central idea.
   e.  analyzing the audience.

49.  After choosing a topic, what is the next step of speech preparation?

   a.  phrasing the central idea
   b.  analyzing the occasion
   c.  selecting the specific purpose
   d.  writing the introduction
  *e.  determining the general purpose

50.  Using Yahoo or another of the subject-based search engines on the Internet is recommended in your textbook as one method of _____ for a speech topic.

    a.  sifting
    b.  consulting
 *c.  brainstorming
    d.  deliberating
    e.  studying

51.  Which of the following is out of place in a speech to inform?

 *a.  advocating
    b.  explaining
    c.  reporting
    d.  demonstrating
    e.  telling

52.  When the general purpose of your speech is to _____, you act primarily as a teacher or lecturer.

 *a.  inform
    b.  convince
    c.  entertain
    d.  persuade
    e.  convert

53.  When the general purpose of your speech is to _____, you act primarily as an advocate.

 *a.  persuade
    b.  entertain
    c.  demonstrate
    d.  commemorate
    e.  inform

54.  "Improving personal relationships" is a poorly phrased specific purpose for a speech because it is

    a.  too technical for a classroom speech.
    b.  written as a sentence rather than a declarative phrase.
    c.  expressed in figurative language.
 *d.  written as a fragment rather than a full infinitive phrase.
    e.  written as a statement rather than a question.

55.    "Knowing how to deal with stress" is a poorly phrased specific purpose for a classroom speech because it

 a. is too technical.
 *b. does not include a reference to the audience.
 c. contains figurative language.
 d. all of the above.
 e. a and c only.

56.    According to your textbook, what is the *most important* early step in the process of developing a successful speech?

 a. creating a preliminary bibliography
 b. researching for speech materials
 *c. formulating the specific purpose
 d. brainstorming for a central idea
 e. selecting the residual message

57.    As a specific purpose statement, "To inform my audience about computer technology" is too

 a. figurative.
 *b. broad.
 c. trivial.
 d. technical.
 e. detailed.

58.    "To persuade my audience that continuing to spend money on the space program is like throwing good money after bad" is a poorly phrased specific purpose statement for a speech because it is

 *a. expressed in figurative language.
 b. written as a declarative sentence rather than a question.
 c. too technical.
 d. all of the above.
 e. a and c only.

59.    "To inform my audience how the campus administration let the cat out of the bag on the proposal to increase tuition" is a poorly phrased specific purpose statement for a speech because it

 a. includes a reference to the audience.
 b. is written as a declarative sentence rather than a question.
 *c. is expressed in figurative language.
 d. all of the above.
 e. a and b only.

60.    "To inform about saving for retirement" is a poorly phrased specific purpose statement because it

    a.    is too specific.
    b.    contains figurative language.
    c.    is written as a statement instead of a question.
   *d.    does not include a reference to the audience.
    e.    is too trivial.

61.    Identify the flaw in the following specific purpose statement for a classroom speech: "To inform my audience about Christianity."

    a.    It's too technical.
   *b.    It's too broad.
    c.    It's too personal.
    d.    It's too figurative.
    e.    It's too specific.

62.    Identify the flaw in the following specific purpose statement for a classroom speech: "To inform my audience about the solar system."

   *a.    It's too general.
    b.    It's too shallow.
    c.    It's too informative.
    d.    It's too remote.
    e.    It's too impersonal.

63.    Identify the flaw in the following specific purpose statement for a classroom speech: "To inform my audience about the stock market."

    a.    It's too figurative.
    b.    It's too detailed.
   *c.    It's too general.
    d.    It's too technical.
    e.    It's too trivial.

64.    "To inform my audience that the National Football League's video replay system should be adopted by college football in order to eliminate officiating errors" is a poor specific purpose statement for an informative speech because

    a.    it is phrased in figurative language.
    b.    it contains more than one distinct idea.
   *c.    the stated goal is persuasive rather than informative.
    d.    all of the above.
    e.    a and b only.

65.    "To inform my audience about the history and rules of water polo" is an example of a

    a.    speech topic.
    b.    general purpose.
    c.    central idea.
    d.    thesis statement.
  *e.    specific purpose.

66.    "To inform my audience about the three basic steps in preventive medicine" is an example of a

    a.    main point.
  *b.    specific purpose.
    c.    thesis statement.
    d.    central idea.
    e.    general purpose.

67.    "To inform my audience about the symptoms, causes, and treatment of chronic fatigue syndrome" is an example of a

  *a.    specific purpose.
    b.    thesis statement.
    c.    general purpose.
    d.    central idea.
    e.    main point.

68.    "To inform my audience how our local water treatment facility ensures the safety of our drinking water" is an example of a

    a.    mission statement.
  *b.    specific purpose.
    c.    transition statement.
    d.    general purpose.
    e.    central idea.

69.    "To inform my audience how a perpetual motion machine works" is an example of a

    a.    general purpose.
    b.    main point.
    c.    central idea.
  *d.    specific purpose.
    e.    thesis statement.

70.    "To inform my audience about the four major elements in rope climbing" is an example of a

    a.    speech topic.
    b.    general purpose.
    c.    central idea.
    d.    thesis statement.
  *e.    specific purpose.

71.    The central idea of a speech should be

     a.    written as a complete sentence.
     b.    expressed as a statement, not a question.
     c.    devoid of figurative language.
  *d.    all of the above.
     e.    a and b only.

72.    The central idea of a speech should be

     a.    expressed as a question.
  *b.    written as a complete sentence.
     c.    determined before the specific purpose.
     d.    all of the above.
     e.    b and c only.

73.    "The laser is a highly versatile instrument with important uses in medicine,
industry, and art" is an example of a

     a.    specific purpose.
  *b.    central idea.
     c.    transition.
     d.    general thesis.
     e.    topic statement.

74.    According to your textbook, "Getting an internship at a major corporation requires a
great deal of work, but the rewards are well worth the effort" is an example of a(n)

     a.    speech proposal.
     b.    specific purpose.
     c.    informative thesis.
     d.    topic statement.
  *e.    central idea.

75.    "The three main methods of harvesting trees in professional logging are selective
cutting, clear cutting, and row thinning" is an example of a

     a.    specific purpose.
     b.    transition.
     c.    general purpose.
     d.    signpost.
  *e.    central idea.

76.    "To understand the role of dance marathons in American popular culture, one needs
to know why they started, how they evolved, and what they are like today" is an
example of a

     a.    mission statement.
     b.    specific purpose.
     c.    transition statement.
  *d.    central idea.
     e.    topic statement.

77.    "The three major factors to consider when purchasing a bicycle are the kind of riding you plan to do, the amount of riding you plan to do, and the amount of money you are willing to spend" is an example of a

    a.   specific purpose.
\*b.   central idea.
    c.   transition.
    d.   general purpose.
    e.   topic statement.

78.    "The value of a classic car is determined by its condition, its rarity, and its desirability to collectors" is an example of a

    a.   speech goal.
    b.   transition statement.
    c.   specific purpose.
    d.   mission statement.
\*e.   central idea.

79.    Chang thinks he'd like to give an informative speech for class on what it's like to be an international student on a U.S. college campus. His specific purpose is "To persuade my audience to be more accepting of international students." His central idea is "An international student's accent, use of English, and cultural customs should be accepted rather than criticized." Has Chang made any mistakes in this process?

    a.   No. Chang has covered all the bases for an informative speech.
    b.   Yes. Chang's specific purpose contains too much figurative language.
    c.   Yes. Chang's central idea contains two or more unrelated ideas.
    d.   Yes. Chang's specific purpose statement is too technical for a classroom speech.
\*e.   Yes. Chang's specific purpose is not suitable for an informative speech.

80.    Orawan plans to give an informative speech about her home country of Thailand. Her specific purpose is "To inform my audience about the interaction of ancient traditions and modern technology in Thai society." Her central idea is "Thailand: Customs and Computers." Has Orawan made any mistakes in this process?

    a.   No. Orawan is off to a good start with her informative speech.
    b.   Yes. Orawan's specific purpose does not meet the assignment.
    c.   Yes. Orawan's specific purpose statement is too trivial.
\*d.   Yes. Orawan's central idea is not written as a complete sentence.
    e.   Yes. Orawan's central idea contains the word "and."

## Short Answer Questions

81.    When your general purpose is to _____inform_____, you act as a teacher or lecturer.

82.    When your general purpose is to _____persuade_____, you act as a partisan or an advocate.

83.    The _____specific purpose statement_____ reveals precisely what the speaker hopes to accomplish in his or her speech.

84.    "To persuade my audience that irradiation of food is not harmful" is an example of a _____specific purpose statement_____.

85.    List at least three questions you should ask about the suitability of your specific purpose for your audience.

    a.    _____

    b.    _____

    c.    _____

    Possible answers include:

    Does my purpose meet the assignment?
    Can I accomplish my purpose in the time allotted?
    Is the purpose relevant to my audience?
    Is the purpose too trivial for my audience?
    Is the purpose too technical for my audience?

86.    The _____central idea_____ usually encapsulates the main points of your speech in a single sentence.

87.    Explain what is wrong with the following poorly written central idea for a persuasive speech: "Something must be done about the homeless in America."

    _____It is too general; it does not indicate what "must be done."_____

88.    Explain what is wrong with the following poorly written central idea for an informative speech: "Origins of soccer."

    _____It is not written as a complete sentence._____

89.    Explain what is wrong with the following poorly written central idea for an informative speech: "What happened to dinosaurs?"

    _____It is written as a question, rather than as a statement._____

90.    Explain what is wrong with the following poorly written central idea for a persuasive speech: "Lawyers who promote frivolous personal injury suits are just a bunch of greedy bums!"

It is expressed with figurative language.

91.    What is wrong with the following specific purpose statement for an informative speech? Rewrite the statement to conform with the criteria given in your textbook for effective specific purpose statements.

Ineffective
  Specific Purpose:          The major beliefs of the Baha'i religion.

Error:                       written as a fragment, not as a full infinitive phrase

More Effective
  Specific Purpose:          To inform my audience about the major beliefs of the Baha'i religion.

92.    What is wrong with the following specific purpose statement for an informative speech? Rewrite the statement to conform with the criteria given in your textbook for effective specific purpose statements.

Ineffective
  Specific Purpose:          To inform my audience about the Civil War.

Error:                       too vague or general; doesn't indicate what specific aspects of the Civil War will be dealt with in the speech.

More Effective
  Specific Purpose:          To inform my audience about the role of women in the Civil War.

93.    What is wrong with the following specific purpose statement for a persuasive speech? Rewrite the statement to conform with the criteria given in your textbook for effective specific purpose statements.

Ineffective
  Specific Purpose:          Why does the United States need to build more nuclear power plants?

Error:                       written as a question, not as a statement

More Effective
  Specific Purpose:          To persuade my audience that the United States needs to build more nuclear power plants.

94.     What is wrong with the following specific purpose statement for a persuasive speech? Rewrite the statement to conform with the criteria given in your textbook for effective specific purpose statements.

Ineffective
Specific Purpose:          To persuade my audience that something must be done to curb the problem of computer theft on our campus.

Error:                     too vague or general; doesn't indicate what the audience should do

More Effective
Specific Purpose:          To persuade my audience that tighter security measures are needed in both the dorms and offices to curb the problem of computer theft on our campus.

95.     What is wrong with the following specific purpose statement for an informative speech? Rewrite the statement to conform with the criteria given in your textbook for effective specific purpose statements.

Ineffective
Specific Purpose:          To inform my audience about astrology.

Error:                     too vague or general; doesn't indicate what specific aspects of astrology will be dealt with in the speech.

More Effective
Specific Purpose:          To persuade my audience that astrology cannot be accepted as scientifically valid. OR, To inform my audience of the origins of astrology in ancient Egypt.

96.     What is wrong with the following specific purpose statement for an informative speech? Rewrite the statement to conform with the criteria given in your textbook for effective specific purpose statements.

Ineffective
Specific Purpose:          To inform my audience about the principles of aerodynamics and how to build a kite.

Error:                     contains more than one distinct idea

More Effective
Specific Purpose:          To inform my audience about the principles of aerodynamics. OR, To inform my audience how to build a kite.

97.    What is wrong with the following specific purpose statement for an informative speech? Rewrite the statement to conform with the criteria given in your textbook for effective specific purpose statements.

Ineffective
Specific Purpose:        The interior design of the White House.

Error:                  written as a fragment, not as a full infinitive phrase

More Effective
Specific Purpose:        To inform my audience of the interior design of the White House.

98.    Supply the general purpose, specific purpose, and central idea for a speech with the following main points:

General Purpose:        To inform

Specific Purpose:        To inform my audience of the major factors that determine the value of a baseball card.

Central Idea:           The major factors that determine the value of a baseball card are the fame of the player, the age of the card, the rarity of the card, and the physical condition of the card.

Main Points:            I.    The first factor determining the value of a baseball card is the fame of the player.
                        II.   The second factor determining the value of a baseball card is the age of the card.
                        III.  The third factor determining the value of a baseball card is the rarity of the card.
                        IV.   The fourth factor determining the value of a baseball card is the physical condition of the card.

99.    Supply the general purpose, specific purpose, and central idea for a speech with the following main points:

General Purpose:        To inform

Specific Purpose:        To inform my audience of three factors that shape our self-esteem.

Central Idea:           Our self-esteem is shaped by our immediate family, by our interactions with friends, and by the media.

Main Points:            I.    Our self-esteem is shaped by our immediate family.
                        II.   Our self-esteem is shaped by our interactions with friends.
                        III.  Our self-esteem is shaped by the media.

100.    Supply the general purpose, specific purpose, and central idea for a speech with the
        following main points:

| | |
|---|---|
| General Purpose: | To inform |
| Specific Purpose: | To inform my audience of the basic steps in making red wine. |
| Central Idea: | There are five basic steps in making red wine: harvesting the grapes, preparing the grapes, fermenting the grapes, pressing the grapes, and aging the wine. |

Main Points:

I.    The first step in making red wine is harvesting the grapes.
II.   The second step in making red wine is preparing the grapes.
III.  The third step in making red wine is fermenting the grapes.
IV.   The fourth step in making red wine is pressing the grapes.
V.    The fifth step in making red wine is aging the wine.

101.    Supply the general purpose, specific purpose, and central idea for a speech with the
        following main points:

| | |
|---|---|
| General Purpose: | To inform |
| Specific Purpose: | To inform my audience about the stages in dealing with the death of a loved one. |
| Central Idea: | The four stages in dealing with the death of a loved one are denial, anger, depression, and acceptance. |

Main Points:

I.    The first stage in dealing with the death of a loved one is denial.
II.   The second stage in dealing with the death of a loved one is anger.
III.  The third stage in dealing with the death of a loved one is depression.
IV.   The fourth stage in dealing with the death of a loved one is acceptance.

102.   Supply the general purpose, specific purpose, and main points for a speech with the following central idea:

General Purpose:      To inform

Specific Purpose:     To inform my audience of the three major causes of decaying bridges in the United States.

Central Idea:         The three major causes of decaying bridges in the United States are overloading, weather, and neglect.

Main Points:
I.    The first major cause of deteriorating bridges in the United States is overloading.
II.   The second major cause of deteriorating bridges in the United States is weather.
III.  The third major cause of deteriorating bridges in the United States is neglect.

103.   Supply the general purpose, specific purpose, and main points for a speech with the following central idea:

General Purpose:      To inform

Specific Purpose:     To inform my audience why Devil's Island was called "the prison from which there is no return."

Central Idea:         Devil's Island was called "the prison from which there is no return" because escape was virtually impossible and because large numbers of prisoners died there.

Main Points:
I.    Devil's Island was called "the prison from which there is no return" because escape was virtually impossible.
II.   Devil's Island was called "the prison from which there is no return" because large numbers of prisoners died there.

104.    Supply the general purpose, specific purpose, and main points for a speech with the following central idea:

| | |
|---|---|
| General Purpose: | To inform |
| Specific Purpose: | To inform my audience of the major factors to consider when buying a notebook computer. |
| Central Idea: | The major factors to consider when buying a notebook computer are price, speed, screen quality, and special features. |
| Main Points: | I.   The first factor to consider when buying a notebook computer is price. |
| | II.  The second factor to consider when buying a notebook computer is speed. |
| | III. The third factor to consider when buying a notebook computer is screen quality. |
| | IV.  The fourth factor to consider when buying a notebook computer is special features. |

## Essay Questions

105.    Your textbook discusses four methods of brainstorming for a speech topic. In a brief essay, identify and explain three of those methods.

106.    Explain the differences between informing and persuading as general speech purposes.

107.    Why is determining the specific purpose such a vital step in the process of preparing a speech?

108.    Your textbook provides five tips for writing specific purpose statements. Identify and briefly explain four of them.

109.    What is the difference between a specific purpose and a central idea? Illustrate your answer by developing a specific purpose statement and a central idea for a hypothetical speech about a topic of your choice.

110.    What are the characteristics of a well-worded central idea? Explain why each characteristic is important.

111.    Imagine that you have been asked to inform a local community group about life as a college student. In a well-developed essay, describe what your general purpose, specific purpose, and central idea would be for this speech. Then draft three main points for a speech on this topic.

# Chapter 5 Analyzing the Audience

## True-False Questions

1. T **F**  The primary purpose of speechmaking is to demonstrate your command of the topic.

2. **T** F  Being audience-centered means that your primary purpose as a speaker is to gain a desired response from the audience.

3. T **F**  The aim of successful speechmaking is to gain a desired response from listeners by any means necessary.

4. T **F**  Being audience-centered means a speaker must sacrifice what she or he really believes to get a favorable response from the audience.

5. T **F**  Adapting to audiences is one of the easiest tasks facing beginning speakers.

6. **T** F  You are most likely to be successful in your classroom speeches if you think of your classmates as a real audience.

7. T **F**  The need for audience analysis and adaptation is one of the major differences between public speaking and everyday conversation.

8. **T** F  An audience's response to a message is invariably colored by its perception of the speaker.

9. T **F**  Unlike beginning speakers, experienced speakers have little need for audience analysis.

10. T **F**  Audience analysis and adaptation affect all aspects of speechmaking except for the delivery of the speech itself.

11. <u>T</u> F    The process of audience analysis and adaptation affects every aspect of speech preparation from choosing a topic to delivering the speech.

12. T <u>F</u>    Public speaking is essentially like acting because once you learn a speech, you can give it over and over without adapting to the different audiences you address.

13. T <u>F</u>    Audience analysis first comes into play after a speaker has chosen a speech topic.

14. T <u>F</u>    Audience analysis first comes into play after a speaker has chosen a specific purpose.

15. T <u>F</u>    Audience analysis is only important after a speaker has completed research for a speech.

16. T <u>F</u>    Audience analysis is only important after a speaker has prepared an outline for the speech.

17. <u>T</u> F    Even when listeners pay close attention, they don't process a speaker's message exactly as the speaker intended.

18. <u>T</u> F    Every speech contains two messages—the one sent by the speaker and the one received by the listener.

19. T <u>F</u>    Egocentrism is the belief that one's culture is superior to all others.

20. <u>T</u> F    Egocentrism means that audiences typically approach speeches by asking "Why is this important for me?"

21. T <u>F</u>    Listeners typically approach a speech with one question uppermost in their minds: "Why is this important to the speaker?"

22. <u>T</u> F    Communication scholars use the term "identification" to refer to the process by which speakers seek to create a bond with audiences by emphasizing common values, goals, and experiences.

23. T <u>F</u>    Communication scholars use the term "identification" to refer to the way speakers use stereotypes to analyze the demographic traits of their audience.

24. <u>T</u> F    Any characteristic of a given audience is potentially important to a speaker analyzing that audience.

25. T <u>F</u>    One of the major demographic traits of audiences is interest in the speaker's topic.

26. <u>T</u> F    Gender, sexual orientation, age, race, ethnicity, and group membership are all factors to consider when conducting a demographic audience analysis.

27.  T̲ F    Recognizing that some of your listeners may have racial, ethnic, cultural, or sexual orientations that bear upon your topic is part of demographic audience analysis.

28.  T F̲    Audience size, the physical setting for the speech, and the audience's disposition toward the topic are all elements of demographic audience analysis.

29.  T̲ F    Audience size, the physical setting for the speech, and the audience's disposition toward the topic, the speaker, and the occasion are all elements of situational audience analysis.

30.  T̲ F    The size of the audience is one of the factors to be considered in situational audience analysis.

31.  T F̲    According to your textbook, sexual orientation is one factor to be considered in situational audience analysis.

32.  T̲ F    According to your textbook, sexual orientation is one factor to be considered in demographic audience analysis.

33.  T̲ F    Although the differences between women and men have diminished in recent years, the gender of listeners is still a major factor in audience analysis.

34.  T F̲    Because men and women in the United States share a much broader range of experiences than they once did, gender is no longer a significant factor in demographic audience analysis.

35.  T F̲    Because religion is private and personal for most people, it is seldom an important element in demographic audience analysis.

36.  T̲ F    The group membership of an audience can provide excellent clues about their interests and attitudes.

37.  T̲ F    As a general rule, the larger your audience, the more formal your speech presentation should be.

38.  T F̲    Knowing how the physical setting might affect your listeners' receptivity to your ideas is an important factor in demographic audience analysis.

39.  T̲ F    Knowing how the physical setting might affect your listeners' receptivity to your ideas is an important factor in situational audience analysis.

40.  T̲ F    Interest, knowledge, and attitude are the three most important factors to consider when determining an audience's disposition toward a speaker's topic.

41.  <u>T</u>  F    The more people know about a topic, the more likely they are to be interested in it.

42.  <u>T</u>  F    No matter what the occasion, listeners will have fairly definite expectations about the kinds of speeches appropriate for the occasion.

43.  T  <u>F</u>    Keeping speeches within strict time limits is an artificial constraint of classroom speeches and is less important for speeches outside the classroom.

44.  T  <u>F</u>    When you construct an audience analysis questionnaire, fixed-alternative questions are especially useful for getting at the strength of a respondent's attitudes.

45.  <u>T</u>  F    When you construct an audience analysis questionnaire, scale questions are especially useful for getting at the strength of a respondent's attitudes.

46.  T  <u>F</u>    When you construct an audience analysis questionnaire, scale questions give respondents the maximum leeway in responding.

47.  T  <u>F</u>    When you construct an audience-analysis questionnaire, open-ended questions are especially valuable because they usually generate clear, unambiguous responses.

48.  T  <u>F</u>    The process of audience adaptation is over by the time a speaker starts delivering the speech.

49.  <u>T</u>  F    Although most of the process of audience adaptation occurs as part of preparing a speech, a speaker may still need to adapt her or his remarks to the audience during the presentation of the speech.

## Multiple Choice Questions *(Students are to indicate the <u>best</u> answer for each question by circling the correct letter.)*

50.    The *primary* purpose of speechmaking is to

  *a.    gain a desired response from listeners.
   b.    learn more about the speech topic.
   c.    gain experience as a speaker.
   d.    try out new ideas with an audience.
   e.    display the speaker's knowledge.

51.    Audience analysis is an important factor in which of the following?

   a.    selecting a topic
   b.    organizing the speech
   c.    choosing supporting materials
  *d.    all of the above
   e.    a and c only

52.    Audience adaptation is an important factor in which of the following?

    a.    choosing the speech topic
    b.    preparing the speech
    c.    presenting the speech
  *d.    all of the above
    e.    a and b only

53.    Audience adaptation is an important factor in which of the following steps of the speechmaking process?

    a.    formulating a specific purpose
    b.    writing an introduction and conclusion
    c.    choosing visual aids
  *d.    all of the above
    e.    a and b only

54.    In her speech introduction, Kailyn asked, "Have you ever looked through old family photo albums and laughed at what people were wearing? Have you ever been amused by the bright colors, huge lapels, and crazy ties worn by characters in old TV shows? Like many of you I've noticed the changes in fashion and feared that my effort to look stylish today may eventually be a source of amusement to my future children." According to your textbook, by seeking to create a bond with her audience through emphasizing their common experiences and fears, Kailyn was engaging in

  *a.    identification.
    b.    stereotyping.
    c.    ethnocentrism.
    d.    comparison.
    e.    inclusion.

55.    To say that people usually want to hear about things that are meaningful to them is to say that people are

    a.    empathic.
    b.    eclectic.
    c.    egotistic.
    d.    egalitarian.
  *e.    egocentric.

56.    The process by which a speaker seeks to create a bond with listeners by emphasizing common values, goals, and experiences is referred to as _____ by communication scholars.

    a.    framing
  *b.    identification
    c.    egocentrism
    d.    structuring
    e.    affiliation

57.    In her speech introduction, Suya said, "Though we are all very different, we are all students here at this university and we are all working toward the completion of a degree. Unfortunately, because of rising tuition, some of us may lose the ability to continue in school." According to your textbook, by seeking to create a bond with her audience through emphasizing their common goals and experiences, Suya was engaging in

   *a.   identification.
    b.   stereotyping.
    c.   ethnocentrism.
    d.   comparison.
    e.   framing.

58.    The fact that audiences are egocentric means that

    a.   listeners believe their cultural group is superior to all other groups.
   *b.   listeners are concerned above all with how a speech will affect them.
    c.   listeners interpret the speech through the speaker's frame of reference.
    d.   all of the above.
    e.   a and b only.

59.    What are the two types of audience analysis discussed in your textbook?

   *a.   demographic and situational
    b.   personal and impersonal
    c.   occupational and educational
    d.   psychological and sociological
    e.   descriptive and analytical

60.    One of the ways speakers analyze audiences is by looking at traits such as age, gender, sexual orientation, religion, group membership, and racial, ethnic and cultural background. According to your textbook, what is this called?

   *a.   demographic audience analysis
    b.   psychological audience analysis
    c.   background audience analysis
    d.   situational audience analysis
    e.   descriptive audience analysis

61.    Which of the following is a demographic characteristic of a speech audience?

   *a.   age
    b.   interest
    c.   size
    d.   attitude
    e.   knowledge

62.    Which of the following is a demographic characteristic of a speech audience?

    a.    interest
    b.    attitude
    c.    size
 *d.    gender
    e.    knowledge

63.    According to your textbook, which of the following is a demographic characteristic of a speech audience?

    a.    knowledge about the subject
    b.    attitude toward the speaker
    c.    interest in the topic
    d.    physical setting
 *e.    cultural background

64.    According to your textbook, which of the following is a demographic characteristic of a speech audience?

    a.    their size
 *b.    their sexual orientation
    c.    their attitude toward the speaker
    d.    their knowledge about the subject
    e.    their attitude toward the occasion

65.    According to your textbook, which of the following is a situational characteristic of a speech audience?

    a.    gender
 *b.    size
    c.    religion
    d.    group membership
    e.    age

66.    According to your textbook, which of the following is a factor in situational audience analysis?

    a.    the audience's cultural background
    b.    the audience's religious beliefs
    c.    the audience's group membership
    d.    the audience's gender
 *e.    the audience's attitude toward the topic

67.    Which of the following is a factor to consider in situational audience analysis?

    a.    gender
    b.    group membership
 *c.    attitude toward the topic
    d.    all of the above
    e.    a and c only

68.    As explained in your textbook, _____ audience analysis usually builds
       on the demographic analysis.

       a.   psychological
       b.   descriptive
       c.   occupational
       d.   background
     *e.   situational


69.    As the size of your audience increases, your presentation should usually become
       more

     *a.   formal.
       b.   flexible.
       c.   extemporaneous.
       d.   punctual.
       e.   informal.


70.    The _____ will usually dictate how long a speech should be.

       a.   size of the audience
     *b.   occasion
       c.   physical setting
       d.   general purpose
       e.   topic


71.    Which of the following elements usually has the greatest impact on the length a
       speech should be?

       a.   the audience's disposition toward the topic
       b.   the physical setting for the speech
       c.   the audience's attitudes toward the speaker
     *d.   the occasion for the speech
       e.   the group membership of the audience


72.    According to your textbook, what are the three primary factors to consider when
       assessing an audience's disposition toward a speech topic?

       a.   gender, knowledge, and opinions
       b.   interest, background, and age
       c.   size, occasion, and group membership
     *d.   knowledge, interest, and attitude
       e.   background, situation, and gender

73. If you were giving a persuasive speech to a general audience on the subject of mandatory retirement, the most important factor to consider when analyzing your audience would probably be its

    a.   economic standing.
    b.   group membership.
    c.   gender.
 *d.   age.
    e.   education.

74. If you were giving a persuasive speech on Medicare to members of the American Association of Retired Persons (AARP), the most important factor to consider when analyzing your audience would probably be the

 *a.   age of the audience.
    b.   gender of the audience.
    c.   audience's attitude toward the speaker.
    d.   physical setting of the speech.
    e.   size of the audience.

75. Ramona is preparing a persuasive speech on environmental issues to present to members of the National Wildlife Federation. The most important factor Ramona should consider when analyzing her audience is probably its

    a.   age.
 *b.   group membership.
    c.   education.
    d.   ethnic background.
    e.   knowledge of the topic.

76. Dimitri plans to give a speech to his classmates about the principles of physics behind the design of hybrid automobiles. The most important factor for Dimitri to consider when analyzing his audience is probably its

    a.   age.
    b.   group membership.
    c.   attitude toward the speaker.
 *d.   knowledge about the topic.
    e.   size.

77. If you were giving an informative speech to your public speaking class about brain aneurysms, the most important factor to consider when analyzing your audience would probably be its

    a.   gender.
 *b.   knowledge about the topic.
    c.   disposition toward the speaker.
    d.   ethnic background.
    e.   physical setting.

78.    Nathan plans to give a speech to his classmates explaining how to create a Web site. The most important factor he should consider when analyzing his audience is probably its

     a.    group membership.
  *b.    knowledge about the topic.
     c.    sexual orientation.
     d.    attitude toward him.
     e.    size.

79.    You are giving a speech on a community building project to a local service organization at its monthly luncheon. Dessert dishes are being cleared away as you walk into the overcrowded, overheated room. The most important situational factor to consider when adapting to your audience would probably be the

     a.    age of your audience.
     b.    audience's attitude toward you.
  *c.    physical setting for your speech.
     d.    education of your audience.
     e.    gender of your audience.

80.    A landlord with a bad reputation among students for her high rent, deceptive advertising, and refusal to return security deposits is speaking to a campus group about how the city's new zoning law will affect students. The most important factor the landlord should consider in her situational audience analysis is probably her listeners'

     a.    gender.
     b.    knowledge of the topic.
  *c.    disposition toward the speaker.
     d.    interest in the topic.
     e.    cultural background.

81.    If you were giving a persuasive speech to a general audience arguing that all children should be required to use standard English in the public schools, the most important factor to consider when analyzing your audience would probably be its

     a.    age.
     b.    religion.
  *c.    ethnic background.
     d.    group membership.
     e.    education.

82.    If you were giving an informative speech to a general audience on the presidency of John F. Kennedy, the most important factor to consider when analyzing your audience would probably be its

  *a.    age.
   b.    religion.
   c.    economic standing.
   d.    gender.
   e.    group membership.

83.    As part of his economics seminar, Geraldo has been invited to give a persuasive speech to a community audience on the subject of Social Security. The most important factor for Geraldo to consider when analyzing his audience is probably its

   a.    occupation.
   b.    gender.
   c.    sexual orientation.
   d.    education.
  *e.    age.

84.    If you were giving a persuasive speech on gun control to members of the National Rifle Association, the most important factor to consider in audience analysis would probably be the

   a.    size of your audience.
  *b.    group membership of your audience.
   c.    economic standing of your audience.
   d.    education of your audience.
   e.    knowledge of your audience.

85.    If you were giving an informative speech to a general audience on Global Positioning Systems technology, the most important factor to consider when analyzing your audience would probably be the

   a.    group membership of the audience.
   b.    size of the audience.
  *c.    knowledge of the audience about the topic.
   d.    gender of the audience.
   e.    physical setting for the speech.

86.    If you were giving an informative speech to a general audience about digital encryption, the most important factor to consider when analyzing your audience would probably be the

   a.    physical setting for the speech.
  *b.    knowledge of the audience about the topic.
   c.    size of the audience.
   d.    occupation of the audience.
   e.    group membership of the audience.

87.    Fran Breit, the golf pro at a local municipal course, has been asked by a social club to give a talk about how to play golf. What is probably the most important factor for Fran to consider in preparing her presentation?

   a.    the age of the audience
   b.    the racial background of the audience
   c.    the time of day the talk will be given
*d.    the audience's knowledge of the topic
   e.    the audience's disposition toward the speaker

88.    Michael is preparing a persuasive speech for class in opposition to gun control. The most important factor for Michael to consider when analyzing his audience is probably its

   a.    knowledge of the topic.
   b.    disposition toward the speaker.
   c.    cultural background.
   d.    religious beliefs.
*e.    attitude toward the topic.

89.    If you were giving an informative speech to a general audience about the war in Vietnam, the most important demographic factor to consider in analyzing your audience would probably be the

   a.    sexual orientation of the audience.
   b.    economic standing of the audience.
   c.    gender of the audience.
*d.    age of the audience.
   e.    education of the audience.

90.    The major advantage of using fixed-alternative questions in an audience analysis questionnaire is that they

   a.    enhance the credibility of the questionnaire.
   b.    get below the surface of respondents' beliefs.
*c.    produce clear, unambiguous answers.
   d.    give respondents maximum leeway in answering.
   e.    require that respondents give truthful answers.

91.    When making up an audience analysis questionnaire, you should use _____ questions to get at the strength of a respondent's attitudes or feelings.

*a.    scale
   b.    fixed-alternative
   c.    leading
   d.    open-ended
   e.    interview

92.    If you were constructing an audience-analysis questionnaire and wanted to learn why some of your listeners do not fasten their seatbelts every time they ride in a motor vehicle, which of the following would be the best kind of question to ask?

    a.    scale question
    b.    leading question
    c.    fixed-alternative question
    d.    demographic question
*e.    open-ended question

93.    A questionnaire item that gives the respondent the widest freedom in answering is called a(n)

    a.    inductive question.
*b.    open-ended question.
    c.    leading question.
    d.    scale question.
    e.    informal question.

94.    If you were constructing an audience-analysis questionnaire and wanted to learn how many of your listeners had ever heard of the Salem witch trials, which of the following would be the best kind of question to ask?

    a.    demographic question
    b.    open-ended question
    c.    leading question
    d.    scale question
*e.    fixed-alternative question

95.    If you were constructing an audience-analysis questionnaire and wanted to learn why some of your listeners had not signed organ donor cards, which of the following would be the best kind of question to ask?

    a.    demographic question
*b.    open-ended question
    c.    leading question
    d.    scale question
    e.    fixed-alternative question

96.    If you were constructing an audience-analysis questionnaire and wanted to learn the strength of your listeners' attitudes for or against animal research, which of the following would be the best kind of question to ask?

    a.    demographic question
    b.    open-ended question
    c.    leading question
*d.    scale question
    e.    fixed-alternative question

97.    The following question from a student audience-analysis questionnaire is an example of what type of question?

    The percent of the U. S. population who speak Spanish in their homes is closest to

    ___    5%
    ___  10%
    ___  20%
    ___  30%

    a.    leading question
    b.    open-ended question
    c.    demographic question
    *d.    fixed-alternative question
    e.    scale question

## Short Answer Questions

98.    Because listeners are ____egocentric____, they typically approach speeches by asking "Why is this important to me?"

99.    Communication scholars use the term ____identification____ to refer to the process by which speakers seek to create a bond with their audiences by emphasizing common values, goals, and experiences.

100.    Age, gender, sexual orientation, religion, group membership, and racial, ethnic or cultural background are among the factors to be considered in ____demographic____ audience analysis.

101.    If you were giving a speech to a general audience about the early days of rock and roll, the ____age____ of your listeners would probably be the most important factor to consider in your demographic audience analysis.

102.    If you were giving a speech to a general audience about the role of women in combat, the ____gender____ of your listeners would probably be the most important factor to consider in your demographic audience analysis.

103.    If you were giving a speech to a general audience on the history of the Watergate crisis, the ____age____ of your listeners would probably be the most important factor to consider in your demographic audience analysis.

104.    As a general rule, the larger your audience, the more ____formal____ your presentation should be.

105.    The three most important factors to consider when determining an audience's disposition toward a speaker's topic are the audience's ____interest____, ____knowledge____, and ____attitude____.

106.   According to your textbook, the five major factors to consider in situational audience analysis are:

    a.   <u>size of the audience</u>

    b.   <u>physical setting of the speech</u>

    c.   <u>the audience's disposition toward the topic</u>

    d.   <u>the audience's disposition toward the speaker</u>

    e.   <u>the audience's disposition toward the occasion</u>

107.   When used in an audience-analysis questionnaire, <u>fixed-alternative</u> questions are valuable because they produce clear, unambiguous answers.

108.   The major advantage of using <u>scale</u> questions in an audience analysis questionnaire is that they help reveal the strength of a respondent's attitudes or feelings.

109.   In constructing an audience analysis questionnaire, you should use <u>open-ended</u> questions when you want to give respondents maximum leeway in answering.

## Essay Questions

110.   What does it mean to say that a public speaker should be "audience-centered"? At what stages in speech preparation should a speaker be concerned about being audience-centered?

111.   Briefly explain the following statement: "To step outside your own frame of reference and see things from another person's point of view is a real achievement. Yet this is exactly what you must learn to do if you are to become a successful speaker."

112.   Explain the following statement: "Every speech situation contains two messages—the one sent by the speaker and the one received by the audience."

113.   Explain why each of the following is an important factor in demographic audience analysis: age; gender; sexual orientation; religion; group membership; racial, ethnic, or cultural background.

114.   Imagine that you are preparing a classroom persuasive speech in favor of abolishing intercollegiate athletics. According to your textbook, what are the three factors to consider in analyzing your audience's disposition toward the topic? In a well-developed essay, explain how differences in each of the three factors might influence your preparation of this speech.

115.   What does it mean to say that people are "egocentric"? What implications does the egocentrism of audiences have for you as a speaker?

116.   What are the three types of questions for audience analysis questionnaires discussed in your text? Give an example of each type and explain the advantages and disadvantages of each.

117.   As your textbook states, "There are two major stages in the process of audience adaptation—the first occurs before the speech, as part of your preparation and rehearsal; the second occurs during the presentation of the speech itself." In a well-developed essay, discuss the steps a speaker might take in adapting her or his speech to the audience in each of these stages.

118.   As a university professor, your research, writing, and teaching in the area of gender-communication has attracted media attention. It seems that nearly everyone is interested in the differences between the communication styles of men and women. You have been asked to address the managers of a large local manufacturing company on the topic of gender communication in the workplace.

   To prepare for your speech, you have arranged a meeting with the company's human resource director—the person who contacted you about giving the speech— in order to learn more about the audience and situation you will be facing. Write an essay in which you discuss (1) the three most important questions you want to ask the resource director about the demographics of your audience, and (2) the three most important questions you want to ask about the situational traits of your audience. Be specific in your questions and explain why each of them is important.

# Chapter 6 Gathering Materials

## True-False Questions

1.  <u>T</u> F     Most library catalogues allow a researcher to look for books by author, title, or subject.

2.  <u>T</u> F     Periodical databases help you locate magazine and journal articles.

3.  T <u>F</u>     As your textbook explains, periodical databases are particularly useful for finding reference works such as encyclopedias.

4.  <u>T</u> F     General periodical databases such as ProQuest Research Library and LexisNexis Academic Universe give you access to the full texts of many articles.

5.  <u>T</u> F     The *Statistical Abstract of the United States* is the standard reference source for numerical information on the social, political, and economic aspects of American life.

6.  <u>T</u> F     Reference works include such items as encyclopedias, biographical aids, and atlases.

7.  <u>T</u> F     The best source for learning about the historical development of a word in the English language is the *Oxford English Dictionary*.

8.  <u>T</u> F     The best known collection of quotations is *Bartlett's Familiar Quotations*.

9.  <u>T</u> F     A gazetteer is a geographical dictionary.

10. T <u>F</u>     As your textbook explains, when you locate an abstract of a magazine article using a computerized periodical database, you should feel free to cite the article in your speech on the basis of the abstract alone.

11. T <u>F</u>     Because it is such a vast source of information, you should use Internet research to replace library research when preparing your speeches.

12.  <u>T</u> F    Experts advise that you use Internet research to supplement, not to replace, library research.

13.  <u>T</u> F    You can find a great deal of information on the Internet, but you cannot always find the same depth of research materials as in a good library.

14.  <u>T</u> F    A search engine is a search aid that indexes Web pages and checks them for sites that match the researcher's request.

15.  T <u>F</u>    Most search engines index about 90 percent of the total number of research sites available on the Internet.

16.  T <u>F</u>    You can almost always count on the reliability of Internet research materials found through major search engines such as Google and Yahoo.

17.  <u>T</u> F    One advantage of using a virtual library for Internet research is that it can give you access to materials from the "Invisible Web" that are not accessible through traditional search engines.

18.  T <u>F</u>    The only way you can use a search engine to find information on the Internet is by conducting a keyword search.

19.  <u>T</u> F    One of the advantages of using the Internet for research is that you can locate information by conducting both subject searches and keyword searches.

20.  <u>T</u> F    A virtual library is a search aid that combines Internet technology with traditional library methods of cataloguing and assessing data.

21.  <u>T</u> F    One advantage of using virtual libraries for speech research is that they contain only material that has been screened for accuracy and reliability.

22.  T <u>F</u>    Yahoo is an example of a virtual library.

23.  <u>T</u> F    One of the strengths of the Internet as a research tool is the access it provides to government documents and publications.

24.  T <u>F</u>    Like magazine and journal articles, most documents posted on the Internet have been subjected to close editorial review.

25.  T <u>F</u>    According to your textbook, the three major criteria against which to test documents that you locate on the Internet are authorship, graphics, and interactivity.

26.  <u>T</u> F    According to your textbook, the three major criteria against which to test documents that you locate on the Internet are authorship, sponsorship, and recency.

27.  T̲ F   If you cannot identify the author of a document on the Web, you should try to determine the sponsoring organization for the document.

28.  T F̲   An interview is an effective way to gather speech materials because it frees you of the need to do research in the library.

29.  T F̲   If you use a tape recorder or a digital recorder in a research interview, you should keep it secret from the person being interviewed.

30.  T̲ F   If you want to record a research interview, you should be sure to get the permission of the person being interviewed.

31.  T̲ F   Your most important task before conducting a research interview is to work out the questions you will ask during the interview.

32.  T F̲   You should avoid asking tough questions during a research interview.

33.  T F̲   As your textbook indicates, you should avoid asking probing questions during a research interview.

34.  T F̲   After conducting an interview you should usually wait a couple of days before reviewing your notes.

35.  T F̲   A preliminary bibliography for research on a speech should usually contain a maximum of three or four sources.

36.  T F̲   If possible, you should write all your research notes from a single book or article on a single index card or sheet of paper.

37.  T̲ F   When taking research notes, it is important to distinguish among direct quotations, paraphrases, and your own ideas.

## Multiple Choice Questions *(Students are to indicate the best answer for each question by circling the correct letter.)*

38.  The _____ is the key to finding information in the library.

   a.   general index
 *b.   catalogue
   c.   periodicals guide
   d.   encyclopedia
   e.   browser

39.    The library's catalogue allows you to search for books by

    a.    author.
    b.    title.
    c.    keyword.
 *d.    all of the above.
    e.    a and b only.

40.    The library catalogue

    a.    lists all the books, periodicals, and other resources owned by the library.
    b.    provides abstracts of magazine and newspaper articles.
    c.    allows a researcher to look for books by author, title, or subject.
    d.    all of the above.
 *e.    a and c only.

41.    Periodical databases

    a.    catalog articles from a large number of journals and magazines.
    b.    are valuable for locating materials in encyclopedias and other reference works.
    c.    often provide abstracts of journal and magazine articles.
    d.    all of the above.
 *e.    a and c only.

42.    Encyclopedias, dictionaries, yearbooks, atlases, gazetteers, and quotation books are all examples of

    a.    research guides.
 *b.    reference works.
    c.    bibliographical aids.
    d.    general indexes.
    e.    special indexes.

43.    A(n) _____ is a research aid that catalogues articles from a large number of journals or magazines.

    a.    abstract
    b.    biographical aid
    c.    reference work
 *d.    periodical database
    e.    keyword index

44.    As part of the research for her persuasive speech on Parkinson's disease, Alissa needs to find recent articles published in general interest periodicals and academic journals. The best resource for her is a

    a.    reliable search engine such as Google.
    b.    yearbook such as *Facts on File* or *World Almanac*.
 *c.    periodical database such as ProQuest or LexisNexis.
    d.    government resource such as FirstGov.
    e.    none of the above.

45.    The best source for numerical data about life in the United States is

    a.    *Who's Who.*
    b.    *Encyclopedia Americana.*
    c.    *World Almanac and Book of Facts.*
    d.    *New York Times Index.*
  *e.    *Statistical Abstract of the United States.*

46.    As part of the research for his informative speech, Malik needs detailed biographical information about United Nations Secretary General Kofi Annan. Which of the following would be the best source for him to consult?

  *a.    *Current Biography*
    b.    *International Editorial Abstracts*
    c.    *World Almanac and Book of Facts*
    d.    *Personal Abstracts*
    e.    *Facts on File*

47.    If you were giving a speech and needed to know the number of people who die each year in the United States from accidental drowning, which of the following would be the best source to consult?

    a.    *Current Biography*
    b.    *Reader's Guide to Periodical Literature*
  *c.    *Statistical Abstract of the United States*
    d.    *Webster's Geographical Dictionary*
    e.    *Encyclopaedia Britannica*

48.    If you needed to learn the number of Americans who own cell phones, which of the following would be the best source to consult?

    a.    *Encyclopedia Americana*
    b.    *U.S. News and World Report*
  *c.    *Statistical Abstract of the United States*
    d.    *Who's Who in America*
    e.    *Social Sciences Index*

49.    If you want to know about the history of a word in the English language, you should turn first to

    a.    *Facts on File.*
    b.    *Roget's Thesaurus.*
    c.    *Encyclopaedia Britannica.*
    d.    *Webster's Geographical Dictionary.*
  *e.    *Oxford English Dictionary.*

50.    You are giving an informative speech about modern music and need to learn the origins of the word "jazz." Which of the following would be the best reference source to consult?

   *a.    *Oxford English Dictionary*
    b.    *Bartlett's Familiar Quotations*
    c.    *World Almanac and Book of Facts*
    d.    *Encyclopedia Americana*
    e.    *Roget's Thesaurus*

51.    You are researching a speech and need to learn how the meaning of the word "science" has changed historically. Which of the following would be the best reference source to consult?

    a.    *Roget's Thesaurus*
    b.    *Encyclopaedia Britannica*
   *c.    *Oxford English Dictionary*
    d.    *Bartlett's Familiar Quotations*
    e.    *Webster's Collegiate Dictionary*

52.    You are researching a speech and need to find a quotation about marriage. Which of the following would be the best reference source to consult?

    a.    *International Who's Who*
    b.    *Oxford English Dictioinary*
    c.    *World Almanac and Book of Facts*
    d.    *Webster's Unabridged Dictionary*
   *e.    *Bartlett's Familiar Quotations*

53.    *Who's Who Among American Women* is an example of a(n)

    a.    encyclopedia.
    b.    special dictionary.
    c.    periodical index.
   *d.    biographical aid.
    e.    yearbook.

54.    According to your textbook, when is it appropriate to cite an abstract of a magazine or journal article in your speech rather than locating and reading the full article?

   *a.    never
    b.    when the article is more than five years old
    c.    when the article is not available on a computerized database
    d.    when the only copy of the article is on the book shelves
    e.    when the article is short enough to be summarized in one paragraph

55.   The two kinds of Internet search aids discussed in your chapter are

   *a.   search engines and virtual libraries.
   b.   browsers and cyberguides.
   c.   electronic catalogues and graphical interfaces.
   d.   Google and Internet Explorer.
   e.   metasearch engines and Web crawlers.

56.   As your textbook explains, virtual libraries are valuable for speech research because they

   a.   contain higher quality information than do traditional search engines.
   b.   access the "invisible Web" that is not indexed by traditional search engines.
   c.   allow a researcher to locate more sources than do traditional search engines.
   d.   all of the above.
   *e.   a and b only.

57.   The search aid that makes it easy to find high-quality Web resources by combining Internet technology with traditional library methods of cataloguing and assessing data is known as a(n)

   a.   abstract index.
   *b.   virtual library.
   c.   periodical database.
   d.   digital reference.
   e.   electronic catalogue.

58.   A _____ is a search aid that combines Internet technology with traditional library methods of cataloguing and assessing data.

   a.   cyber catalogue
   b.   metasearch engine
   *c.   virtual library
   d.   reference locator
   e.   Web crawler

59.   As your textbook explains, the best kind of search aid for locating reliable, high quality information on the Internet is a(n)

   a.   search engine.
   b.   electronic catalogue.
   c.   metasearch engine.
   d.   research pilot.
   *e.   virtual library.

60.    According to your textbook, the three criteria for judging the reliability of research documents located on the Internet are authorship, sponsorship, and

    a.    interest.
    b.    formality.
    c.    interactivity.
  *d.    recency.
    e.    graphics.

61.    What are the three criteria discussed in your textbook for assessing the soundness of documents found on the Internet?

    a.    length, accuracy, and graphics
    b.    interactivity, objectivity, and authorship
    c.    graphics, sponsorship, and accuracy
    d.    creativity, reliability, and length
  *e.    authorship, sponsorship, and recency

62.    According to your textbook, the three criteria for judging the reliability of documents located on the Internet are recency, authorship, and

    a.    indexing.
  *b.    sponsorship.
    c.    interactivity.
    d.    graphics.
    e.    creativity.

63.    If you can't identify the author of a document on the Internet, your textbook recommends that you

    a.    look up the year the document was published.
    b.    bookmark the document and return to it later.
  *c.    try to determine the sponsoring organization for the document.
    d.    double check the accuracy of the document's URL.
    e.    search for the document in the library.

64.    According to your textbook, when quoting an Internet document during a speech, a speaker should identify the

    a.    search aid used to find the document.
    b.    author of the document if the author's name is known.
    c.    organization responsible for the document if the author's name is not known.
    d.    all of the above.
  *e.    b and c only.

65.    In her speech on depression, Aida said: "According to materials I located through a Google search, almost 20 million American adults suffer from a depressive illness serious enough to interfere with their jobs and their family life." According to your textbook, has Aida made any mistakes in citing her sources?

    a.    No. Aida gave the audience a clear statistic from the Internet.
    b.    Yes. Aida should have given the exact statistic instead of rounding it off to 20 million.
*c.    Yes. Aida should have identified the organization that sponsored the Web site.
    d.    Yes. Aida should have stated the statistic without mentioning where she found it.
    e.    No. Aida cited Google, which is a reputable Internet search engine.

66.    According to your textbook, when quoting an Internet document during a speech, a speaker should identify the

    a.    full URL of the document.
*b.    author or sponsoring organization responsible for the document.
    c.    search aid used to find the document.
    d.    all of the above.
    e.    a and b only.

67.    According to your textbook, when citing an Internet document in a speech bibliography, you should include the

    a.    .date on which you accessed the document.
    b.    organization responsible for the document if the author's name is not known.
    c.    URL of the document.
*d.    all of the above.
    e.    b and c only.

68.    According to your textbook, when citing an Internet document in a speech bibliography, you should include the

    a.    title of the document.
    b.    author or sponsoring organization responsible for the document.
    c.    date on which you accessed the document.
*d.    all of the above.
    e.    a and b only.

69.    The most important task when preparing to conduct a research interview is

*a.    devising questions to ask during the interview.
    b.    deciding whether or not to record the interview.
    c.    choosing what to wear during the interview.
    d.    selecting an appropriate interviewing style.
    e.    deciding whether to take notes during the interview.

70. According to your textbook, when preparing questions for a research interview, you should

    a. avoid questions you can answer without the interview.
    b. organize questions alphabetically by subject.
    c. arrange questions in the order you want to ask them.
    d. all of the above.
\*e. a and c only.

71. When taking research notes, you should

    a. take only a few notes so you do not get too much information.
    b. put all the notes from each source on a single index card or sheet of paper.
\*c. distinguish among quotations, paraphrases, and your own ideas.
    d. record notes only when you're sure you'll use the information in your speech.
    e. all of the above.

72. When taking research notes, you should

    a. put all notes from each source on a single index card or sheet of paper.
    b. record notes only when you're sure you'll use the information in your speech.
    c. take all notes as direct quotations.
    d. all of the above.
\*e. none of the above.

73. Antonio is researching his speech on West Nile Virus. According to your textbook, Antonio should

    a. make a preliminary bibliography.
    b. think about his research materials as he is gathering them.
    c. distinguish among direct quotations, paraphrases, and his own ideas.
\*d. all of the above.
    e. a and c only.

74. Claudia is researching her speech on the use of hydrogen fuel cells as an energy source. According to your textbook, Claudia should

    a. make a separate entry for each note.
    b. take notes only from sources she knows she will cite in the speech.
    c. use index cards if she writes notes by hand.
    d. all of the above.
\*e. a and c only.

75. The preliminary bibliography

    a. is based on the speaker's personal knowledge about the topic.
\*b. lists each source that looks as if it might be helpful in speech.
    c. should be prepared after the speaker has finished researching the speech.
    d. should contain a maximum of three or four sources.
    e. identifies sources that the speaker is sure will be used in the speech.

76.   Ivan has decided to give his persuasive speech on stem-cell research. Which of the following tips for doing research discussed in your textbook should he keep in mind as he works on the speech?

&ast;a.   include a subject heading on each note.
  b.   put all the information from each source on a single note.
  c.   use a different format for notes from Internet sources and library documents.
  d.   all of the above.
  e.   a and c only.

77.   The two major formats mentioned in your textbook for citing works in a speech bibliography are from the

  a.   American Library Association (ALA) and National Bibliography Center (NBC).
  b.   Educational Testing Service (ETS) and American Style Manual (ASM).
  c.   International Citation Index (ICI) and American Communication Association (ACA).
  d.   Social Science Manual (SSM) and Humanities Bibliography Guide (HBG).
&ast;e.   Modern Language Association (MLA) and American Psychological Association (APA).

78.   According to your textbook, which of the following is a guideline for preparing a preliminary bibliography?

&ast;a.   Write a brief note on why the source may be valuable for your speech.
  b.   Include only those sources that you are certain to use in your speech.
  c.   Try to get as many sources as possible on each index card or sheet of paper.
  d.   all of the above
  e.   b and c only

## Short Answer Questions

79.   A(n) _____periodical database_____ is a research aid that catalogues articles from a large number of journals and magazines.

80.   A(n) _____abstract_____ is a summary of a magazine or journal article, written by someone other than the original author.

81.   The standard reference source published by the United States government for numerical information on American life is _____Statistical Abstract of the United States_____.

82.   The _____Oxford English Dictionary_____ is the best source for learning about the historical evolution of a word in the English language.

83.   According to your textbook, when is it appropriate to cite an abstract of a magazine or journal article in your speech rather than locating and reading the full article?

  _____One should never cite an article in a speech on the basis of the abstract alone._____

84.    A(n) _____virtual library_____ is a search aid that combines Internet technology with traditional library methods of cataloguing and assessing data.

85.    What are the three criteria discussed in your textbook for assessing the soundness of documents found on the Internet?

    a.    _____authorship_____

    b.    _____sponsorship_____

    c.    _____recency_____

86.    When doing research, you should prepare a _____preliminary bibliography_____ that includes all the books or articles you find that look as if they might be useful in your speech.

## Essay Questions

87.    What is a reference work? Identify and explain four of the kinds of reference works discussed in your textbook.

88.    What is a periodical database? In your answer, be sure to give an example of a periodical database and to explain the kinds of information most periodical databases provide.

89.    When is an interview an effective means of gathering information for a speech?

90.    Your textbook describes six steps an interviewer should take during a research interview to help make the interview process go smoothly. In a well-developed essay, identify and explain four of these steps.

91.    Explain the following statement: "Every interview is unique. Just as a speaker adapts to an audience during a speech, so must an interviewer adapt to the person being interviewed."

92.    Once an interview is over, the interviewer still has two major tasks to complete the interview process. What are they and why are they important?

93.    What is a preliminary bibliography? Why is preparing a preliminary bibliography an important step in researching a speech?

94.    Explain the five guidelines presented in the text for taking research notes efficiently.

# Chapter 7 Supporting Your Ideas

## True-False Questions

1. <u>T</u> F     The selection and use of supporting materials for a speech involves critical thinking skills.

2. <u>T</u> F     One of the main reasons to use examples in a speech is that they put abstract ideas into concrete terms that listeners can easily understand.

3. T <u>F</u>     According to your textbook, the two basic types of supporting materials are facts and hypothetical examples.

4. T <u>F</u>     Research has shown that examples have little effect on listeners' beliefs and actions.

5. T <u>F</u>     Although examples work very well to clarify ideas in an informative speech, they are less effective in a persuasive speech.

6. <u>T</u> F     Examples are particularly effective as supporting materials because they help get the audience involved in a speech.

7. <u>T</u> F     Brief examples can be used either to illustrate a point or to introduce a topic.

8. <u>T</u> F     A hypothetical example describes an imaginary or fictitious situation.

9. <u>T</u> F     Hypothetical examples can be especially powerful as supporting materials when they create scenarios that involve the audience.

10. <u>T</u> F     Whenever you use a hypothetical example in a speech, it is usually a good idea to follow it with statistics or testimony to show that the example is not unrealistic.

11.  T <u>F</u>    Because of their high credibility, you should use only factual examples in your speeches.

12.  T <u>F</u>    As a speaker, you should usually avoid examples when explaining complex or unfamiliar ideas.

13.  T <u>F</u>    As your textbook makes clear, a vivid, richly textured extended example is usually effective regardless of how well it is delivered.

14.  T <u>F</u>    As your textbook explains, statistics are the most effective type of supporting material because they are difficult to manipulate or distort.

15.  <u>T</u> F    The mean—popularly called the average—is determined by summing all the items in a group and dividing by the number of items.

16.  T <u>F</u>    The median is determined by summing all the items in a group and dividing by the number of items.

17.  <u>T</u> F    The median is the middle number in a group of numbers arranged in order from highest to lowest.

18.  <u>T</u> F    The mode is the number that occurs most frequently in a group of numbers.

19.  T <u>F</u>    It is seldom necessary to cite the source of statistics in a speech.

20.  <u>T</u> F    Your textbook recommends using visual aids to make statistics easier for listeners to comprehend.

21.  T <u>F</u>    Research has shown that the more statistics you use, the more effective your speech is likely to be.

22.  T <u>F</u>    Unlike testimony, which can easily be quoted out of context, statistics are difficult to manipulate for biased purposes.

23.  <u>T</u> F    In most cases, you should round off statistics when presenting them in a speech.

24.  <u>T</u> F    To be most effective in a speech, statistics need to be interpreted and explained in terms that are meaningful to the audience.

25.  T <u>F</u>    Using strong, credible testimony is the best way to add human interest to a speech.

26.  <u>T</u> F    Acceptable testimony can include either statements from recognized experts or from ordinary people with special expertise on the topic.

27.  <u>T</u> F    Peer testimony is made up of opinions from ordinary people with firsthand experience or insight on a topic.

28.  T F̲    Peer testimony is highly credible in a speech because it comes from people who are recognized experts on the topic.

29.  T F̲    It is seldom necessary to name the people you quote or paraphrase in a speech.

30.  T̲ F    When you use testimony in a speech, it is acceptable either to paraphrase or to use a direct quotation.

31.  T F̲    Examples and testimony are most effective in persuasive speeches, while statistics work best in informative speeches.

32.  T F̲    Statistics are most effective in persuasive speeches, while examples and testimony work best in informative speeches.

33.  T F̲    It is seldom a good idea to use examples and testimony in the same speech.

## Multiple Choice Questions *(Students are to indicate the best answer for each question by circling the correct letter.)*

34.    Using _____ is the best way to pull listeners into your speeches.

   a.  peer testimony
   b.  statistics
  *c.  extended examples
   d.  visual aids
   e.  brief examples

35.    The more _____ your examples, the greater impact they are likely to have.

   a.  hypothetical
   b.  complex
   c.  unusual
   d.  expert
  *e.  vivid

36.    Examples are especially helpful as supporting materials because they

  *a.  personalize your ideas.
   b.  are not overly technical.
   c.  quantify a speaker's ideas.
   d.  are harder to manipulate than statistics or testimony.
   e.  enhance the speaker's credibility.

37.    Your textbook presents each of the following as a tip for using examples in a speech *except*

   a.    use examples to personalize your ideas.
   b.    practice delivery to enhance your extended examples.
   c.    make your examples vivid and richly textured.
*d.    combine examples with causal reasoning.
   e.    use examples to clarify your ideas.

38.    Alisha began the introduction of her speech by saying:

   Have you ever been knocked down so hard by life that you didn't feel you'd ever get back up? This has happened to me many times, the first being when I tried to ride a bicycle when I was very young. Today I want to discuss with you some basic strategies for coping with life's challenges.

   What kind of supporting material did Alisha use in her introduction?

   a.    expert testimony
*b.    brief example
   c.    metaphor
   d.    hypothetical example
   e.    simile

39.    According to your textbook, an imaginary story that makes a general point is called a(n)

   a.    mythical example.
   b.    artificial example.
   c.    spurious example.
*d.    hypothetical example.
   e.    synthetic example.

40.    According to your textbook, an imaginary story that makes a general point is called a(n)

   a.    anecdote.
   b.    simulated example.
*c.    hypothetical example.
   d.    narrative.
   e.    illustration.

41.    Accomplished speakers consider _____ "the very life of the speech."

   a.    statistics
   b.    causal reasoning
   c.    testimony
*d.    examples
   e.    emotional appeals

42.    In a speech about valley fever, a potentially deadly disease that has reached serious proportions in several southwestern states, a speaker said:

> After being plagued by asthma attacks in Hawaii for six years, Lori Crown hoped to find relief by moving to the dryer climate in Bakersfield, California. A few months after arriving in Bakersfield, Crown was suffering from severe headaches, swollen feet, painful bumps on her hands and legs, and a prolonged fever. The diagnosis—valley fever.
>
> To combat the disease, Crown has to take fluconazole, an antifungal drug that costs $685 for a one-month supply of pills. Although the drug helps, Crown still gets painful headaches, frequent fevers, and debilitating fatigue. "It's so frustrating," Crown says. "One day I'll feel fine, then I'll be in bed for the next three." Most days she wishes she had stayed in Hawaii.

According to your textbook, what kind of supporting material is used in this statement?

   a.    scientific example
*b.    extended example
   c.    hypothetical example
   d.    illustrative example
   e.    expert example

43.    Ryan began his speech by saying:

> Imagine that you are on a deserted island—palm trees sway in the breeze, the warm sun is on your face, and the smell of tropical flowers is in the air. Suddenly, the sound of distant drums breaks your euphoria. What do you do—panic? What would you do if you found yourself in such a situation?

What kind of supporting material did Ryan use in his introduction?

   a.    peer testimony
   b.    extended metaphor
   c.    synthetic example
   d.    artificial simile
*e.    hypothetical example

44.    Which of the following is recommended by your textbook as a way to enhance the effectiveness of your examples?

   a.    Practice delivery to enhance your extended examples.
   b.    Avoid using examples drawn from your personal experience.
   c.    Make your examples vivid and richly textured.
   d.    all of the above
*e.    a and c only

45.    According to your textbook, what kind of supporting material is used in the following speech excerpt:

> Imagine yourself driving down the freeway on your way to work. You see lights flashing in your rear view mirror. You turn to see the police officer pulling you over. Were you speeding? No, says the officer, but he needs to search your vehicle as part of a new program to stop drug trafficking. Does he have a warrant? He says he doesn't need one. You protest, but the officer carries out his search anyway. The officer finds nothing, but by the time he is done, you are very late for work.

  a.    analogical example
*b.    hypothetical example
  c.    causal example
  d.    synthetic example
  e.    metaphorical example

46.    Research indicates that the impact of examples is greatly enhanced when they are combined with _____ that show(s) the examples to be typical.

  a.    analogies
  b.    causal reasoning
  c.    credibility statements
  d.    emotional appeals
*e.    statistics

47.    Which of the following statistical measures corresponds to what is popularly called "the average"?

  a.    the medial
*b.    the mean
  c.    the medium
  d.    the mode
  e.    the median

48.    What is the mean in the following set of numbers: 100, 300, 500, 500, 600?

  a.    300
*b.    400
  c.    500
  d.    550
  e.    600

49.    What is the median in the following set of numbers: 200, 300, 500, 600, 600?

  a.    200
  b.    350
  c.    440
*d.    500
  e.    600

50.    What is the mode in the following set of numbers: 300, 400, 400, 600, 800?

    a.   300
\*b.   400
    c.   450
    d.   500
    e.   700

51.    To say that the *mean* salary of a major league baseball player is $2.3 million is to say that

    a.   no major league baseball player makes less than $2.3 million.
    b.   more major league baseball players earn $2.3 million than any other salary.
\*c.   when you average all the salaries paid to major leaguers, the result is $2.3 million.
    d.   when you list all the players' salaries in order, $2.3 million is the middle salary.
    e.   none of the above.

52.    To say that the *median* salary of a major league baseball player is $800,000 is to say that

    a.   more major league baseball players earn $800,000 than any other salary.
    b.   when you average all the salaries paid to major leaguers, the result is $800,000.
\*c.   when you list all the players' salaries in order, $800,000 is the middle salary.
    d.   no major league baseball player makes less than $800,000.
    e.   none of the above.

53.    To say that the *mode* salary of a major league baseball player is $600,000 is to say that

\*a.   more major league baseball players earn $600,000 than any other salary.
    b.   when you list all the players' salaries in order, $600,000 is the middle salary.
    c.   when you average all the salaries paid to major leaguers, the result is $600,000.
    d.   no major league baseball player makes less than $600,000.
    e.   none of the above.

54.    The main value of using statistics in a speech is to

    a.   lend realism to the speech.
    b.   enhance the speaker's credibility.
    c.   make the speech more vivid.
    d.   avoid relying on testimony.
\*e.   quantify the speaker's ideas.

55.    To give statistics greater impact, a speaker should

    a.   avoid using visual aids with the statistics.
    b.   cite exact numbers rather than rounding off.
\*c.   avoid using too many statistics.
    d.   combine the statistics with technical language.
    e.   conceal the source of the statistics.

56.    To ask if the statistics from a survey are "representative" is to ask if

    a.    statistical measures were used correctly in presenting the survey results.
    b.    the survey results represent statistics that a wide range of experts agree are accurate.
  *c.    the sample group surveyed accurately represents the group about whom a claim is being made.
    d.    all of the above.
    e.    a and b only.

57.    According to your textbook, when you use statistics in a speech, you should usually

  *a.    round off complicated statistics.
    b.    combine the statistics with a hypothetical example.
    c.    use a large number of statistics.
    d.    increase your speaking rate when giving statistics.
    e.    manipulate the statistics to make a point.

58.    When using statistics in a speech, you should usually

    a.    manipulate the statistics to make your point.
    b.    cite exact numbers rather than rounding off.
    c.    increase your speaking rate when giving statistics.
  *d.    avoid using too many statistics.
    e.    conceal the source of the statistics.

59.    Each of the following is mentioned in your textbook as a tip for using statistics *except*

    a.    use statistics sparingly.
    b.    use visual aids to clarify statistical trends.
    c.    round off complicated statistics.
    d.    identify the source of your statistics.
  *e.    avoid using statistics found on the Internet.

60.    According to your textbook, when evaluating statistics you should ask whether they

    a.    are from a reliable source.
    b.    use statistical measures correctly.
    c.    are representative of what they claim to measure.
  *d.    all of the above.
    e.    b and c only.

61.    According to your textbook, a good way to clarify statistical trends is to

    a.    increase your speaking rate when giving statistics.
    b.    consult the *Guinness Book of World Records*.
    c.    use exact numbers rather than rounding off.
  *d.    use visual aids when presenting statistics.
    e.    make sure the statistics are from unbiased sources.

62.    How does the following excerpt from a classroom speech violate the guidelines for the use of statistics presented in your textbook?

>   I discovered on the Internet that each year for every 100,000 students living in college dormitories there are 4 cases of bacterial meningitis.

    a.    It doesn't round off the statistics.
    b.    It doesn't state the statistics clearly.
  *c.    It doesn't cite a qualified source for the statistics.
    d.    all of the above.
    e.    b and c only.

63.    How does the following excerpt from a classroom speech violate the guidelines for using statistics presented in your textbook?

>   One magazine reports that U.S. consumers pay more than $300 billion a year on products to cover the manufacturers' liability costs. This amounts to a staggering $4,000 per household. On a specific basis, product liability costs account for $11.50 of every $12 dose of vaccine we give our children, and over $100 of the cost of a football helmet.

    a.    It doesn't relate statistics to the audience.
  *b.    It doesn't identify the source of statistics.
    c.    It doesn't use statistics to quantify ideas.
    d.    all of the above
    e.    a and b only

64.    How does the following excerpt from a classroom speech violate the guidelines for supporting materials presented in your textbook?

>   According to a CNN/*USA Today* poll taken last month, 57.63 percent of those surveyed support legislation to ban the cloning of human beings.

    a.    It doesn't use a qualified source for statistics.
  *b.    It doesn't round off statistics.
    c.    It doesn't use up-to-date statistics.
    d.    all of the above
    e.    a and c only

65.    The main value of using expert testimony in a speech is to

    a.    enhance the vividness of the speaker's ideas.
    b.    gain attention in the introduction of the speech.
  *c.    build the credibility of speakers who are not experts on their topics.
    d.    keep the audience's attention throughout the body of the speech.
    e.    relate the speaker's ideas directly to the audience.

66.    According to your textbook, if you quoted Dr. Anthony D'Allesandro, a world-renowned transplant surgeon, on the organ shortage problem, what kind of testimony would you be using?

    a.    valid
    b.    peer
    c.    professional
  *d.    expert
    e.    unbiased

67.    According to your textbook, if you quoted Harvard business professor John B. Matthews on the strengths and weaknesses of U.S. business schools, you would be using _____ testimony.

    a.    peer
    b.    professional
  *c.    expert
    d.    unbiased
    e.    valid

68.    To paraphrase is to

    a.    create a new way of describing an event.
    b.    violate ethical standards of public speaking.
    c.    use someone else's words so you don't have to credit them.
  *d.    give the gist of someone's statement in your own words.
    e.    use testimony for persuasive speeches.

69.    According to your textbook, when presenting testimony in a speech, you should usually paraphrase the testimony, rather than quote it verbatim, if

    a.    the quotation is more than two or three sentences long.
    b.    you need to alter the quotation so it will say what you need to prove your point.
    c.    the wording of the quotation is obscure or cumbersome.
    d.    all of the above.
  *e.    a and c only.

70.    To give the gist of someone's statement in your own words is to

  *a.    paraphrase.
    b.    hypothesize.
    c.    corroborate.
    d.    testify.
    e.    quote.

71.    According to your textbook, if you quoted Joy Perkins Newman, a National
       Institutes of Health researcher, on the causes of adolescent depression, what kind of
       testimony would you be using?

    a.    peer
   *b.    expert
    c.    professional
    d.    scientific
    e.    direct

72.    Using expert testimony is an excellent way to lend _____ to your
       speeches.

    a.    vividness
    b.    reliability
    c.    concreteness
   *d.    credibility
    e.    professionalism

73.    According to your textbook, if you quoted your cousin about her experience digging
       for dinosaur bones last summer, you would be using _____ testimony.

   *a.    peer
    b.    personal
    c.    paraphrased
    d.    ordinary
    e.    direct

74.    In her speech about spouse abuse, Nilofer said:

       According to the director of the local battered woman's shelter,
       spouse abuse has become a more serious problem in the past ten
       years than ever before.

       According to your textbook, what kind of supporting material did Nilofer use?

    a.    peer testimony
    b.    scientific testimony
   *c.    expert testimony
    d.    hypothetical testimony
    e.    logical testimony

75.    When Julia Wang quoted former U.S. Social Security Commissioner Dorcas Hardy
       in her speech on reforming the Social Security system, she was using what your
       textbook calls _____ testimony.

    a.    peer
    b.    legitimate
    c.    professional
    d.    accurate
   *e.    expert

76.     According to your textbook, if you quoted tsunami survivor Suvik Jayaratne on the hardships that continue to face residents trying to rebuild their lives in Sri Lanka, you would be using _____ testimony.

*a.    peer
 b.    informal
 c.    representative
 d.    professional
 e.    expert

77.     In her speech about child abuse, Kim included the following statement:

 The effects of child abuse last long after the child has grown to adulthood. As one victim of child abuse stated in a local newspaper article just last week, "I know it sounds crazy, but sometimes I still wake up in fear in the middle of the night. Even worse, I find myself raging at my own children and treating them like my parents treated me."

According to your textbook, what kind of supporting material did Kim use?

*a.    peer testimony
 b.    extended testimony
 c.    authoritative testimony
 d.    expert testimony
 e.    valid testimony

78.     According to your textbook, if you quoted Juanita Ramirez, a resident of Los Angeles, on the psychological effects of the 1994 Los Angeles earthquake, you would be using _____ testimony.

 a.    private
 b.    personal
 c.    expert
 d.    occasional
*e.    peer

79.     Which of the following would probably be the most reliable source of testimony in a speech about the impact of automobile exhaust on air pollution?

 a.    the president of General Motors
 b.    a sociology professor at Yale University
*c.    the U.S. Environmental Protection Agency
 d.    a public relations officer at Ford Motors
 e.    the head of the Better Business Bureau

80.    What guideline presented in your textbook for using supporting materials is followed in this speech excerpt?

> According to the Office for Substance Abuse Prevention, alcohol is the leading cause of death among young adults. Furthermore, of college students currently enrolled in the United States, more than 240,000 will eventually lose their lives to alcohol. Two hundred forty thousand—that's the current student population of this university six times over.

  *a.    Relate statistics to the audience.
    b.    Use extended examples to personalize ideas.
    c.    Paraphrase sources whenever presenting testimony.
    d.    all of the above
    e.    b and c only

81.    What suggestion presented in your textbook for using supporting materials is used in the following speech excerpt?

> Since it first opened for business, McDonald's has sold over 100 billion hamburgers. To give you an idea how many hamburgers that is, think of it this way: Since each McDonald's burger (with the bun) is about 2 inches thick, 100 billion hamburgers stacked on top of each other would reach over 3 million miles—fifteen times as far as the moon.

  *a.    explain your statistics
    b.    present testimony from qualified sources
    c.    use examples to quantify ideas
    d.    quote or paraphrase accurately
    e.    use statistics to personalize ideas

82.    What suggestion presented in your textbook for using statistics is followed in the following speech excerpt?

> If it seems as if you spend a lot of time going back and forth from your job, it's probably because you do. According to figures compiled by management consultant Jeff Davidson, the average American commutes 157,600 miles to and from work during his or her working life. That's equal to driving six times around the earth.

    a.    use statistics to quantify ideas
    b.    identify the source of statistics
    c.    relate statistics to the audience
  *d.    all of the above
    e.    b and c only

## Short Answer Questions

83.     According to your textbook, the three basic kinds of supporting materials are
        _____examples_____ , _____statistics_____ , and _____testimony_____ .

84.     According to your textbook, an imaginary story that makes a general point is called
        a(n) _____hypothetical_____ example.

85.     The _____mean_____, popularly called the average, is determined by adding up all
        the items in a group and dividing by the number of items.

86.     The _____median_____ is the middle figure in a group once the numbers are put in
        order from highest to lowest.

87.     The number that occurs the most in a group of numbers is the _____mode_____.

88.     According to your textbook, what three questions should you ask when evaluating
        statistics?

        a.     _____Are the statistics representative?_____

        b.     _____Are statistical measures used correctly?_____

        c.     _____Are the statistics from a reliable source?_____

89.     If you quoted Charles McCreery, director of the Pacific Tsunami Warning Center,
        on the new systems in place for early detection of possible tsunamis, you would be
        using _____expert_____ testimony.

90.     If you quoted your brother who plays football in high school about steroid use
        among high school athletes, you would be using _____peer_____ testimony.

91.     If you quoted the head of the United States Centers for Disease Control on chronic
        fatigue syndrome, you would be using _____expert_____ testimony.

92.     If you quoted Nobel Prize winning novelist Toni Morrison on recent developments
        in popular literature, you would be using _____expert_____ testimony.

93.     If you quoted your roommate in a speech about the stress of being a college student,
        you would be using _____peer_____ testimony.

94.    If you quoted your younger cousin in a speech about her experience playing youth soccer, you would be using _____peer_____ testimony.

95.    When you give the gist of someone else's statement in your own words, rather than quoting that person verbatim, you are _____paraphrasing_____.

## Essay Questions

96.    Why are examples such effective ways to support ideas in a speech?

97.    Explain the differences among the three types of examples discussed in the textbook. How can each be used effectively to support a speaker's ideas?

98.    Explain the following statement: "Strictly speaking, statistics don't lie. But they can be easily manipulated and distorted." In your answer, include three examples of how statistics can be unethically manipulated and distorted.

99.    Explain the differences among the mean, the median, and the mode as statistical measures.

100.    Your textbook provides six tips for the effective use of statistics in a speech. Identify and explain four of these tips.

101.    Explain why each of the following would or would not be a reliable source of statistics in a speech about the environmental impact of drilling for oil in U.S. national parks.

    a.    the president of Shell Oil
    b.    a spokesperson for the National Wildlife Federation
    c.    a professor of economics at Stanford University

102.    What is the difference between peer testimony and expert testimony? Are there cases where the lines begin to blur? What are the principal benefits of using each kind of testimony in a speech?

103.    Identify and explain the four major guidelines discussed in your textbook for using testimony effectively in a speech.

104.    Each of the following statements violates at least one of the criteria presented in your textbook for the use of supporting materials. Identify the flaw (or flaws) in each statement.

    a.    As Matt Damon stated in a recent interview, America must act now to protect its national parks. If we do not take action right away, Damon said, the park system may be permanently damaged.

    b.    According to a study by American Airlines, the quality of service in the U.S. airline industry has never been better.

    c.    Every day 15,000 people die of starvation. That's one person every 4.5 seconds. A half-billion people are chronically hungry. The U.S. Bureau of Labor states that over a billion people are trying to subsist on less than $300 a year for a family of four. Of that billion people, one-half are starving. An additional 1 billion people in 40 nations try to live on 27 cents a day.

105.    What are the three major types of supporting materials used in public speeches? Evaluate the use of all three types in the following speech excerpt. Be sure to deal with *all* the supporting materials in the excerpt, and be specific in your evaluation.

    Wetlands include swamps, marshes, lakes, any area that is full of water. In addition to providing habitat for thousands of different animals, wetlands are a major barrier to the damage caused by the flooding of lakes and rivers. According to William Niering, "Because they hold water like sponges, wetlands prolong and moderate runoff after heavy precipitation or snow melt. Without wetlands, floods would ravage the American landscape."

    Wetlands also help protect the quality of America's water supply. Mark Christianson, a lobbyist for environmental issues, stated in the *Nebraska Law Review* that "Filtration of pollution is one of the most valuable functions of wetlands. Wetlands can recycle amazing amounts of polluted water."

    Yet despite their many benefits, America's wetlands are being destroyed by business interests and urban sprawl. Imagine a canteen full of water. This canteen could provide almost a week's worth of refreshment in a hot desert. But what if there was a small hole in the canteen? Then the water might last just five days, or four, or maybe just two. This is what is happening to America's wetlands. More than 11 million acres of American wetlands—an expanse twice the size of New Jersey—have been drained in the past three decades. Ten times that amount have been lost since the Pilgrims arrived. Environmentalists report that today we are losing wetlands at an average rate of 458,246 acres each year. The hole in the canteen is dripping.

106.    Each of the following statements violates at least one of the criteria for effective supporting materials. Explain the flaw (or flaws) in each statement.

a.    According to the Department of Health and Human Services, last year there were 6,157,246 students enrolled in American colleges and universities. For the first time in American history, women outnumbered men on campus—52 percent to 48 percent. Moreover, a recent magazine reports that 35 percent of all college students are now over the age of thirty.

b.    A random poll taken recently in Washington, D.C., showed that 78 percent of those interviewed opposed term limitations on U.S. senators and representatives. Clearly, then, the American people oppose such limitations.

c.    In the words of one observer, "As we enter the new millennium, the American public school system is just not working as it should." For example, in 1979 national test scores in English, math, and science were all lower than in 1969. As further evidence, test scores in the local school district declined by 10 percent during the 1980s.

107.    Each of the following statements violates at least one of the criteria for effective supporting materials. Explain the flaw (or flaws) in each statement.

a.    According to a survey sponsored by Verizon Wireless, Americans believe that the quality of customer service provided by cell phone companies has never been better than it is now.

b.    As Angelina Jolie stated in a recent interview, American foreign policy toward Cuba must be revised before the U.S. causes even more damage to the lives of the average Cuban.

c.    Nearly 5,000 drivers aged 70 or older were killed in automobile accidents last year. That's a 33 percent increase over the past 10 years. There are currently 24 million U.S. drivers over age 70, and within 20 years there will be more than 30 million. The National Highway Safety Traffic Administration notes that the fatality rate for drivers 85 and older is nine times as high as the rate for drivers aged 25 to 69, while a 1990 study points out that 18 percent of fatalities to pedestrians were caused by drivers over the age of 70.

---

# Chapter **8** Organizing the Body of the Speech

## True-False Questions

1. T <u>F</u>   Clear organization is usually less important in speaking than in writing.

2. <u>T</u> F   Audiences find well-organized speakers to be more credible than poorly organized speakers.

3. <u>T</u> F   How well a speech is organized affects how listeners view the speaker's competence and trustworthiness.

4. <u>T</u> F   Research suggests that using a clear, specific method of speech organization can enhance your ability to deliver a speech fluently.

5. T <u>F</u>   The introduction of a speech usually should be prepared before the body.

6. <u>T</u> F   According to your textbook, it is usually best to prepare the body of the speech before the introduction.

7. T <u>F</u>   Once you know the main points of your speech, you should then formulate your specific purpose.

8. <u>T</u> F   Most speeches should contain from two to five main points.

9. T <u>F</u>   According to your textbook, most speeches should contain from five to eight main points.

10. T <u>F</u>   If a speech is 45 minutes long, an audience can be expected to keep track of as many as a dozen main points.

11. T <u>F</u>   The time given to each main point in the body of a speech should be exactly the same.

12.  T̲ F    When developing a speech, you should try to roughly balance the amount of time devoted to each main point.

13.  T̲ F    The most effective order for the main points of a speech depends upon the topic, the specific purpose, and the audience.

14.  T̲ F    Chronological organization is used primarily for informative speeches.

15.  T F̲    Speeches arranged in causal order usually have three main points.

16.  T F̲    When arranging a speech in causal order, you must deal first with the causes of an event and then explain its effects.

17.  T̲ F    Problem-solution order is used most often in persuasive speeches.

18.  T F̲    Speeches arranged in problem-solution order are divided into four main parts.

19.  T F̲    In topical order the main points proceed from top to bottom, left to right, front to back, east to west, or some similar route.

20.  T F̲    When arranged in topical order, the main points of a speech usually follow a time sequence.

21.  T F̲    Speeches arranged in spatial order follow a time sequence.

22.  T̲ F    Speeches arranged in chronological order follow a time pattern.

23.  T F̲    Although using a consistent pattern of wording for main points is common practice among writers, it is less important in public speaking.

24.  T F̲    Unlike writers, good speakers seldom use connectives between main points.

25.  T̲ F    Transitions state both the idea the speaker is leaving and the one the speaker is coming to.

26.  T F̲    "Now that we have explored the problem, let's turn to the solution" is an example of an internal preview.

27.  T̲ F    According to your textbook, the following statement is an example of a transition: "So much for the present; now let's turn our attention to the future."

28.  T F̲    According to your textbook, the following statement is an example of an internal summary: "So much for the present; what about the future?"

29.  T F̲    According to your textbook, an internal summary must be used after every main point in a speech.

30.  T <u>F</u>     A public speaker should avoid using transitions and internal summaries together.

31.  <u>T</u> F     "The most important point to remember about . . ." is an example of a signpost.

32.  <u>T</u> F     "Above all, you need to know . . ." is an example of a signpost.


**Multiple Choice Questions** (*Students are to indicate the <u>best</u> answer for each question by circling the correct letter.*)

33.  According to your textbook, how well a speech is organized likely will influence

    a.  how clearly the audience understands the speech.
    b.  how the audience views the competence of the speaker.
    c.  how confident the speaker feels about his or her delivery.
 *d.  all of the above.
    e.  a and b only.

34.  The _____ is the longest and most important part of the speech.

 *a.  body
    b.  blueprint
    c.  introduction
    d.  conclusion
    e.  frame

35.  According to your textbook, what is the *most* important reason for limiting the number of main points in a speech?

    a.  It is hard to maintain parallel wording if there are too many main points.
    b.  It is hard to phrase the central idea if a speech has too many main points.
    c.  It is hard to organize supporting materials if there are too many main points.
    d.  It is hard to deliver a speech extemporaneously if it has too many main points.
 *e.  It is hard for the audience to keep track of too many main points.

36.  The most effective order of main points in a speech depends above all on your topic, purpose, and

 *a.  audience.
    b.  research.
    c.  visual aids.
    d.  credibility.
    e.  delivery.

37.    Which organizational pattern would probably be most effective for arranging the main points of a speech with the specific purpose "To inform my audience how to start an online business"?

    a.    spatial
    b.    technical
    c.    causal
    d.    comparative-advantages
  *e.    chronological

38.    What organizational pattern would probably be most effective for arranging the main points of a speech with the specific purpose "To inform my audience about three major ways to block junk mail from their e-mail system"?

  *a.    topical
    b.    logistical
    c.    chronological
    d.    technical
    e.    causal

39.    When the main points of a speech follow a time pattern, they are organized in

    a.    problem-solution order.
    b.    spatial order.
    c.    topical order.
    d.    causal order.
  *e.    chronological order.

40.    Which organizational pattern would probably be most effective for arranging the main points of a speech with the specific purpose, "To inform my audience how to set up an online banking system to pay your bills"?

  *a.    chronological
    b.    problem-solution
    c.    spatial
    d.    causal
    e.    comparative-advantage

41.    Which organizational pattern would probably be most effective for arranging the main points of a speech with the specific purpose "To persuade my audience to support stricter drug testing for Olympic athletes"?

    a.    chronological
  *b.    problem-solution
    c.    thematic
    d.    spatial
    e.    causal

42.    Here are the main points for a speech about the major steps involved in a successful job interview:

    I.    The first step is preparing for the interview before it takes place.
    II.    The second step is presenting yourself well during the interview itself.
    III.    The third step is following up after the interview.

These main points are arranged in _____ order.

    a.    topical
    b.    spatial
 *c.    chronological
    d.    informative
    e.    causal

43.    Here are the main points for a speech explaining the reasons for the current shortage of teachers.

    I.    Teachers are leaving the profession because of low pay.
    II.    Teachers are leaving the profession because of excessive bureaucracy.
    III.    Teachers are leaving the profession because of inadequate facilities.

These main points are arranged in _____ order.

    a.    ascending
    b.    consecutive
    c.    chronological
    d.    descending
 *e.    topical

44.    Here are the main points for a speech about the methods used by Feng Shui consultants.

    I.    Feng Shui consultants use light cures to redirect energy.
    II.    Feng Shui consultants use sound cures to generate new energy.
    III.    Feng Shui consultants use weight cures to bring feelings of stability.
    IV.    Feng Shui consultants use living cures to nourish life and growth.

These main points are arranged in _____ order.

    a.    formal
    b.    professional
    c.    problem-solution
 *d.    topical
    e.    causal

45.    Here are the main points for an informative speech about the history of chocolate:

   I.    Chocolate was originally used in Mexico as a drink by the Aztecs.
   II.    Chocolate was introduced to Europe after the Spanish conquered the Aztecs.
   III.    Chocolate was first made into candy during the 1800s.
   IV.    Chocolate's popularity and uses continue to expand today.

   These main points are arranged in _____ order.

   a.    causal
   b.    analytical
   c.    descriptive
   *d.    chronological
   e.    spatial

46.    Here are the main points for an informative speech about the process of drying and storing garden herbs.

   I.    The first step is to prepare the herbs for drying by rinsing and gathering stems together.
   II.    The second step is to hang the herb bunches upside down in a dry place.
   III.    The third step is to strip the dried leaves and store the herbs properly.

   These main points are arranged in _____ order.

   a.    topical
   *b.    chronological
   c.    descriptive
   d.    practical
   e.    spatial

47.    Here are the main points for an informative speech about the civil rights movement.

   I.    The 1954 Supreme Court decision in *Brown vs. Board of Education* marked the beginning of the modern civil rights movement.
   II.    In 1963 peaceful protests and violent police responses in Birmingham, Alabama, dramatically increased support for the civil rights movement.
   III.    In 1965 the Voting Rights Act was passed, marking the major legislative achievement of the civil rights movement.

   These main points are arranged in _____ order.

   a.    spatial
   b.    historical
   c.    descriptive
   *d.    chronological
   e.    topical

48.    Which organizational pattern would be most effective for arranging the main points
       of a speech with the specific purpose "To inform my audience about the major steps
       in setting up a home aquarium"?

       *a.    chronological
        b.    causal
        c.    problem-solution
        d.    informative
        e.    Monroe's motivated sequence

49.    When main ideas follow a directional pattern, they are organized in

        a.    geographical order.
        b.    topical order.
       *c.    spatial order.
        d.    causal order.
        e.    chronological order.

50.    Which organizational pattern would probably be most effective for arranging the
       main points of a speech with the central idea "There are five basic positions of the
       feet in ballet"?

        a.    visual
        b.    chronological
        c.    problem-solution
        d.    causal
       *e.    topical

51.    Which pattern of organization would probably be most effective for arranging the
       main points of a speech with the specific purpose "To persuade my audience that
       high school and college football programs should act now to reduce the incidents of
       serious injuries in their sport."

        a.    spatial
        b.    causal
       *c.    problem-solution
        d.    chronological
        e.    topical

52.    What organizational pattern would probably be most effective for arranging the
       main points of a speech with the central idea "Estate taxes should be retained
       because they preserve opportunity for all, because their elimination would increase
       the national deficit, and because they are consistent with American values of
       fairness and justice"?

        a.    causal
        b.    formal
        c.    problem-solution
       *d.    topical
        e.    economic

53. Which organizational pattern would probably be most effective for arranging the main points of a speech with the specific purpose "To inform my audience about the major geographical regions of Mexico?"

   a. causal
   b. chronological
   c. topical
   d. problem-solution
   *e. spatial

54. Jackson had been a rodeo fan since childhood. In his informative speech, he gave a presentation with the following main points. Jackson's points were arranged in _____ order.

   I. Rodeos began in the Old West as contests of skill among cowboys during cattle roundups.
   II. By 1920 rodeos had become a popular spectator sport for the general public.
   III. Today rodeos combine traditional western events with a circuslike atmosphere and the marketing techniques of big business.

   a. topical
   b. formal
   *c. chronological
   d. analytical
   e. spatial

55. Which organizational method is used in a speech with the following main points?

   I. Many citizens are victimized every year by incompetent lawyers.
   II. A bill requiring lawyers to stand for recertification every 10 years will do much to help solve the problem.

   a. legal
   b. topical
   c. chronological
   *d. problem-solution
   e. analytical

56. Here are the main points for an informative speech about the anatomy of the human ear.

   I. The outer ear includes the ear flap and the ear canal.
   II. The middle ear includes the eardrum and three tiny, interconnected bones.
   III. The inner ear includes the cochlea, the semicircular canals, and the auditory nerve.

   These main points are arranged in _____ order.

   *a. spatial
   b. descending
   c. chronological
   d. ascending
   e. topical

57.   Which organizational method is used in a speech with the following main points?

      I.    The outermost section of the Egyptian burial tomb was the entrance passage.
      II.   The next section of the Egyptian burial tomb was the antechamber.
      III.  The third section of the Egyptian burial tomb was the treasury.
      IV.  The innermost section of the Egyptian burial tomb was the burial chamber.

*a.   spatial
 b.   logical
 c.   chronological
 d.   progressive
 e.   descriptive

58.   Here are the main points for a speech on the subject of hearing loss.

      I.    Hearing loss can be caused by genetic and environmental factors.
      II.   Hearing loss can lead to significant changes in a person's daily life.

These main points are arranged in _____ order.

 a.   logical
 b.   scientific
 c.   analytical
 d.   topical
*e.   causal

59.   Because of his family's medical history, Devin Hardaway decided to give his informative speech on sickle-cell anemia. When he finished work on the speech, it had the following main points.

      I.    Sickle-cell anemia is a hereditary blood disease caused by abnormal blood cells.
      II.   The effects of sickle-cell anemia include liver damage, blindness, paralysis, and early death.

Devin's main points were arranged in _____ order.

 a.   topical
 b.   medical
 c.   analytical
 d.   formal
*e.   causal

60.    Here are the main points for a speech about the impact of global warming:

     I.    Global warming has had a major impact in North America.
     II.   Global warming has had a major impact in South America.
     III.  Global warming has had a major impact in Europe.
     IV.  Global warming has had a major impact in Asia.
     V.   Global warming has had a major impact in Africa.

These main points are arranged in _____ order.

   a.   directional
\*b.   spatial
   c.   chronological
   d.   causal
   e.   problem-solution

61.    Which organizational method is used in a speech with the following main points?

     I.    As a social worker, Jane Addams founded the settlement house movement in Chicago.
     II.   As a reformer, Jane Addams campaigned for child-labor laws, unemployment compensation, and better public sanitation.
     III.  As a suffragist, Jane Addams fought to give women the vote.
     IV.  As a writer, Jane Addams is best known for her autobiographical *Twenty Years at Hull House*.

\*a.   topical
   b.   spatial
   c.   chronological
   d.   descriptive
   e.   formal

62.    Here are the main points for an informative speech about the major categories of dog breeds:

     I.    The working dogs do rescue, police, herding, and guide jobs.
     II.   The hound dogs are hunters that specialize in small animals.
     III.  The terrier dogs make good watchdogs.
     IV.  The toy dogs are primarily house pets.

These points are organized in _____ order.

   a.   spatial
   b.   descriptive
   c.   chronological
   d.   illustrative
\*e.   topical

63. Which of the following organizational patterns is used more than any other method of speech organization because of its applicability to almost any subject?

    a. chronological
    b. spatial
    c. problem-solution
 *d. topical
    e. causal

64. Which organizational pattern is reflected in a speech with the following the main points?

    I. Soda lime glass is used in almost all ordinary glass products.
    II. Lead crystal glass is used mostly for luxury glass products.
    III. Heat resistant glass is used for cooking and scientific products.

    a. causal
    b. informative
    c. chronological
 *d. topical
    e. descriptive

65. Which organizational pattern would probably be most effective for arranging the main points of a speech with the specific purpose "To inform my audience about the three major kinds of drone aircraft used by the U.S. military"?

    a. analytical
 *b. topical
    c. causal
    d. spatial
    e. chronological

66. A speech about the equipment used in the sport of ice hockey should probably use a(n) _____ organizational pattern.

    a. analogical
    b. chronological
 *c. topical
    d. problem-solution
    e. causal

67. Which organizational pattern would probably be most effective for arranging the main points of a speech with the specific purpose "To inform my audience of the four factors that make a classic car collectible"?

    a. analogical
    b. spatial
    c. problem-solution
 *d. topical
    e. causal

68.    A speech with the specific purpose "To inform my audience of the four major factors to consider when choosing a cell-phone plan" would most likely be arranged in _____ order.

   a.   causal
   b.   chronological
   c.   problem-solution
   d.   objective
  *e.   topical

69.    A speech with the specific purpose "To inform my audience of the steps involved in the process of making ice cream" would most likely be arranged in _____ order.

   a.   formal
   b.   causal
  *c.   chronological
   d.   progressive
   e.   spatial

70.    A speech with the specific purpose "To inform my audience how outbreaks of bird flu move from region to region" would most likely be organized in _____ order.

   a.   natural
   b.   analytical
   c.   progressive
   d.   scientific
  *e.   spatial

71.    A speech with the specific purpose "To inform my audience how to take pictures like a professional" would most likely be arranged in _____ order.

   a.   causal or chronological
   b.   topical or causal
   c.   spatial or topical
   d.   chronological or spatial
  *e.   topical or chronological

72.    A speech with the specific purpose "To inform my audience of the major features of the Empire State Building" would most likely be organized in _____ order.

   a.   chronological or spatial
   b.   causal or topical
  *c.   topical or spatial
   d.   chronological or causal
   e.   causal or spatial

73.    A speech about the causes and effects of domestic violence would most likely be organized in _____ order.

   *a.   causal
    b.   problem-solution
    c.   consequential
    d.   informative
    e.   analytical

74.    A speech with the specific purpose "To inform my audience about the causes of domestic violence and its effects on society" would most likely be arranged in _____ order.

    a.   legal
   *b.   causal
    c.   informative
    d.   problem-solution
    e.   chronological

75.    Problem-solution order is most appropriate for organizing _____ speeches.

    a.   acceptance
   *b.   persuasive
    c.   after-dinner
    d.   commemorative
    e.   informative

76.    Here are the main points for a speech about the components of a medieval coat of armor.

      I.    The head was protected by a helmet.
      II.   The torso was protected by shoulder pieces, palates, a breastplate, a skirt of tasses, and a tuille.
      III.  The arms and hands were protected by brassards, elbow pieces, and gauntlets.
      IV.   The legs and feet were protected by cuisses, knee pieces, jambeaux, and sollerets.

    These main points are arranged in _____ order.

    a.   topical
    b.   informative
    c.   chronological
    d.   structural
   *e.   spatial

77.    Here are the main points for a persuasive speech about the environmental hazards created by discarded computers.

    I.    Discarded computers have become a major source of lead and radiation pollution in landfills.

    II.    Solving this problem requires government regulation and personal action by consumers and businesses.

These main points are arranged in _____ order.

    a.    spatial
    b.    ascending
    c.    chronological
*d.    problem-solution
    e.    descending

78.    If the following transition were used in a persuasive speech, the speech would most likely be organized in _____ order.

Now that I've told you about declining voter involvement in this country, let's look at what we can do about it.

    a.    causal
    b.    spatial
    c.    comparative-advantages
*d.    problem-solution
    e.    topical

79.    Here are the main points for a persuasive speech on adult illiteracy.

    I.    Adult illiteracy has reached crisis proportions in the United States.

    II.    Solving the problem will require continued action by government and individual citizens alike.

These main points are arranged in _____ order.

    a.    spatial
    b.    topical
*c.    problem-solution
    d.    comparative-advantage
    e.    causal

80.　A soccer player herself, Jenine is very concerned about the growing number of serious injuries at all levels of the sport. When the time came for her persuasive speech, she presented a speech with the following main points:

> I.　In the past ten years serious soccer injuries have risen dramatically among players of all ages and skill levels.
> II.　The best way to control this problem is through changes in rules and training.

Jenine's main points were arranged in _____ order.

* a.　problem-solution
  b.　chronological
  c.　problem-cause-solution
  d.　topical
  e.　motivated sequence

81.　If the following connective were used between the last two main points in an informative speech, the speech would most likely be organized in _____ order.

> So far we have seen that the earliest roller coasters were developed in Russia and by the mid-1920s were very popular throughout the United States. Today, U.S. amusement parks attract millions of visitors because of their adventurous roller coasters. Let's take a look now at what the future holds for roller coasters.

  a.　spatial
* b.　chronological
  c.　analytical
  d.　formal
  e.　topical

82.　If the following internal summary were used in an informative speech, the speech would most likely be organized in _____ order.

> On our tour of campus thus far, we have moved from the student union on the east side of campus and around the perimeter. We've taken in the engineering campus on the north, the design college on the west side, and the school of education on the south.

  a.　causal
  b.　formal
  c.　analytical
* d.　spatial
  e.　topical

83.    If the following connective were used between the two main points of a persuasive speech, the speech would most likely be organized in _____ order.

>    Now that we have seen how the U.S. is facing a shortage of qualified teachers, let's turn to steps that should be taken to remedy the situation.

   a.    causal
   b.    analytical
  *c.    problem-solution
   d.    consecutive
   e.    topical


84.    Words or phrases that indicate when a speaker has completed one thought and is moving on to another are called

   a.    transfers.
   b.    internal summaries.
   c.    speech bridges.
  *d.    transitions.
   e.    signposts.


85.    "Now that we have seen the causes of unrest in central Africa, we shall turn to their effects . . ." is an example of a(n)

   a.    internal preview.
  *b.    transition.
   c.    internal summary.
   d.    signpost.
   e.    main point.


86.    After discussing the first main point in his speech on sustainable agriculture, Rasheed said:

>    So far, I have explained the problems associated with our present agricultural system. Next, I will explain what sustainable agriculture is and why it is vastly superior to the current system.

   According to your textbook, what type(s) of connective(s) did Rasheed use?

   a.    bridge
   b.    internal summary
  *c.    transition
   d.    all of the above
   e.    b and c only

87.    After discussing the first main point of her speech on the exploration of Mars, Jeanne said:

> Let's take a moment to recap. To this point we have seen that scientists have made important discoveries about the terrain of Mars, including its channels, basins, and polar caps. Now let's move on from the terrain of Mars and look at the planet's atmosphere.

According to your textbook, what type(s) of connective(s) did Jeanne use?

    a.    internal summary
    b.    transition
    c.    bridge
    d.    all of the above
*e.    a and b only

88.    According to your textbook, if the following statement occurred in the body of a speech, it would be an example of what kind of connective?

> In order to get a better understanding of how the proposed copper mine will harm the environment, we shall consider its effects on the land, its effects on the water, and its effects on wildlife.

    a.    signpost
*b.    internal preview
    c.    transition
    d.    internal summary
    e.    bridge

89.    According to your textbook, if the following statement occurred in the body of a speech, it would be an example of what kind of connective?

> Now that we have learned about the history of Mormonism, let's consider its major beliefs.

    a.    marker
    b.    signpost
*c.    transition
    d.    bridge
    e.    link

90.    According to your textbook, if the following statement occurred in the body of a speech, it would be an example of what kind of connective?

> In addition to helping people in need, working as a hospital volunteer provides you with valuable job experience.

    a.    link
    b.    signpost
    c.    marker
*d.    transition
    e.    bridge

91.    According to your textbook, if the following statement occurred in the body of a speech, it would be an example of what kind of connective?

We have spent a lot of time talking about the problem of computer viruses. Now let's look at some solutions.

&ast;a.    transition
　b.    internal preview
　c.    internal summary
　d.    all of the above
　e.    a and c only

92.    According to your textbook, if the following statement occurred in the body of a speech, it would be an example of what kind of connective?

So, first, to what extent will you be protected by wearing a seatbelt?

　a.    transition
&ast;b.    signpost
　c.    rhetorical question
　d.    internal preview
　e.    bridge

93.    According to your textbook, if the following statement occurred in the body of a speech, it would be an example of which kind of connective?

As we have seen so far, ignorance about the disease and how it spreads, cultural norms that make it nearly impossible for women to protect themselves, and rampant poverty all contribute to the rapid growth of AIDS among women in Africa.

　a.    repetition
　b.    internal checkpoint
　c.    transitional marker
&ast;d.    internal summary
　e.    signpost

94.    According to your textbook, if the following statement occurred in the body of the speech, it would be an example of what kind of connective?

Let's pause for a moment to see what we have found thus far. First we have seen that America's criminal justice system does not effectively deter crime. Second we have seen that prison programs to rehabilitate criminals have failed.

&ast;a.    internal summary
　b.    transition
　c.    bridge
　d.    internal preview
　e.    enumeration

95.    While working on the body of your speech, you realize that the steps of the process you just explained are fairly complex. You decide that you need to review those steps before moving on to the next main point. To accomplish this task, you would probably add a(n)

    a.    transition.
    b.    checkpoint.
  *c.    internal summary.
    d.    supplement.
    e.    signpost.

96.    While working on the body of your speech, you see the need to let the audience know what the upcoming subpoints will be. You decide to add a(n)

    a.    transition.
  *b.    internal preview.
    c.    organizational bridge.
    d.    internal summary.
    e.    structural link.

97.    According to your textbook, if the following statement occurred in the body of a speech, it would be an example of what kind of connective?

    In discussing the problem of childhood asthma, we shall look at the symptoms of the disease, its causes, and current treatments.

    a.    signpost
  *b.    internal preview
    c.    transition
    d.    internal summary
    e.    bridge

98.    According to your textbook, brief statements that help listeners follow your ideas by indicating exactly where you are in the speech are called

    a.    markers.
  *b.    signposts.
    c.    transitions.
    d.    bridges.
    e.    links.

99.    According to your textbook, "My second point is . . ." is an example of a(n)

    a.    transition.
    b.    bridge
  *c.    signpost.
    d.    enumeration.
    e.    marker.

## Short Answer Questions

100.    A speech narrating a series of historical events will usually be arranged in
____chronological____ order.

101.    A speech demonstrating how to build a soapbox derby car will probably be
arranged in ____chronological____ order.

102.    The following main points are arranged in ____chronological____ order.

    I.    The rise of the American film industry started with the age of silent movies
          from 1910 to 1930.
    II.   The American film industry was at its peak during the Golden Age of
          Hollywood from 1930 to 1950.
    III.  Since 1950 the American film industry has withstood the rise of television
          and the development of home video systems.

103.    Because it is adaptable to such a wide variety of topics and purposes, __topical__
order is used more than any other pattern of speech organization.

104.    A speech with the specific purpose "To inform my audience of the causes,
symptoms, and treatment of diabetes" will probably be arranged in ____topical____
order.

105.    A speech with the specific purpose "To inform my audience of three serious
consequences of not getting enough sleep" would most likely be arranged in
____topical____ order.

106.    The following main points are arranged in ____topical____ order.

    I.    High-protein diets are high in protein and low in carbohydrates.
    II.   High carbohydrate diets are high in carbohydrates and low in protein.
    III.  Fasting diets involve total abstention from food for a long period of time.

107.    The following main points are arranged in ____topical____ order.

    I.    As a painter, Picasso tested the limits of abstraction.
    II.   As a sculptor, Picasso often incorporated "found" objects.
    III.  As a printmaker, Picasso gave vent to his whimsy and eroticism.

108.    The following main points are arranged in ____topical____ order.

    I.    The first major type of environmental pollution is land pollution.
    II.   The second major type of environmental pollution is air pollution.
    III.  The third major type of environmental pollution is water pollution.

109.    The following main points are arranged in ____topical____ order.

    I.    Rabies in people is almost always caused by the bite of an infected animal.
    II.    The symptoms of rabies include drooling, changes in temperament, sudden changes in voice, and abnormal positioning of the limbs.
    III.    It is vital that people exposed to rabies seek prompt medical treatment.

110.    Speeches arranged in ____spatial____ order follow a directional pattern from top to bottom, east to west, or some other route.

111.    The following main points are arranged in ____spatial____ order.

    I.    The raised right arm and torch of the Statue of Liberty symbolize America's role as a beacon light of liberty to people the world over.
    II.    The body of the Statue of Liberty is lined with staircases, which give a good view of the inside contours.
    III.    The base of the Statue of Liberty contains a plaque with the poignant lines beginning "Give me your tired, your poor . . . ."

112.    A speech whose specific purpose is to show a cause-effect relationship is usually organized in ____causal____ order.

113.    The following main points are arranged in ____causal____ order.

    I.    The effects of airborne pollution continue to poison the air in major cities across the United States.
    II.    The major causes of airborne pollution are industrial and automobile contaminants.

114.    The following main points are arranged in ____problem-solution____ order.

    I.    Gambling addiction is an increasingly serious problem throughout the United States.
    II.    The problem of gambling addiction can best be solved by a combination of education and rehabilitation.

115.    ____Connectives____ are words or phrases that join one thought to another and indicate the relationship between them.

116.    Technically, ____transitions____ state both the idea the speaker is leaving and the one she or he is coming to.

117.    A(n) ____internal preview____ works just like the preview statement in the introduction, except that it comes in the body of the speech.

118.    "The final point I'd like to present . . . " is an example of a(n) ____signpost____ .

## Essay Questions

119.  Explain each of the following guidelines for main points in a speech. Why is it important to follow each guideline?

   a.  Limit the number of main points.
   b.  Balance the amount of time devoted to main points.
   c.  Keep main points separate.
   d.  Try to use the same pattern of wording for all main points.

120.  What is wrong with the following set of main points for a speech about different kinds of pianos? Explain the problem and then rewrite the main points to solve it.

   I.   Grand pianos are the largest and most expensive pianos.
   II.  Upright pianos take up less floor space and have poorer tone quality than grand pianos.
   III. Electronic pianos are often used in jazz and rock music, while player pianos, which produce music automatically, were popular in the late 1800s.

121.  Write an essay in which you (a) identify the four kinds of speech connectives explained in your textbook, (b) give an example of each, and (c) discuss the role of each in a speech.

122.  What is wrong with the following set of main points for a speech about preventive medicine? Explain the problem and then rewrite the main points to solve it.

   I.   The first basic step in preventive medicine is maintaining a well-balanced diet.
   II.  Learning how to cope with stress is another basic step in preventive medicine.
   III. The third basic step in preventive medicine is keeping a regular exercise program.

123.  Describe and give an example of each of the following methods of speech organization:

   a.  chronological
   b.  spatial
   c.  topical
   d.  problem-solution

124.  For speeches with the following specific purpose statements, what organizational pattern of main points would be most appropriate? Explain your choice in each case.

   a.  To inform my audience of the major stages in the development of professional baseball.
   b.  To inform my audience about the interior design of a medieval castle.
   c.  To persuade my audience that consumer fraud in America is a serious problem that requires action at both the state and federal levels.
   d.  To inform my audience about the three basic moves in tae kwon do.
   e.  To inform my audience how to paint the exterior of a house.

---

# Chapter 9 Beginning and Ending the Speech

## True-False Questions

1. <u>T</u> F     Regardless of what other methods you use to gain attention, you should almost always relate the topic to your audience in the introduction of a speech.

2. T <u>F</u>     It is seldom a good idea to discuss the importance of your topic in the introduction of a speech.

3. T <u>F</u>     If your topic is clear in the body of the speech, there is no need to state it in the introduction.

4. <u>T</u> F     A startling introduction is effective only if it is firmly related to the speech topic.

5. T <u>F</u>     Opening your speech with a lengthy quotation is an excellent way to gain the attention of your audience.

6. <u>T</u> F     Using visual aids is an acceptable method of gaining attention in the introduction of a speech.

7. <u>T</u> F     It is usually a good idea to restate your topic at some point in the introduction, even if the listeners already know it.

8. T <u>F</u>     Goodwill is the audience's perception of whether a speaker is qualified to speak on a given topic.

9. <u>T</u> F     Credibility is the audience's perception of whether a speaker is qualified to speak on a given topic.

10.  T  F    Goodwill is the audience's perception of whether the speaker has the best interests of the audience in mind.

11.  T  F    Establishing goodwill is more likely to be necessary in the introduction of a persuasive speech than in the introduction of an informative speech.

12.  T  F    Establishing credibility is an important function of a speech introduction.

13.  T  F    Establishing goodwill is more likely to be necessary in the introduction of an informative speech than in the introduction of a persuasive speech.

14.  T  F    Establishing goodwill is especially necessary in the introduction of a speech presented to a hostile audience.

15.  T  F    One function of a preview statement is to signal that the body of the speech is about to begin.

16.  T  F    The preview statement is usually the last component of an introduction and serves as a bridge to the body of the speech.

17.  T  F    A preview statement is usually necessary in the introduction even when a speaker is addressing an audience that is well-informed about the topic.

18.  T  F    The preview statement in a speech introduction identifies the main points to be discussed in the body.

19.  T  F    A preview statement is especially important in a speech introduction when a speaker is addressing a hostile audience.

20.  T  F    Under normal circumstances the introduction should constitute about 10 to 20 percent of a speech.

21.  T  F    Under normal circumstances, you should work out the exact wording of your introduction after you have finished preparing the body of your speech.

22.  T  F    As your textbook explains, working out a speech introduction in detail can help reduce a speaker's sense of stage fright.

23.  T  F    A "rhetorical question" is a question that the audience answers mentally rather than out loud.

24.  T  F    When you use a rhetorical question to gain attention in a speech introduction, you should state the question, pause a moment, and then give the answer.

25. T **F**    One function of a speech conclusion is to establish the credibility of the speaker.

26. T **F**    Arousing the curiosity of the audience is one of the major functions of a speech conclusion discussed in your textbook.

27. T **F**    It is inappropriate for a public speaker to say anything so obvious as "in conclusion."

28. T **F**    The only way to convey that your speech is ending is through the use of words such as "In conclusion."

29. **T** F    A speech conclusion that builds in power and intensity as it moves toward the closing line is known as a crescendo ending.

30. T **F**    A speech conclusion that builds in power and intensity as it moves toward the closing line is known as a dissolve ending.

31. T **F**    The crescendo conclusion is essentially a matter of the speaker getting louder and louder as the speech comes to an end.

32. **T** F    The conclusion of Martin Luther King's "I Have a Dream" is a good example of a crescendo ending.

33. **T** F    A dissolve ending is a conclusion that generates emotional appeal by fading step by step to a dramatic final statement.

34. T **F**    The conclusion should normally make up about 25 percent of a speech.

35. T **F**    It is overly repetitious to restate the central idea in the conclusion of a speech.

36. **T** F    Using a quotation is one of the most common and effective ways to conclude a speech.

37. T **F**    When concluding a speech, it is inappropriate to refer back to ideas mentioned in the introduction.

38. **T** F    Referring back to the introduction in your conclusion is a good way to give the speech psychological unity.

39. **T** F    The conclusion should normally comprise about 5 to 10 percent of a speech.

40. **T** F    One function of a speech conclusion is to reinforce the speaker's central idea.

**Multiple Choice Questions** *(Students are to indicate the <u>best</u> answer for each question by circling the correct letter.)*

41.   According to your textbook, when you are in a formal speaking situation the most effective way of gaining the initial attention of your audience after you walk to the lectern is

    a.   asking someone to lower the lights.
    b.   beginning to speak loudly and clearly.
    c.   rapping your hand lightly on the lectern until everyone is quiet.
  *d.   looking directly at the audience without saying a word.
    e.   asking everyone to be quiet and pay attention.

42.   Which of the following is a basic objective of a speech introduction?

    a.   reinforce the central idea
    b.   preview the main points
    c.   gain the attention of the audience
    d.   all of the above
  *e.   b and c only

43.   All of the following are basic objectives of a speech introduction *except*

    a.   establish credibility and goodwill.
  *b.   support your main points.
    c.   reveal the topic of the speech.
    d.   preview the body of the speech.
    e.   get the audience's attention and interest.

44.   According to your textbook, which of the following is one of the four major objectives of a speech introduction?

  *a.   reveal the topic
    b.   identify the audience
    c.   reinforce the central idea
    d.   all of the above
    e.   a and c only

45.   Which of the following would you expect to find in a well-constructed speech introduction?

    a.   a statement establishing the speaker's credibility
    b.   a statement gaining the audience's attention
    c.   a statement previewing the main points of the speech
  *d.   all of the above
    e.   a and b only

46.    Even when you use other interest-arousing lures in a speech introduction, you should always

    a.    startle the audience.
    b.    use a rhetorical question.
\*c.    relate the topic to the audience.
    d.    tell an interesting story.
    e.    present striking statistics.

47.    When preparing a speech introduction, you should usually

    a.    preview the main points to be discussed in the body.
    b.    gain the attention and interest of your audience.
    c.    establish your credibility on the speech topic.
\*d.    all of the above.
    e.    a and b only.

48.    When preparing a speech introduction, you should usually

    a.    reveal the topic of the speech.
    b.    support the central idea with evidence.
    c.    preview the main points of the speech.
    d.    all of the above.
\*e.    a and c only.

49.    Which of the following would you be *most* likely to find in a speech introduction?

    a.    a visual aid
\*b.    a preview statement
    c.    an internal summary
    d.    a research citation
    e.    a quotation

50.    Which of the following would you *most* likely find in a speech introduction?

    a.    a transition
    b.    an internal summary
    c.    a lengthy quotation
\*d.    a startling statement
    e.    a causal argument

51.    Which of the following would you *most* likely find in a speech introduction?

\*a.    a credibility statement
    b.    a transition
    c.    a causal argument
    d.    an internal summary
    e.    a call to action

52.    Which of the following would you *least* likely find in a speech introduction?

    a.    a preview statement
    b.    an announcement of the topic
    c.    a brief quotation
    d.    a credibility statement
  *e.    an internal summary

53.    Which of the following would you *least* likely find in a speech introduction?

    a.    a preview statement
  *b.    a call to action
    c.    a credibility statement
    d.    a provocative quotation
    e.    a startling statement

54.    If you were giving an informative speech to your classmates on the subject of photokinesis, you would probably include a _____ in your introduction.

    a.    quotation
    b.    startling statement
    c.    rhetorical question
    d.    story
  *e.    definition

55.    In the introduction of his speech on the Special Olympics, Mason mentioned that he had attended the events last year to cheer on a family friend who was competing in some races. Sharing this information with the audience helped Mason achieve which goal of a speech introduction?

    a.    relating to the audience
    b.    generating emotional appeal
    c.    stating the importance of the topic
  *d.    establishing credibility
    e.    previewing the body

56.    Which objective of a good speech introduction is fulfilled by the following statement?

      Today we will explore the three most important forms of intellectual property protection—copyrights, trademarks, and patents.

  *a.    preview the body
    b.    establish the speaker's goodwill
    c.    state the importance of the topic
    d.    summarize the introduction
    e.    relate to the audience

57.     The following passage from a speech introduction is an example of _____.

>   After attending a seminar on currency security, I became fascinated by the technology developed by the Treasury Department to prevent the counterfeiting of paper money. I learned more about the subject by reading information from the Treasury Department, as well as by interviewing Donna Marshall, a security expert at Bank of America.

>   a.   revealing the topic
>   b.   previewing the body
>   c.   stating the importance of the topic
>  *d.   establishing the speaker's credibility
>   e.   relating to the audience

58.     Paul began his speech as follows:

>   They called Lou Gehrig the iron horse. This tireless worker played an astounding 2,130 consecutive baseball games even though he suffered 17 hand fractures during those years. This would be like one of us never missing a day of school for over 13 years. Can you imagine completing kindergarten through your senior year with perfect attendance? Never taking a sick day, never a college visit day, or even senior skip day. And, to match Gehrig, you would also have to end your school career with an A average.

>   What method for gaining attention and interest did Paul use?

>   a.   revealing the general purpose
>  *b.   relating the topic to the audience
>   c.   previewing the body of the speech
>   d.   stating the importance of the topic
>   e.   summarizing the central idea

59.     Tobias began his informative speech by saying:

>   You hear a noise under the hood of your car, so you pull over to the side of the road. Your engine goes dead; you try to start the car, but it just sits there. Then you see a lot of black smoke. What's happened? Why won't your car go anywhere?

>   What method for gaining attention and interest did Tobias use?

>   a.   establishing goodwill with the audience
>  *b.   arousing the curiosity of the audience
>   c.   stating the importance of the topic
>   d.   presenting a startling statement
>   e.   establishing his credibility as a speaker

60.    Rachel began her speech as follows:

      I want all of you to think about your day. What did you eat? How active were you? How late will it be before you get to bed? These are the kinds of questions I would like to talk about this evening.

      What method(s) for gaining attention and interest did Rachel use?

    a.   questioning the audience
    b.   stating the importance of the topic
    c.   relating the topic to the audience
    d.   all of the above
 *e.   a and c only

61.    When used in a speech introduction, telling a story, asking a question, making a startling statement, and referring to the occasion are all methods of

    a.   previewing the body of the speech.
    b.   enhancing the speaker's credibility.
    c.   establishing goodwill with the audience.
    d.   revealing the topic of the speech.
 *e.   gaining the attention of the audience.

62.    According to your textbook, a speaker who attempts to establish goodwill in the introduction of a speech is aiming to convince the audience that she or he

    a.   will not talk for a long time.
 *b.   has the best interests of the audience in mind.
    c.   is willing to take questions at the end of the speech.
    d.   will avoid using illogical arguments.
    e.   is qualified to speak on the topic.

63.    If Leonardo DiCaprio were to deliver a speech about the future of medical care in the United States, his *main* task in the introduction of his speech would probably be to

    a.   gain attention.
    b.   reveal the topic.
 *c.   establish credibility.
    d.   preview the body.
    e.   define key terms.

64.    In the introduction to his speech on the art of digital photography, Seung mentioned that he works part-time at a camera shop and has had some of his pictures printed in the newspaper. By sharing this information with his audience, Seung was seeking to accomplish which goal of a speech introduction?

    a.   gain attention
    b.   preview the speech
    c.   reveal the topic
    d.   relate to the audience
 *e.   establish credibility

65. According to your textbook, the following passage from a speech introduction is an example of a(n) _____.

> I became interested in canine companions two years ago when my older sister, who was paralyzed in a car accident, received a canine companion named Lucky. Since then I have learned more about the subject by watching Lucky, by talking with my sister, and by reading a number of articles and pamphlets.

   a. preview statement
   b. narrative statement
   *c. credibility statement
   d. attention statement
   e. thesis statement

66. Jason began the introduction of his informative speech with these words:

> How many of you just can't wait until spring break? How many of you plan to hit the road about a minute after your last class lets out? How many of you are looking forward to having a great time?

   Which objective of a speech introduction were these words designed to fulfill?

   a. reveal the topic of the speech
   b. indicate the importance of the topic
   *c. gain the attention of the audience
   d. enhance the credibility of the speaker
   e. preview the main points of the speech

67. If Celine Dion were to deliver a speech on international diplomacy, her main task in the introduction would be to

   a. reveal the topic of her speech.
   b. gain attention and interest.
   c. preview the body of her speech.
   *d. establish her credibility on the topic.
   e. state the importance of her topic.

68. When you advocate a highly unpopular position, it is particularly important to _____ in the introduction of your speech.

   a. tell a story
   b. define unclear terms
   c. have a concise preview statement
   d. state the importance of the topic
   *e. establish goodwill toward the audience

69.    When preparing an introduction for a speech to a hostile audience, you should be especially careful to

    a.    preview the body of the speech.
 *b.    establish credibility and goodwill.
    c.    state the importance of the topic.
    d.    use statistics in the introduction.
    e.    arouse the curiosity of the audience.

70.    If a real estate developer were speaking to a group of citizens opposed to the creation of a shopping center in their neighborhood, the most important objective of her or his introduction would probably be to

    a.    gain the attention of the audience.
    b.    reveal the topic of the speech.
    c.    relate the topic to the audience.
    d.    state the importance of the topic.
 *e.    create goodwill with the audience.

71.    Creating goodwill is especially important in the introduction of a(n) _____ speech.

    a.    commemorative
    b.    acceptance
 *c.    persuasive
    d.    after-dinner
    e.    informative

72.    According to your textbook, the following passage from a speech introduction is an example of a(n) _____.

    Today I would like to share what I have learned about attention deficit disorder by first discussing its effects on people and then looking at the treatments that can be used to help people who suffer from this condition.

    a.    opening statement
    b.    attention statement
 *c.    preview statement
    d.    credibility statement
    e.    transition statement

73.    When preparing a speech introduction, you should usually

    a.    practice the introduction no more than two or three times.
    b.    make sure the introduction takes up 25 percent of the speech.
 *c.    complete the introduction after the body of the speech.
    d.    stick with the first introduction that comes to mind.
    e.    use humor to gain the audience's attention and interest.

74. According to your textbook, the following passage from a speech introduction is an example of a(n) _____.

> In order for you to understand why the mariachi are significant to Hispanic culture, I will give you a brief overview of the history of the mariachi, their style of dress, and the ways they are used in entertainment today.

   *a.   preview statement
   b.   credibility statement
   c.   transition statement
   d.   attention statement
   e.   summary statement

75. The best time to work out the exact wording of a speech introduction is

   a.   shortly after you determine the central idea.
   b.   before you work out the conclusion.
   c.   when you prepare your speaking outline.
   *d.   after you prepare the body of the speech.
   e.   as you rise to deliver an extemporaneous speech.

76. According to your textbook, the best time to work out the exact wording of a speech introduction is

   a.   while you are researching the speech.
   b.   as you rise to deliver a persuasive speech.
   c.   at the same time you formulate the specific purpose.
   *d.   after you prepare the body of the speech.
   e.   before you finish phrasing the central idea.

77. What does your textbook say about preparing an effective speech conclusion?

   a.   Make your conclusion about 5 to 10 percent of the entire speech.
   b.   Work especially hard on establishing your credibility in the conclusion.
   c.   Keep an eye out for concluding materials as you research the speech.
   d.   all of the above
   *e.   a and c only

78. What does your textbook say about preparing effective speech conclusions?

   a.   Be sure to reinforce your credibility before ending the speech.
   b.   The best conclusion is likely to be the one that comes to mind first.
   c.   Leave most of the conclusion to chance so it will sound natural.
   *d.   Make your conclusion about 5 to 10 percent of the entire speech.
   e.   Use an extended example in the conclusion for emotional appeal.

79.    According to your textbook, which of the following statements about speech conclusions is true?

    a.    The conclusion should take up about 25 percent of a speech.

    b.    Ending a speech abruptly is an excellent way to reinforce the speaker's central idea.

    c.    The last sentence of a speech should usually offer to answer questions from the audience.

 *d.    All four methods of reinforcing the central idea can be combined in a single conclusion.

    e.    It is usually best to let a conclusion grow out of the inspiration of the moment.

80.    Which of the following does your textbook mention as a means of reinforcing the central idea in the conclusion of a speech?

 *a.    end with a quotation

    b.    end with a visual aid

    c.    end with thanking the audience

    d.    all of the above

    e.    a and c only

81.    Which of the following is recommended in your textbook as a way to reinforce the central idea in a speech conclusion?

    a.    speed up your rate of delivery

 *b.    refer back to the introduction

    c.    ask for questions from the audience

    d.    all of the above

    e.    b and c only

82.    Which of the following is recommended in your textbook as a way to reinforce the central idea in a speech conclusion?

    a.    end with a quotation

    b.    make a dramatic statement

    c.    refer to the introduction

 *d.    all of the above

    e.    a and b only

83.    According to your textbook, in addition to reinforcing the central idea, a speech conclusion should also

    a.    secure the audience's attention.

    b.    build your credibility as a speaker.

    c.    reveal the topic of the speech.

    d.    provide a clear preview statement.

 *e.    signal the end of the speech.

84.　Which of the following would you *least* likely find in a speech conclusion?

    a.　dramatic statement
    b.　summary of the main points
  *c.　a statement to arouse curiosity
    d.　a reference to the introduction
    e.　a brief quotation

85.　Which of the following would you *most* likely find in a speech conclusion?

    a.　a causal argument
    b.　an extended example
  *c.　a provocative quotation
    d.　a rhetorical question
    e.　an internal preview

86.　Which of the following would you *most* likely find in a speech conclusion?

    a.　a preview statement
    b.　an announcement of the topic
    c.　a lengthy quotation
  *d.　a reference to the introduction
    e.　a statement of goodwill

87.　Which of the following would you *most* likely find in a speech conclusion?

    a.　a preview statement
    b.　an announcement of the topic
    c.　a gesture of goodwill
    d.　a credibility statement
  *e.　a restatement of the central idea

88.　Which of the following would you *most* likely find in a speech conclusion?

    a.　a personal story
  *b.　a reference to the introduction
    c.　an internal preview
    d.　a credibility statement
    e.　a visual aid

89.　Which of the following would you *least* likely find in a speech conclusion?

  *a.　a credibility statement
    b.　a provocative quotation
    c.　a call to action
    d.　a reference to the introduction
    e.　a summary of the main points

90.    The conclusion of Martin Luther King's "I Have a Dream" speech is an example of a

   a.  dissolve ending.
   b.  connective ending.
 *c.  crescendo ending.
   d.  cascade ending.
   e.  diminutive ending.

91.    According to your textbook, when a speaker concludes a speech by fading out on an emotional note she or he is using a _____ ending.

   a.  descending
   b.  crescendo
   c.  cascade
 *d.  dissolve
   e.  reflective

92.    According to your textbook, a(n) _____ ending is a conclusion that builds force until reaching a peak of power and intensity.

 *a.  crescendo
   b.  cascade
   c.  dissolve
   d.  reflective
   e.  ascending

93.    The conclusion of a speech is an appropriate time to

   a.  add supporting materials you could not work into the body.
 *b.  reinforce your listeners' commitment to the central idea.
   c.  apologize for any mistakes you made during the speech.
   d.  all of the above.
   e.  b and c only.

94.    Referring back to your introduction in the conclusion of your speech is recommended as a way to

   a.  secure the audience's attention.
   b.  reinforce your credibility as a speaker.
   c.  move the audience to action.
 *d.  give the speech psychological unity.
   e.  develop a dissolve ending.

95.    An appeal to action is most appropriate in the conclusion of a(n) _____ speech.

   a.  informative
   b.  after-dinner
   c.  acceptance
   d.  commemorative
 *e.  persuasive

96.     A(n) _____ is most appropriate in the conclusion of a persuasive speech.

    *a.   appeal to action
    b.    lengthy quotation
    c.    internal summary
    d.    extended example
    e.    definition

97.     In her persuasive speech, Josina concluded with the following statement:

    So the next time you see flyers around campus announcing a blood drive, decide that this will be your moment to get involved—to do something worthwhile, to take a step that may help save someone's life.

    What method of concluding her speech did Josina use?

    a.    extended example
    b.    internal summary
    c.    reference to the introduction
    *d.   appeal to action
    e.    causal reasoning

## Short Answer Questions

98.     What are the four major objectives of a speech introduction?

    a.    ____get the attention and interest of the audience____

    b.    ____reveal the topic of the speech____

    c.    ____establish the speaker's credibility and goodwill____

    d.    ____preview the body of the speech____

99.     When you use a ____rhetorical____ question in the introduction of a speech, you expect the audience to answer mentally rather than out loud.

100.    According to your textbook, no matter what other methods of gaining attention you use in a speech introduction, you should always ____relate the topic to the audience.____

101.    Establishing ____credibility____ in a speech introduction is a matter of getting your audience to perceive you as qualified to speak on the topic.

102.    The ____preview statement____ provides a lead-in from the introduction to the body of the speech.

103.    List six methods you can use to gain the attention and interest of an audience in the introduction of a speech.

a.  _____

b.  _____

c.  _____

d.  _____

e.  _____

f.  _____

The textbook discusses seven methods:

Relate the topic to the audience.
State the importance of the topic.
Startle the audience.
Arouse the curiosity of the audience.
Question the audience.
Begin with a quotation.
Tell a story.

The textbook also mentions five additional methods:

Refer to the occasion.
Invite audience participation.
Use audio equipment or visual aids.
Relate to a previous speaker.
Begin with humor.

Any six of these twelve methods should constitute a satisfactory answer.

104.    The two major functions of a speech conclusion are to __signal the end of the__ __speech__ and to ___reinforce the central idea___.

105.    One way to let an audience know that you are coming to the end of a speech is by saying something like "In conclusion." Another way is by your manner of _____delivery_____.

106.    When you use a(n) _____crescendo_____ ending, the speech builds in force until it reaches a zenith of power and intensity in the conclusion.

107.    The four methods discussed in the text for reinforcing the central idea in a speech conclusion are:

a.  _____summarize the main points_____

b.  _____end with a quotation_____

c.  _____make a dramatic statement_____

d.  _____refer to the introduction_____

## Essay Questions

108.   List and explain the four objectives of a speech introduction.

109.   What is the first thing a speaker must do in the introduction? Why?

110.   What are six methods a speaker can use in a speech introduction to gain the attention and interest of an audience? Identify each and offer a brief explanation.

111.   What is a preview statement? Why should the introduction of a speech nearly always include a preview statement?

112.   Which should you usually prepare first—the introduction of a speech or the body? Why?

113.   Explain the two main functions of a speech conclusion.

114.   List and explain the four methods presented in your textbook for reinforcing the central idea in the conclusion of a speech.

115.   Explain the following statement: "You can let your audience know your speech is coming to an end both by what you say and by your manner of delivery."

116.   What are the requirements of a good speech introduction? Evaluate the following complete introduction to a classroom speech in light of those requirements. Be specific in your answer.

> Imagine yourself walking through a large department store. You admire the new fashions, fiddle with the cameras, gawk at the jewelry, and check out the stereo equipment. Now imagine you can have any of those items for free—all you have to do is steal them.
>
> The temptation is great—so great that shoplifting has become one of the most frequent and expensive crimes in the United States. According to *Time* magazine, there are 150 million incidents of shoplifting in the U.S. each year, and the total value of goods stolen by shoplifters amounts to about $10 billion annually.
>
> And who pays for this? We all do. The value of stolen merchandise, the increased cost of store security, the time consumed in legal proceedings—all are passed on to us in higher prices and higher taxes. The Retail Merchants Association estimates that honest shoppers pay as much as 10 percent more to offset the cost of shoplifting.
>
> Although shoplifting is sometimes called an invisible crime, I have learned to see it in my job as a salesperson at Sears. By doing library research and by talking with security personnel at Sears, I have come to realize how widespread and how complex a problem shoplifting is. Today I would like to discuss with you the kinds of shoplifters and the security procedures used to fight them.

117.    What are the requirements of a good speech introduction? Evaluate the following complete introduction to a classroom speech in light of those requirements. Be specific in your answer.

"An attack on the United States with a biological or chemical weapon is an eventuality that must be addressed." That warning comes from Steven Rosenthal of the U.S. Food and Drug Administration. As Rosenthal's warning suggests, we must be prepared to deal with the threat of smallpox. Smallpox is a deadly disease, but vaccination dealt with it in the past and will do so again.

Today, I will give you information that will help you understand the current situation with regard to smallpox. We'll focus on the smallpox threat, the smallpox virus, and the smallpox vaccine.

118.    What are the requirements of a good speech introduction? Evaluate the following complete introduction to a classroom speech in light of those requirements. Be specific in your answer.

The body as we know it was not designed to participate in athletic events under the high demands that athletes face today. This leads to injuries and creates a need for trained professionals to deal with these injuries. I have taken several classes in my pursuit of an athletic training certificate. Today I will talk about what athletic trainers do to prevent injuries, how they assess injuries, and how they work with injuries in rehabilitation.

119.    What are the requirements of a good speech introduction? Evaluate the following complete introduction to a classroom speech in light of those requirements. Be specific in your answer.

"Oh beautiful for spacious skies, for amber waves of grain; for purple mountains majesty above the fruited plain."

Most of us are familiar with the song "America the Beautiful" and its description of our natural resources. Let's step back a minute, though, and consider what the picture might look like in the future. What if the amber waves of grain withered and died because the water table had been disrupted and contaminated? Or consider if the fruited plain was no more than a barren landscape because floods had washed away all the topsoil.

Because I believe that we have to protect our environment, I want to talk with you about one of America's most precious resources and how it is being destroyed.

120.    What are the requirements of a good speech introduction? Evaluate the following complete introduction to a classroom speech in light of those requirements. Be specific in your answer.

A brain aneurysm has been described as "the worst headache you can imagine." But the outcome is much worse than a headache. Here are the statistics: one-third of the people with a ruptured aneurysm die before they get to the hospital; another third of the people with a ruptured aneurysm die after they get to the hospital. The final third? They survive, but 40 percent of them suffer long-term neurological damage. Today I would like to explore this subject with you.

121.    What are the requirements of a good speech introduction? Evaluate the following complete introduction to a classroom speech in light of those requirements. Be specific in your answer.

The most dangerous source of radiation in the United States might be right here in this classroom. The threat is not nuclear power or medical x-rays. Yet according to the Environmental Protection Agency, it threatens up to eight million American homes.

The threat I am talking about is radon, a colorless, odorless gas that may cause as many as 20,000 deaths from lung cancer each year in the United States.

Today we will explore the threat caused by radon gas. We will begin by learning more about radon itself—what it is, where it comes from, and why it is so dangerous. Then we will look at some solutions to the problem—steps that can be taken by government and by individual citizens to control the dangers of radon in our homes.

# Chapter 10 Outlining the Speech

**True-False Questions**

1.  T <u>F</u>     The preparation outline should be drawn up before a speaker begins research for a speech.

2.  <u>T</u> F     When making a preparation outline, you should state your main points and subpoints in full sentences to ensure that you develop your ideas fully.

3.  <u>T</u> F     When making an outline, you should place the main points farthest to the left and less important ideas progressively farther to the right.

4.  <u>T</u> F     You should include your specific purpose statement with your preparation outline.

5.  <u>T</u> F     Including the specific purpose with your preparation outline makes it easier to assess how well you have constructed the speech to accomplish your purpose.

6.  <u>T</u> F     The visual framework of a preparation outline shows the relationships among the speaker's ideas.

7.  <u>T</u> F     According to your textbook, the introduction, body, and conclusion should all be labeled in a speech preparation outline.

8.  <u>T</u> F     In a preparation outline, the specific purpose is usually stated before the introduction.

9.  T <u>F</u>     In a preparation outline, the specific purpose is usually stated after the introduction.

10. T <u>F</u>     In a preparation outline, the specific purpose and central idea are identified by Roman numerals.

11.  <u>T</u>  F    In the most common system of outlining, main points are identified by Roman numerals and subpoints by capital letters.

12.  T  <u>F</u>    In the most common system of outlining, main points are identified by capital letters.

13.  T  <u>F</u>    Stating main points in a word or two is usually sufficient for a preparation outline.

14.  <u>T</u>  F    A preparation outline should include transitions and internal summaries.

15.  T  <u>F</u>    According to your textbook, transitions and other connectives should be identified with Roman numerals on a speech preparation outline.

16.  <u>T</u>  F    A preparation outline should include your final bibliography.

17.  T  <u>F</u>    "Dogs" would be an appropriate title for a speech to inform an audience about the major breeds of show dogs.

18.  T  <u>F</u>    It is seldom necessary to include a formal bibliography in the preparation outline for a classroom speech.

19.  <u>T</u>  F    According to your textbook, the two major bibliographic formats are those developed by the Modern Language Association (MLA) and the American Psychological Association (APA).

20.  <u>T</u>  F    According to your textbook, your final bibliography should include the URL for Internet sources.

21.  T  <u>F</u>    A speaking outline is usually longer and more detailed than a preparation outline.

22.  T  <u>F</u>    The speaking outline follows a different pattern of symbolization and indentation from the preparation outline.

23.  T  <u>F</u>    The speaking outline is a more complete version of the preparation outline.

24.  <u>T</u>  F    In the speaking outline, main points are indicated by Roman numerals.

25.  T  <u>F</u>    A speaking outline should be written on both sides of an index card or sheet of paper.

26.  <u>T</u>  F    You should keep your speaking outline as brief as possible.

27.  T  <u>F</u>    According to your textbook, a speaking outline is a full-sentence, expanded version of your preparation outline.

28.  T  <u>F</u>    It is seldom necessary to write out quotations in full in a speaking outline.

29.  T  <u>F</u>    A bibliography is usually included as part of the speaking outline.

30.   T F      A speaking outline should usually include directions for delivering the speech.

31.   T F      Delivery cues should be included on both the preparation and speaking outlines.

32.   T F      You should label the body and conclusion in both the preparation and
              speaking outlines.

33.   T F      Main points must be written out in full sentences in both the preparation
              outline and the speaking outline.

34.   T F      As your textbook explains, phrasing your speech title as a question can be
              highly effective.

## Multiple Choice Questions (Students are to indicate the *best* answer for each question by circling the correct letter.)

35.   Outlining is an important part of public speaking because

   a.   an outline helps the speaker compile an organized preliminary bibliography.
 *b.   an outline helps ensure that ideas flow clearly from one to another.
   c.   an outline helps the speaker choose an interesting, sharply focused topic.
   d.   all of the above.
   e.   a and b only.

36.   Outlining is important to public speaking because an outline helps a speaker

   a.   judge whether each part of the speech is fully developed.
   b.   ensure that ideas flow clearly from one to another.
   c.   solidify the structure of a speech.
 *d.   all of the above.
   e.   b and c only.

37.   According to your textbook, outlining is important to public speaking because an
     outline helps you judge whether

   a.   your main points are properly balanced.
   b.   your speech will be interesting to the audience.
   c.   you have adequate supporting materials for your main points.
   d.   all of the above.
 *e.   a and c only.

38.   According to your textbook, which of the following should be included in a
     preparation outline?

   a.   research notes
   b.   connectives
   c.   a bibliography
   d.   all of the above
 *e.   b and c only

39.     Two types of speech outlines discussed in your textbook are the

    a.     preparation outline and the delivery outline.
    b.     rough draft outline and the polished outline.
  *c.     preparation outline and the speaking outline.
    d.     speaking outline and the audience outline.
    e.     audience outline and the preparation outline.

40.     According to your textbook, which of the following should be included in a preparation outline?

    a.     a bibliography
    b.     a specific purpose statement
    c.     directions for delivering the speech
    d.     all of the above
  *e.     a and b only

41.     Which of the following should be included in a preparation outline?

  *a.     the central idea
    b.     a general purpose statement
    c.     the preliminary bibliography
    d.     directions for delivering the speech
    e.     all of the above

42.     According to your textbook, Raul should include which of the following in his preparation outline?

    a.     transitions
    b.     the central idea
    c.     a bibliography
  *d.     all of the above
    e.     b and c only

43.     According to your textbook, as Bekah prepares her preparation outline for her speech on spiders, she should remember to include all of the following *except*

    a.     a specific purpose statement.
    b.     labels for the introduction, body, and conclusion.
    c.     transitions, internal previews, and internal summaries.
  *d.     directions for delivering the speech.
    e.     a bibliography.

44.     Which of the following should be included in a preparation outline?

    a.     the final bibliography
    b.     a specific purpose statement
    c.     transitions, internal previews, and internal summaries
    d.     the central idea
  *e.     all of the above

45.    Which of the following is mentioned in your textbook as a guideline for a preparation outline?

  *a.    Label the introduction, body, and conclusion.
   b.    Identify the specific purpose with a Roman numeral.
   c.    Position the title so it appears immediately before the central idea.
   d.    Include a startling statement in the introduction to get attention.
   e.    Use parallel wording for subpoints and sub-subpoints.

46.    All of the following are necessary in a preparation outline *except*

   a.    labels for the introduction, body, and conclusion.
  *b.    directions for delivering the speech.
   c.    transitions, internal previews, and internal summaries.
   d.    a consistent pattern of indentation and symbolization.
   e.    a specific purpose statement.

47.    According to your textbook, the specific purpose statement in a preparation outline should be written

   a.    in capital letters.
   b.    at the end of the introduction.
   c.    immediately before the first main point.
   d.    after the preview statement.
  *e.    before the text of the outline itself.

48.    According to your textbook, when making a preparation outline, you should

   a.    label transitions and internal summaries.
   b.    indicate the introduction, body, and conclusion with Roman numerals.
   c.    state the specific purpose as a separate unit before the outline itself.
   d.    all of the above.
  *e.    a and c only.

49.    A preparation outline

   a.    should be as brief as possible.
  *b.    states main points and subpoints in full sentences.
   c.    contains the speaker's preliminary bibliography.
   d.    all of the above.
   e.    b and c only.

50.    In a preparation outline, main points should be

  *a.    positioned farthest to the left.
   b.    indicated by Arabic numerals.
   c.    written in key words to jog the memory.
   d.    listed after subpoints.
   e.    stated as questions.

51.    The main points in a preparation outline are

     a.    identified by capital letters.
   *b.    located farthest to the left.
     c.    listed immediately after the specific purpose.
     d.    all of the above.
     e.    a and b only.

52.    The main points in a preparation outline are

   *a.    identified by Roman numerals.
     b.    identified by capital letters.
     c.    located farther to the right than subpoints.
     d.    identified by Arabic numbers.
     e.    written in phrases, not full sentences.

53.    Which of the following is a correctly worded main point for a speech preparation outline?

     a.    Leadership.
     b.    What are the major types of leadership?
     c.    Two major types of leadership.
   *d.    There are two major types of leadership.
     e.    Leadership: major types.

54.    Which of the following is a correctly worded main point for a speech preparation outline?

     a.    The danger of smallpox in the United States.
     b.    What is the danger of smallpox in the United States?
   *c.    Smallpox poses a real danger to the United States.
     d.    Smallpox: a genuine danger to the United States.
     e.    Smallpox.

55.    Which of the following is a correctly worded main point for a speech preparation outline?

     a.    Myths about day care.
     b.    Is day care good for children?
     c.    The pros and cons of day care: research results.
   *d.    Research shows that there are both advantages and disadvantages to day care.
     e.    Knowing the advantages and disadvantages of day care for your child.

56.    Which of the following is a correctly worded main point for a speech preparation outline?

     a.    The human eye as a means of identification.
   *b.    Researchers are working on ways to use the iris as a means of identification.
     c.    Did you know that each person's iris has a unique pattern?
     d.    Using the human eye as a means of identification.
     e.    Through your eyes only.

57.    Which of the following is a correctly worded main point for a speech preparation outline?

   a.    Wolves.
   b.    Did you know that all domestic dogs are descended from the wolf?
  *c.    The ancestry of the domestic dog can be directly traced to the wolf.
   d.    The place of the wolf in the ancestry of the domestic dog.
   e.    Wolves and the domestic dog.

58.    Which of the following is a correctly worded main point for a speech preparation outline?

   a.    Computer-generated graphics as special effects.
  *b.    Many movie special effects are created with computer-generated graphics.
   c.    How are special effects created with computer-generated graphics?
   d.    The use of computer-generated graphics to create special effects in movies.
   e.    Computer-generated graphics.

59.    Which of the following is a correctly worded main point for a speech preparation outline?

   a.    Causes.
   b.    Migraine headaches and their causes.
   c.    Causes of migraine headaches.
  *d.    There are three major causes of migraine headaches.
   e.    Why people get migraine headaches.

60.    Subpoints in a preparation outline are indicated

   a.    by Roman numerals.
   b.    by Arabic numbers.
  *c.    by capital letters.
   d.    in the same manner as sub-subpoints.
   e.    in the same manner as main points.

61.    Subpoints in a preparation outline are

   a.    listed just before the conclusion.
   b.    written in key words to jog the memory.
   c.    indicated by Roman numerals.
   d.    indented farther to the left than main points.
  *e.    written in full sentences.

62.    Arranged in random order below are a main point, two subpoints, and two sub-subpoints from a speech preparation outline. Which is the main point?

   a.    Melanoma is the least common but most deadly form of skin cancer.
   b.    Each year about 7,400 people die from melanoma in the U.S.
   c.    Basal cell carcinoma is the most common type of skin cancer.
  *d.    Two types of skin cancer are melanoma and basal cell carcinoma.
   e.    Of all skin cancers diagnosed in the U.S., only 4 percent are melanoma.

63.     Arranged in random order below are a main point, two subpoints, and two sub-subpoints from a speech preparation outline. Which is the main point?

    a.     The largest members of the hawk family are Old World vultures.
*b.     Raptors are powerful birds of prey with hooked beaks and sharp talons.
    c.     Among Falconiformes, the hawk family is the largest and most diverse.
    d.     The hawk family includes eagles, hawks, kites, harriers, and vultures.
    e.     There are two orders of Raptors—Falconiformes and Strigiformes.

64.     Arranged in random order below are a main point, one subpoint, and three sub-subpoints from a speech preparation outline. Which is the main point?

    a.     Included among those remedies are some highly bizarre—and even dangerous—practices.
    b.     A third remedy was wrapping the patient's neck with a piece of flannel soaked in foul-smelling salve.
    c.     One remedy was bleeding the patient by taking out a pint or two of blood.
*d.     Over the years, people have tried many remedies to combat the common cold.
    e.     Another remedy was soaking the patient with huge quantities of baking soda dissolved in water.

65.     Arranged in random order below are a main point, two subpoints, and two sub-subpoints from a speech preparation outline. Which is the main point?

    a.     One example of this kind of phobia is the child who is bitten by a dog and who remains fearful of dogs thereafter.
    b.     Most phobias are caused by a frightening experience, usually in childhood.
*c.     Phobias can develop either in childhood or adulthood.
    d.     Another example is the child who develops a fear of heights after falling off a ladder.
    e.     Some phobias seem to develop suddenly in adulthood without any apparent cause.

66.     Arranged in random order below are a main point, two subpoints, and two sub-subpoints from a speech preparation outline. Which is the *first* subpoint?

    a.     The purpose of a manager interview is to evaluate those people who survive the screening interview.
    b.     The 20 percent who do pass the screening interview get invited back for a manager interview.
    c.     The two types of job interviews used by most companies are the screening interview and the manager interview.
    d.     Usually about 80 percent of job applicants do not pass the screening interview.
*e.     The purpose of a screening interview is just what the name implies—to screen out people the company doesn't want to hire.

67. Arranged below are a main point, two subpoints, and two sub-subpoints from a speech preparation outline. Which is the *second* subpoint?

   a. *Meteorologica* was written around 340 B.C.
   *b. After Thales, Aristotle was the major figure in ancient meteorology.
   c. The science of meteorology first developed in ancient Greece.
   d. Aristotle presented his theories in a book called *Meteorologica*.
   e. In 640 B.C., Thales identified the winter and summer solstices.

68. According to your textbook, a speech title should

   a. include a catchy quotation.
   *b. attract the audience's attention.
   c. be stated as a full sentence.
   d. all of the above.
   e. b and c only.

69. A speech title should

   a. attract the attention of the audience.
   b. be brief.
   c. suggest the main thrust of the speech.
   *d. all of the above.
   e. a and c only.

70. A catchy speech title is fine as long as it is

   a. phrased as a question.
   *b. relevant to the speech.
   c. written as a full sentence.
   d. all of the above.
   e. b and c only.

71. "Adventures in the Grand Canyon" is an appropriately worded

   *a. speech title.
   b. general purpose statement.
   c. main point for a preparation outline.
   d. specific purpose statement.
   e. central idea.

72. According to your textbook, which of the following should be included in a speaking outline?

   a. key words or phrases to jog the speaker's memory
   b. cues for delivering the speech
   c. statistics and quotations that might be easily forgotten
   *d. all of the above
   e. a and b only

73. Both a preparation outline and a speaking outline should

   a. include delivery cues.
   b. briefly sketch the speaker's ideas.
   *c. use a consistent pattern of symbolization and indentation.
   d. be written entirely in full sentences.
   e. contain a bibliography.

74. When preparing a speaking outline, you should

   a. follow the visual framework of the preparation outline.
   b. make sure the outline is plainly legible.
   c. keep the outline as brief as possible.
   *d. all of the above.
   e. b and c only.

75. According to your textbook, the main reason to keep a speaking outline brief is to

   a. help the speaker feel more confident and secure.
   b. make the speech clearer for the audience.
   c. ensure that the outline fits on a single note card.
   d. make it easier for the speaker to gesture.
   *e. help the speaker maintain eye contact with the audience.

76. According to your textbook, a speaking outline usually

   a. includes a preliminary bibliography.
   b. fills more than five note cards.
   c. includes the speech introduction written out word-for-word.
   d. contains mostly complete sentences.
   *e. includes the quotations a speaker plans to use.

77. Erica has completed her final preparation outline and is preparing her speaking outline for her speech on macrobiotic foods. According to your textbook, as Erica prepares her speaking outline, she should remember to

   a. include a bibliography.
   b. make sure the outline is plainly legible.
   c. keep the outline as brief as possible.
   d. all of the above.
   *e. b and c only.

78. When Terrence creates a speaking outline for his informative speech on hockey, he should

   a. include cues for delivering the speech.
   b. write out quotations he plans to use in the speech.
   c. follow the visual framework of the preparation outline.
   *d. all of the above.
   e. a and b only.

79.    In a speaking outline, subpoints are

    a.    set off in parentheses.
    b.    written in full sentences.
   *c.    identified by capital letters.
    d.    all of the above.
    e.    a and b only.

80.    According to your textbook, in a speaking outline, the conclusion should be

    a.    written out word for word.
   *b.    labeled as a separate part of the speech.
    c.    set off in parentheses.
    d.    all of the above.
    e.    a and c only.

81.    According to your textbook, a speaking outline

    a.    includes the final bibliography.
    b.    states the specific purpose at the start of the outline.
   *c.    contains delivery cues for the speaker.
    d.    all of the above.
    e.    a and b only.

## Short Answer Questions

82.    A detailed outline for the planning stage of a speech is called a ____preparation____ outline.

83.    When making a ____preparation____ outline, you should state your main points and subpoints in full sentences to ensure that you develop your ideas fully.

84.    In a speech outline, main points are identified by ____Roman numerals____, while subpoints are identified by ____capital letters____.

85.    A bibliography is often included as part of the ____preparation____ outline.

86.    A ____speaking____ outline should include cues for delivering the speech.

87.    A ____speaking____ outline should be kept as brief as possible.

88.    The textbook gives four guidelines for a speaking outline. They are:

    a.    ____Follow the visual framework used in the preparation outline.____

    b.    ____Make sure the outline is plainly legible.____

    c.    ____Keep the outline as brief as possible.____

    d.    ____Include cues for delivering the speech.____

89.    In the left-hand column below is a blank portion of a preparation outline for an informative speech on skin cancer. In the right-hand column, arranged in random order, are a main point, a subpoint, and three sub-subpoints. Use them to fill in the outline.

|                   Outline                   |                   Main Point and Subpoints                   |
| --- | --- |
| I. | The amount of ultraviolet radiation you are exposed to depends in part on where you live. |
|    A. | Certain health and skin conditions are also contributing causes to the development of skin cancer. |
|      1. | There are several causes of skin cancer. |
|      2. | Exposure to ultraviolet radiation from the sun is the most common cause of skin cancer. |
|    B. | The amount of ultraviolet radiation you are exposed to also depends on the time of day you are in the sun. |

**Discussion:**  When filled in, the outline should look like this:

I.    There are several causes of skin cancer.

    A.    Exposure to ultraviolet radiation from the sun is the most common cause of skin cancer.

        1.    The amount of ultraviolet radiation you are exposed to depends in part on where you live.

        2.    The amount of ultraviolet radiation you are exposed to also depends on the time of day you are in the sun.

    B.    Certain health and skin conditions are also contributing causes to the development of skin cancer.

90.    In the left-hand column below is a blank portion of a preparation outline for an informative speech on maple syrup. In the right-hand column, arranged in random order, are a main point, two subpoints, and two sub-subpoints. Use them to fill in the outline.

|  | Outline | Main Point and Subpoints |
|---|---|---|
| I. | | It also requires less time and labor. |
| | A. | In the modern method, sap is collected through a system of pipelines. |
| | B. | The pipeline method yields more sap than the bucket method. |
| | 1. | In the traditional method, sap is collected in buckets. |
| | 2. | There are two major methods of collecting sap from maple trees. |

**Discussion:**  When filled in, the outline should look like this:

I.    There are two major methods of collecting sap from maple trees.

    A.    In the traditional method, sap is collected in buckets.

    B.    In the modern method, sap is collected through a system of pipelines.

        1.    The pipeline method yields more sap than the traditional method.

        2.    It also requires less time and labor.

91.   In the left-hand column below is a partially blank outline from a speech about advertising strategies. In the right-hand column, arranged in random order, are the subpoints and sub-subpoints to fill in the outline. Choose the appropriate subpoint or sub-subpoint for each blank in the outline.

| Outline | Main Point and Subpoints |
|---|---|
| I. Advertisers use various types of visual strategies to persuade consumers to buy their products. | Advertisers use shocking images because, says London advertising consultant Robert Bean, "the real risk in advertising is to not be noticed at all." |
| A. | Cigarette ads always show images of beautiful, healthy people smoking, not elderly people suffering from emphysema or lung cancer. |
| 1. | Another type of visual strategy is to use visually shocking images to gain attention. |
| 2. | Another example is car ads that show images of a car high on a mountain rather than sitting in a traffic jam on an urban highway. |
| B. | At other times the shock is offensive, as in sexually explicit alcohol ads. |
| 1. | One type of visual strategy is to use illusions and appealing images. |
| 2. | Bean notes that sometimes the shock is humorous, such as a radio company in Chicago that gained attention by posting their ads upside down. |
| 3. | |

**Discussion:**   When filled in, the outline should look like this:

I.        Advertisers use various types of visual strategies to persuade consumers to buy their products.

   A.        One type of visual strategy is to use illusions and appealing images.

      1.        Cigarette ads always show images of beautiful, healthy people smoking, not elderly people suffering from emphysema or lung cancer.

      2.        Another example is car ads that show images of a car high on a mountain rather than sitting in a traffic jam on an urban highway.

   B.        Another type of visual strategy is to use visually shocking images to gain attention.

      1.        Advertisers use shocking images because, says London advertising consultant Robert Bean, "the real risk in advertising is to not be noticed at all."

      2.        Bean notes that sometimes the shock is humorous, such as a radio company in Chicago that gained attention by posting their ads upside down.

      3.        At other times the shock is offensive, as in sexually explicit alcohol ads.

92.    In the left-hand column below is a blank portion of a preparation outline for an informative speech on diamonds. In the right-hand column, arranged in random order, are a main point, two subpoints, and two sub-subpoints. Use them to fill in the outline.

| Outline | Main Point and Subpoints |
|---|---|
| I. | A carat is equal to 0.2 grams. |
| A. | Usually the greater the carat weight, the more valuable the diamond. |
| 1. | The carat is a unit of weight, not size. |
| 2. | One way to judge the quality of a diamond is by its carat weight. |
| B. | This is about the weight of a carob seed, from which the word "carat" is derived. |

**Discussion:**   When filled in, the outline should look like this:

I.        One way to judge the quality of a diamond is by its carat weight.

   A.        The carat is a unit of weight, not size.

      1.        A carat is equal to 0.2 grams.

      2.        This is about the weight of a carob seed, from which the word "carat" is derived.

   B.        Usually the greater the carat weight, the more valuable the diamond.

93.  In the left-hand column below is a blank portion of a preparation outline for an informative speech about diabetes. In the right-hand column, arranged in random order, are a main point, a subpoint, and three sub-subpoints. Use them to fill in the outline.

|            Outline            |              Main Point and Subpoints              |
| ----------------------------- | -------------------------------------------------- |
| I.                            | Insulin injections are literally a lifesaver for millions of people with diabetes. |
|   A.                 | In the future, it may be possible to take insulin orally, without the discomfort of injections. |
|     1.     | Before insulin was developed in 1921, diabetes was usually a fatal disease. |
|     2.     | Diabetes can be combated by injections of insulin and by control of diet. |
|     3.     | Today, daily injections of insulin allow even severe diabetics to live normal lives. |

**Discussion:**  When filled in, the outline should look like this:

I.  Diabetes can be combated by injections of insulin and by control of diet.

   A.  Insulin injections are literally a life-saver for millions of people with diabetes.

      1.  Before insulin was developed in 1921, diabetes was usually a fatal disease.

      2.  Today daily injections of insulin allow even severe diabetics to live normal lives.

      3.  In the future it may be possible to take insulin orally, without the discomfort of injections.

## Essay Questions

94.  Explain the following statement: "As plans and blueprints are essential to architecture, so are outlines essential for effective public speaking."

95.  What does it mean to say that a speech outline has a "visual framework"? Why is that framework important to a speaker?

96.  What should a preparation outline include in addition to the main points, subpoints, and sub-subpoints?

97.  When making a preparation outline, why is it important to state main points and subpoints in full sentences?

98.  What are the criteria for an effective speech title? Explain the three kinds of titles discussed in your text.

99.  In a well-developed essay, explain the similarities and differences between a preparation outline and a speaking outline. Be sure to consider what a preparation outline includes that is not part of a speaking outline.

100. Explain the four guidelines presented in your textbook for an effective speaking outline.

101. In the left-hand column below is a partially blank outline from a speech about child abuse. In the right-hand column, arranged in random order, are the subpoints and sub-subpoints to fill in the outline. Choose the appropriate subpoint or sub-subpoint for each blank in the outline.

| Outline | Main Point and Subpoints |
|---|---|
| I.   Child abuse continues to be a serious problem in the United States. | There is an unusually high rate of criminal activity among adults who were abused as children. |
|      A. | In the short run, children suffer serious injuries and even death. |
|           1. | This averages out to almost 3,500 cases per day. |
|           2. | These statistics are even more alarming once we recognize that for every reported case of child abuse, five more go unreported. |
|      B. | One study showed that abused children are ten times more likely to be arrested for violent crimes as adults than are non-abused children. |
| II.  The consequences of child abuse are tragic in both the short run and the long run. | In addition to these injuries, some 2,000 children die each year from severe abuse. |
|      A. | Last year alone there were more than 1.3 million reported cases of child abuse. |
|           1. | Victims of child abuse often grow up to become child abusers themselves as adults. |
|           2. | Injuries to abused children include bruises, burns, cuts, broken bones, internal bleeding, and damage to organs such as the kidneys and the liver. |
|      B. | |
|           1. | Another study revealed that 90 percent of the inmates at San Quentin prison were abused as children. |
|                a. | This figure breaks down further to 146 cases per hour. |
|                b. | In the long run, victims of child abuse often continue to be affected by it as adults. |
|           2. | |

**Discussion:**   When filled in, the outline should look like this:

I.      Child abuse continues to be a serious problem in the United States.

    A.      Last year alone there were more than 1.3 million reported cases of child abuse.

        1.      This averages out to almost 3,500 cases per day.

        2.      This figure breaks down further to 146 cases per hour.

    B.      These statistics are even more alarming once we recognize that for every reported case of child abuse, five more go unreported.

II.     The consequences of child abuse are tragic in both the short run and the long run.

    A.      In the short run children suffer serious injuries and even death.

        1.      Injuries to abused children include bruises, burns, cuts, broken bones, internal bleeding, and damage to organs such as the kidneys and the liver.

        2.      In addition to these injuries, some 2,000 children die each year from severe abuse.

    B.      In the long run victims of child abuse often continue to be affected by it as adults.

        1.      There is an unusually high rate of criminal activity among adults who were abused as children.

            a.      One study showed that abused children are ten times more likely to be arrested for violent crimes as adults than are non-abused children.

            b.      Another study revealed that 90 percent of the inmates at San Quentin prison were abused as children.

        2.      Victims of child abuse often grow up to become child abusers themselves as adults.

102.    In the left-hand column below is a partially blank outline from a speech about the symptoms and treatment of frostbite. In the right-hand column, arranged in random order, are the subpoints and sub-subpoints to fill in the outline. Choose the appropriate subpoint or sub-subpoint for each blank in the outline.

<table>
<tr><td>Outline</td><td>Main Point and Subpoints</td></tr>
<tr><td>I.    There are several symptoms of frostbite.</td><td>Another method of warming is to lightly cover the affected areas with warm towels.</td></tr>
<tr><td>A.</td><td>If you take the wrong steps in treating frostbite, you can cause permanent damage to the affected areas.</td></tr>
<tr><td>B.</td><td>As frostbite develops, the skin first changes to a grayish-yellow color.</td></tr>
<tr><td>C.</td><td>First, get the victim indoors as quickly as possible.</td></tr>
<tr><td>II.    The key to treating frostbite is knowing what to do and what not to do.</td><td>When the affected areas become flushed, discontinue warming and have the victim gently exercise them to stimulate circulation.</td></tr>
<tr><td>A.</td><td>Second, do not rub or massage the affected areas.</td></tr>
<tr><td>1.</td><td>Once the victim is indoors, warm the affected areas until they become flushed.</td></tr>
<tr><td>2.</td><td>As frostbite intensifies, the affected areas feel extremely cold, turn numb, and may turn from a grayish-yellow to a bluish color.</td></tr>
<tr><td>a.</td><td rowspan="2">As frostbite intensifies, the affected areas feel extremely cold, turn numb, and may turn from a grayish-yellow to a bluish color.</td></tr>
<tr><td>b.</td></tr>
<tr><td>3.</td><td>If you take the right steps in treating frostbite, you can usually prevent permanent damage to the affected areas.</td></tr>
<tr><td>B.</td><td>Third, do not break any blisters that may have formed.</td></tr>
<tr><td>1.</td><td>One method of warming is to immerse the affected areas in warm water.</td></tr>
<tr><td>2.</td><td>In severe cases, the frostbite victim may experience mental confusion and impaired judgment.</td></tr>
<tr><td>3.</td><td>First, do not apply hot water or strong heat.</td></tr>
</table>

**Discussion:**   When filled in, the outline should look like this:

I.        There are several symptoms of frostbite.

        A.        As frostbite develops, the skin first changes to a grayish-yellow color.

        B.        As frostbite intensifies, the affected areas feel extremely cold, turn numb, and may turn from a grayish-yellow to a bluish color.

        C.        In severe cases, the frostbite victim may experience mental confusion and impaired judgment.

II.       The key to treating frostbite is knowing what to do and what not to do.

        A.        If you take the right steps in treating frostbite, you can usually prevent permanent damage to the affected areas.

                1.        First, get the victim indoors as quickly as possible.

                2.        Once the victim is indoors, warm the affected areas until they become flushed.

                        a.        One method of warming is to immerse the affected areas in warm water.

                        b.        Another method of warming is to lightly cover the affected areas with warm towels or blankets.

                3.        When the affected areas become flushed, discontinue warming and have the victim gently exercise them to stimulate circulation.

        B.        If you take the wrong steps in treating frostbite, you can cause permanent damage to the affected areas.

                1.        First, do not apply hot water or strong heat.

                2.        Second, do not rub or massage the affected areas.

                3.        Third, do not break any blisters that may have formed.

---

# Chapter 11 Using Language

## True-False Questions

1. <u>T</u> F    As your textbook explains, language and thought are closely linked.

2. <u>T</u> F    The words we use to label an event determine to a great extent how we respond to that event.

3. T <u>F</u>    If the meaning of a word is clear to you, you can assume that it is also clear to your audience.

4. T <u>F</u>    The denotative meaning of a word includes all the feelings, associations, and emotions that the word touches off in different people.

5. <u>T</u> F    The connotative meaning of a word is more variable, figurative, and subjective than its denotative meaning.

6. <u>T</u> F    The connotative meaning of a word includes all the feelings, associations, and emotions that the word touches off in different people.

7. T <u>F</u>    Connotative meaning is precise, literal, and objective.

8. <u>T</u> F    One way to think of a word's denotative meaning is as its dictionary definition.

9. T <u>F</u>    Denotative meaning gives words their emotional power.

10. T <u>F</u>    A speech dominated by abstract words will almost always be clearer than one dominated by concrete words.

11. <u>T</u> F    The more abstract a word, the more ambiguous it will be.

12. T <u>F</u>    A public speaker needs to use big words to impress the audience.

13. <u>T</u> F    It is often possible to use words accurately without using them clearly.

14. T <u>F</u>    A speaker should avoid using familiar words because they make a speech sound trite.

15. T <u>F</u>   As your textbook explains, if you want to sound eloquent, you should use words that are unfamiliar to the audience.

16. T <u>F</u>   In dealing with technical topics, a speaker has little choice but to use technical language.

17. T <u>F</u>   Abstract words are usually clearer to listeners than are concrete words.

18. <u>T</u> F   Concrete words add to the imagery of language use by creating sensory impressions.

19. T <u>F</u>   "She darted around the bookstore like a hummingbird in a flower garden" is an example of metaphor.

20. <u>T</u> F   "She darted around the bookstore like a hummingbird in a flower garden" is an example of simile.

21. T <u>F</u>   "Air pollution is eating away at the monuments in Washington, D.C., like a giant Alka-Seltzer tablet" is an example of metaphor.

22. <u>T</u> F   "His smile flashed on and off like a neon sign" is an example of simile.

23. <u>T</u> F   "Air pollution is eating away at the monuments in Washington, D.C., like a giant Alka-Seltzer tablet" is an example of simile.

24. T <u>F</u>   "Silence settled over the audience like a block of granite" is an example of metaphor.

25. <u>T</u> F   "Silence settled over the audience like a block of granite" is an example of simile.

26. T <u>F</u>   "History is a drama with many acts" is an example of simile.

27. <u>T</u> F   "History is a drama with many acts" is an example of metaphor.

28. T <u>F</u>   "Her sense of humor was a continual bubble of joy" is an example of simile.

29. <u>T</u> F   "Her sense of humor was a continual bubble of joy" is an example of metaphor.

30. <u>T</u> F   "Your success as a family, our success as a society, depends not on what happens in the White House, but on what happens inside your house" is an example of antithesis.

31. <u>T</u> F   "Ask not what your country can do for you; ask what you can do for your country" is an example of antithesis.

32. T <u>F</u>   "Ask not what your country can do for you; ask what you can do for your country" is an example of metaphor.

33.  T <u>F</u>    Using metaphor is an excellent way to enhance the rhythm of a speech.

34.  <u>T</u> F    Language has a rhythm created by the choice and arrangement of words.

35.  T· <u>F</u>    Language has a rhythm created by the speaker's choice of supporting materials.

36.  <u>T</u> F    The use of repetition in a speech usually results in parallelism.

37.  T <u>F</u>    Antithesis and alliteration are excellent ways to enhance the imagery of a speech.

38.  <u>T</u> F    Alliteration as a means of creating rhythm in a speech refers to repeating the initial consonant sound of close or adjoining words.

39.  <u>T</u> F    Using language with a strong rhythm can increase the impact of a speaker's words.

40.  <u>T</u> F    There is a difference between one's everyday personal style and one's developed style as a public speaker.

41.  <u>T</u> F    Language needs to be appropriate to a speaker himself or herself, as well as to the audience, topic, and occasion.

42.  <u>T</u> F    You can seldom be too cautious in avoiding language that may confuse or offend your audience.

43.  T <u>F</u>    The main reason to use inclusive language in your speeches is to avoid being accused of political incorrectness.

44.  T <u>F</u>    Using the masculine pronoun "he" in a speech is an inclusive way to designate "all persons."

45.  <u>T</u> F    Using inclusive language is an important aspect of audience adaptation in public speaking.

46.  <u>T</u> F    Using inclusive language is important in public speaking both as a matter of audience adaptation and as a matter of accuracy in language.

47.  T <u>F</u>    According to your textbook, "Despite progress in recent years, homosexuals still face many forms of discrimination" is a good example of inclusive language.

48.  T <u>F</u>    As your textbook explains, using inclusive language in a speech is important primarily as a matter of political correctness.

49.  <u>T</u> F    According to your textbook, using inclusive language in a speech is a matter of personal courtesy.

**Multiple Choice Questions** *(Students are to indicate the <u>best</u> answer for each question by circling the correct letter.)*

50.    According to your textbook, language is important because it

    a.    mirrors reality.
\*b.    gives meaning to events.
    c.    has unambiguous connotations.
    d.    is separate from thought.
    e.    all of the above.

51.    Language helps to shape our sense of reality by

    a.    causing events.
\*b.    giving meaning to events.
    c.    communicating events.
    d.    mirroring events.
    e.    reflecting events.

52.    The denotative meaning of a word is

    a.    what the word suggests or implies.
    b.    based on the audience's sense of appropriateness.
    c.    usually more abstract than its connotative meaning.
    d.    often too technical to be used in a speech.
\*e.    its literal or dictionary meaning.

53.    The connotative meaning of a word is

    a.    its dictionary definition.
    b.    determined by the speaker.
    c.    concrete and precise.
\*d.    what the word suggests or implies.
    e.    usually too technical for a general audience.

54.    As your textbook explains, connotative meaning gives words their _____ power.

    a.    logical
    b.    definitional
\*c.    emotional
    d.    rhythmical
    e.    ethical

55.    As a speaker, you would probably use more connotative words if you wanted to

\*a.    arouse an emotional response.
    b.    appear as impartial as possible.
    c.    explain a technical concept.
    d.    enhance your credibility.
    e.    exploit the rhythm of language.

56.    Jerome wants his audience to appreciate the harsh reality of life for migrant workers in the United States. In addition to using strong supporting materials, he decides to use words with connotative meanings because he knows they will help him

    a.    have stronger delivery.
    b.    appear as impartial as possible.
  *c.    arouse an emotional response.
    d.    add rhythm to his language.
    e.    increase his accuracy.

57.    Each of the following is discussed in your textbook as a basic criterion for the effective use of language in public speaking *except*

    a.    use language clearly.
    b.    use language vividly.
    c.    use language appropriately.
  *d.    use language technically.
    e.    use language accurately.

58.    Which of the following is discussed in your textbook as a way to use language clearly?

    a.    use familiar words
    b.    choose concrete words
    c.    eliminate clutter
  *d.    all of the above
    e.    a and b only

59.    Kathryn wants to create concern among her listeners about the infringements on civil liberties she fears are resulting from the war on terrorism. She has decided to use words with strong connotative meanings because she knows they will help her

    a.    enhance her credibility.
  *b.    arouse an emotional response.
    c.    appear as impartial as possible.
    d.    all of the above.
    e.    b and c only.

60.    Which of the following is discussed in your textbook as a basic criterion for the effective use of language in public speaking?

    a.    use language clearly
    b.    use language accurately
    c.    use language vividly
  *d.    all of the above
    e.    a and b only

61.    Which of the following is discussed in your textbook as a basic criterion for the effective use of language in public speaking?

    a.    use language clearly
    b.    use language technically
    c.    use language clearly
    d.    all of the above
  *e.    a and c only

62.    Which of the following is discussed in your textbook as a basic criterion for the effective use of language in public speaking?

    a.    use language technically
    b.    use language appropriately
    c.    use language clearly
    d.    all of the above
  *e.    b and c only

63.    Which of the following words is the most general and abstract?

  *a.    language
    b.    novel
    c.    *Moby Dick*
    d.    book
    e.    publication

64.    Which of the following words is the most concrete and specific?

  *a.    Mozart
    b.    composer
    c.    classical music
    d.    entertainment
    e.    music

65.    Which of the following words is the most general and abstract?

    a.    roll
    b.    croissant
    c.    baked good
    b.    bread
  *e.    food

66.    Which of the following words is the most concrete and specific?

    a.    music
    b.    human activity
  *c.    Dave Matthews Band
    d.    entertainment
    e.    rock bands

67.    Which of the following words is the most concrete and specific?

    a.    fruit
    b.    tree
    c.    plant
  *d.    apricot
    e.    organism

68.    Which of the following words is the most concrete and specific?

    a.    performer
    b.    actress
  *c.    movie star
    d.    entertainer
    e.    celebrity

69.    To use language vividly your textbook recommends that speakers employ

    a.    metaphor and rhyme.
  *b.    imagery and rhythm.
    c.    concrete words and quotations.
    d.    testimony and examples.
    e.    antithesis and parallelism.

70.    Phrases such as "dry as a bone," "clear as a bell," "dark as night," and "smart as a whip" should be avoided in speeches because they are

    a.    abstract.
  *b.    clichés.
    c.    similes.
    d.    connotative.
    e.    figurative.

71.    "Asking the current administration to police its corruption is like putting Dracula in charge of the blood bank" is an example of

    a.    metaphor.
    b.    parallelism.
  *c.    simile.
    d.    rhythm.
    e.    repetition.

72.    "The Philippine Islands look like giant pieces of broken emerald that were dropped into the South China Sea by some giant" is an example of

  *a.    simile.
    b.    rhythm.
    c.    parallelism.
    d.    metaphor.
    e.    repetition.

73.   "Just like an iceberg, the most important dimensions of culture are below the
      surface" is an example of

 *a.   simile.
  b.   antithesis.
  c.   repetition.
  d.   alliteration.
  e.   metaphor.

74.   "Jesse Owens won his races in the 1936 Olympic games like a cheetah going after
      its prey" is an example of

  a.   metaphor.
  b.   alliteration.
  c.   antithesis.
  d.   repetition.
 *e.   simile.

75.   "Freedom is like a drum; strike it anywhere and it resounds everywhere" is an
      example of

  a.   metaphor.
  b.   repetition.
  c.   antithesis.
  b.   rhythm.
 *e.   simile.

76.   "A master politician, he worked the crowd with oiled precision" is an example of

  a.   antithesis.
  b.   repetition.
  c.   personification.
 *d.   metaphor.
  e.   simile.

77.   To help her audience understand how it felt to be a woman living under the
      Taliban, Sima stated, "Some Afghani women lived their lives in dark caves, cut off
      from the modern world, breathing only the stale air of information filtered through
      the ideology of the Taliban." In this statement, Sima used

 *a.   metaphor.
  b.   antithesis.
  c.   personification.
  d.   repetition.
  e.   simile.

78.   "Memories are like fingerprints—no two sets are ever the same" is an example of

  a.   metaphor.
 *b.   simile.
  c.   antithesis.
  d.   repetition.
  e.   personification.

79.    "Our mission is to right wrong, to do justice, and to serve humanity" is an example of

    a.    simile.
    b.    antithesis.
    c.    metaphor
    d.    imagery.
*e.    parallelism.

80.    "The roots of education are bitter, but the fruit is sweet" is an example of

    a.    parallelism.
*b.    metaphor.
    c.    simile.
    d.    repetition.
    e.    rhythm.

81.    "Her cheek was soft yet vibrant—a beautiful piece of copper-colored silk," is an example of

    a.    simile.
    b.    antithesis.
*c.    metaphor.
    d.    abstraction.
    e.    repetition.

82.    "My teacher was a gardener nurturing the seeds of knowledge" is an example of

    a.    repetition.
    b.    simile.
    c.    antithesis.
*d.    metaphor.
    e.    abstraction.

83.    In his speech on the importance of regular exercise, Aymil stated, "Taking the first step toward a healthier lifestyle requires three commitments: discipline, determination, and desire." In this statement, Aymil used

    a.    metaphor.
    b.    simile.
    c.    antithesis.
    d.    repetition.
*e.    alliteration.

84.    According to your textbook, "Let every nation know that we shall pay any price, bear any burden, meet any hardship, support any friend, oppose any foe to assure the survival and the success of liberty" is an example of

    a.    metaphor.
*b.    parallelism.
    c.    identification.
    d.    antithesis.
    e.    simile.

85.  "Unfortunately, many Americans live on the outskirts of hope—some because of their poverty, some because of their color, and all too many because of both" is an example of

   a.   simile.
   b.   antithesis.
   c.   personification.
  *d.   parallelism.
   e.   analogy.

86.  Your textbook recommends using repetition and parallelism to enhance the
     _____ of your speeches.

  *a.   rhythm
   b.   credibility
   c.   emotional appeal
   d.   appropriateness
   e.   imagery

87.  When used effectively, repetition in a speech

   a.   unifies a sequence of ideas.
   b.   helps to build a strong cadence.
   c.   reinforces an idea.
  *d.   all of the above.
   e.   b and c only.

88.  _____ is the repetition of the initial consonant sound of close or adjoining words.

   a.   Antithesis
   b.   Assonance
   c.   Anaphora
   d.   Arthimeria
  *e.   Alliteration

89.  "We will be candid, consistent, and confident" is an example of

   a.   metaphor.
   b.   antithesis.
   c.   simile.
  *d.   alliteration.
   e.   repetition.

90.  "Ask not what your country can do for you; ask what you can do for your country" is an example of

  *a.   antithesis.
   b.   simile.
   c.   metaphor.
   d.   imagery.
   e.   alliteration.

91. "We must come to realize that we are responsible not only for preparing you for the world, but for preparing the world for you" is an example of

    a.   metaphor.
 *b.   antithesis.
    c.   appropriateness.
    d.   formalism.
    e.   simile.

92. "Let us never negotiate out of fear. But let us never fear to negotiate" is an example of

    a.   imagery.
 *b.   antithesis.
    c.   repetition.
    d.   metaphor.
    e.   illustration.

93. "We must put an end to war—or war will put an end to us" is an example of

 *a.   antithesis.
    b.   simile.
    c.   illustration.
    d.   metaphor.
    e.   analogy.

94. "We will read all these names. We will linger over them. We will learn their stories, and we will weep" is an example of

    a.   simile.
    b.   repetition.
    c.   alliteration.
    d.   all of the above.
 *e.   b and c only.

95. "A voter without a ballot is like a soldier without a bullet" is an example of

    a.   simile.
    b.   parallelism.
    c.   personification.
    d.   all of the above.
 *e.   a and b only.

96. "Government of the people, by the people, for the people" is an example of

    a.   alliteration.
    b.   parallelism.
    c.   repetition.
 *d.   all of the above.
    e.   b and c only.

97.     "A dream deferred dries up like a raisin in the sun" is an example of

     a.   simile.
     b.   metaphor.
     c.   alliteration.
     d.   all of the above.
   *e.   a and c only.

98.     "The task is heavy, the toil is long, and the trials will be severe" is an example of

     a.   simile.
     b.   parallelism.
     c.   alliteration.
     d.   all of the above.
   *e.   b and c only.

99.     Which of the following does your textbook identify as a guideline for using language appropriately?

     a.   use language appropriate to the topic
     b.   use language appropriate to the speaker
     c.   use language appropriate to the audience
   *d.   all of the above
     e.   a and c only

100.    Which of the following is mentioned in your textbook as a basic criterion for the effective use of language?

   *a.   use language appropriately
     b.   use language persuasively
     c.   use language credibly
     d.   use language emphatically
     e.   use language forcefully

101.    In her speech about classical ballet, Kyndra mentioned, but did not explain, the terms *entrechat* and *arabesque*. Since most of her listeners were unfamiliar with ballet, what error did Kyndra make in her use of language?

     a.   She did not use language appropriate to the occasion.
     b.   She did not use language appropriate to the topic.
   *c.   She did not use language appropriate to the audience.
     d.   She did not use language appropriate to the setting.
     e.   She did not use language appropriate to the speaker.

102.    Which of the following are mentioned in your textbook as guidelines for the use of inclusive language in public speaking?

     a.   Avoid the generic "he."
     b.   Avoid the use of "man" when referring to both men and women.
     c.   Use names that groups currently use to identify themselves.
   *d.   all of the above
     e.   a and b only

103.   Which of the following are mentioned in your textbook as guidelines for the use of inclusive language in public speaking?

    a.   Avoid stereotyping jobs and social roles by gender.
    b.   Avoid pointing out personal traits that have no bearing on the topic at hand.
    c.   Avoid emotional appeal when discussing issues of race, gender, or disability.
    d.   all of the above
 *e.   a and b only

104.   "Police officers need extra life insurance to protect their wives and children," said city council member Heather Carpenter. Carpenter's language violated which of the guidelines for inclusive language discussed in your textbook?

    a.   Avoid the generic "he."
    b.   Avoid excluding listeners because of their age.
    c.   Avoid identifying personal traits that are unrelated to the topic.
 *d.   Avoid stereotyping jobs and social roles by gender.
    e.   Use names that groups use to identify themselves.

105.   "Surgeons and their wives deserve the financial protection offered by these caps on monetary awards in malpractice suits." This statement violates which of the guidelines for inclusive language discussed in your textbook?

 *a.   Avoid stereotyping jobs and social roles by gender.
    b.   Avoid excluding listeners because of their occupation.
    c.   Use names that groups use to identify themselves.
    d.   all of the above
    e.   b and c only

## Short Answer Questions

106.   The ____denotative____ meaning of a word is its literal or dictionary meaning.

107.   The ____connotative____ meaning of a word includes all of the associations and feelings the word touches off in different people, while the ____denotative____ meaning of a word is best thought of as its dictionary definition.

108.   The ____denotative____ meaning of a word is precise, literal, and objective, whereas the ____connotative____ meaning of a word is variable, figurative, and subjective.

109.   As your textbook explains, language should be appropriate to the topic, the audience, the occasion, and the _____speaker_____.

110.   Three methods explained in your textbook for using language clearly are:

a.   _____use concrete words_____

b.   _____use familiar words_____

c.   _____eliminate clutter_____

111.   Rearrange the following words in order from most general and abstract to most concrete and specific:

transportation, Ford products, vehicles, Mustangs, automobiles

(transportation, vehicles, automobiles, Ford products, Mustangs)

112.   Rearrange the following words in order from the most general and abstract to the most concrete and specific:

physics, Einstein, science, intellectual endeavor, physicist

(intellectual endeavor, science, physics, physicist, Einstein)

113.   Using _____concrete_____ words is the key to creating effective verbal imagery.

114.   A _____simile_____ is a figurative comparison that always contains the word "like" or "as."

115.   A form of creating imagery in a speech that involves an implied comparison between things that are essentially different is termed _____metaphor_____.

116.   The similar arrangement of a pair or series of related words is a language device called _____parallelism_____.

117.   When you repeat the initial consonant sound of close or adjoining words, you are using the language device known as _____alliteration_____.

118.   Here are four words whose meaning is roughly synonymous—walk, trudge, stroll, march. Select the appropriate word to complete each of the following sentences.

a.   On spring afternoons we like to _____stroll_____ through the botanical gardens.
b.   I was too tired to do anything but _____trudge_____ home.
c.   We had a great time watching the bands _____march_____ by during the parade.
d.   If you _____walk_____ instead of drive, you'll improve your cardiovascular fitness.

119.   Here are four words whose meaning is roughly synonymous—madness, eccentricity, obsession, infatuation. Select the most appropriate word to complete each of the following sentences.

a.   Professor Schwartz never wears an overcoat even on the coldest days. That's his personal _____eccentricity_____.
b.   My friend Jean has every Beatles record ever made. She's gone beyond collecting to the point of _____obsession_____.
c.   Sue's love for Ben Affleck isn't real love. It's just _____infatuation_____.
d.   My public speaking instructor thinks I'm going to deliver six speeches this semester. That's _____madness_____.

120.   In public speaking, the use of language should be appropriate to:

a.   _____the audience_____

b.   _____the occasion_____

c.   _____the topic_____

d.   _____the speaker_____

## Essay Questions

121.   Explain the following statement: "Language does not mirror reality. Instead, language helps create our sense of reality by giving meaning to events."

122.   Explain the following statement: "On most occasions when we are looking for 'just the right word,' what we are really looking for is just the right idea."

123.   Explain the following statement: "Language is not neutral. The words we use to label an event determine to a great extent how we respond to it."

124.   What are the differences between connotative meaning and denotative meaning? Be sure to illustrate your answer with examples of each kind of meaning.

125.   Explain the differences between abstract and concrete words. Why are public speakers usually advised to rely on the latter rather than on the former?

126.   Identify and explain the four criteria given in your textbook for using language effectively.

127.   What is the difference between using language accurately and using language clearly? Explain the three criteria given in your textbook for using language clearly.

128.   What is "clutter" in a public speech? Why is it a barrier to effective speechmaking? How can it be combated?

129.   What is the difference between imagery and rhythm in the language of a speech? Identify and explain two devices each for enhancing the imagery and the rhythm of a speech.

130.   Identify and explain the four criteria for language appropriateness discussed in your textbook.

131.   Explain the following statement: "Public speakers need to use inclusive language both as a matter of audience adaptation and as a matter of accuracy in language use."

132.   One of the greatest differences between writing an essay and giving a speech is that the listener, unlike the reader, cannot turn to a dictionary or reread an author's words to discover their meaning. How does this complicate the task of a public speaker? Explain three specific steps a speaker can take to make his or her meaning clear despite these complications.

**Discussion:** These three steps need not be limited to material dealt with in Chapter 11. Students might focus their answers on such matters as using familiar words, eliminating clutter, and the like, but they might also mention such matters as using clear patterns of organization, providing connectives between ideas, etc.

133.    In the column on the left are statements as they could have been made by a speaker. The column on the right shows what the speaker actually said. In each case explain what elements of language usage make the statements on the right more effective.

|  | Less Effective | More Effective |
|---|---|---|
| a. | The impact of freedom in one part of the world has a great impact on freedom in other parts of the world. | Freedom is like a drum; strike it anywhere and it resounds everywhere. (Adlai Stevenson) |

**Discussion:** The more effective statement is improved primarily by its use of simile and also by its use of imagery and parallel structure.

|  | | |
|---|---|---|
| b. | We should always negotiate from a position of strength, and we should always be willing to negotiate. | Let us never negotiate out of fear. But let us never fear to negotiate. (John F. Kennedy) |

**Discussion:** The more effective statement is distinguished by the speaker's use of antithesis. It is also enhanced by the alliteration in "never negotiate."

|  | | |
|---|---|---|
| c. | Now is the time to ensure democracy for all citizens, to put an end to segregation, and to abolish racial injustice. | Now is the time to make real the promises of democracy. Now is the time to rise from the dark and desolate valley of segregation to the sunlit path of racial justice. Now is the time to lift our nation from the quicksand of racial injustice to the solid rock of brotherhood. (Martin Luther King) |

**Discussion:** The more effective statement is more vivid, more forceful, and more rhythmical because of the speaker's use of repetition, parallelism, metaphor, and imagery.

134.    What does it mean to say that language should be appropriate to the topic of a speech? Explain.

135.    What does it mean to say that language should be appropriate to the speaker? Explain.

136.    Identify and explain five of the criteria for inclusive language discussed in your textbook.

_____

# Chapter 12 Delivery

## True-False Questions

1.   T  <u>F</u>     Good speech delivery should call attention to itself.

2.   <u>T</u>  F     Good speech delivery conveys a speaker's ideas without calling attention to itself.

3.   <u>T</u>  F     Nonverbal communication is based on a person's use of voice and body, rather than on the use of words.

4.   T  <u>F</u>     One of the advantages of speaking from a manuscript is that it frees a speaker from the need to establish eye contact with the audience.

5.   T  <u>F</u>     Speaking from a manuscript allows for greater spontaneity and directness than does speaking extemporaneously.

6.   <u>T</u>  F     A manuscript speech is written out word for word and read to the audience.

7.   T  <u>F</u>     Speaking from memory is most effective when a speaker wants to be very responsive to feedback from the audience.

8.   <u>T</u>  F     When speaking impromptu, you should do your best to look calm and confident no matter how nervous you may be feeling.

9.   T  <u>F</u>     Impromptu speaking gives more precise control over thought and language than does extemporaneous speaking.

10.   <u>T</u>  F     An impromptu speech is delivered with little or no immediate preparation.

11.   T  <u>F</u>     Speaking impromptu and speaking extemporaneously are essentially alike.

12.  T F    An extemporaneous speech is carefully prepared and practiced in advance.

13.  T F    "Conversational quality" in a speech means that the speaker talks the same as she or he would in ordinary conversation.

14.  T F    The "conversational quality" of extemporaneous speaking means that a speech has been well rehearsed yet sounds spontaneous to the audience

15.  T F    No two people have exactly the same vocal characteristics.

16.  T F    A speaker always sounds louder to a listener than to the speaker.

17.  T F    Pitch is the relative highness or lowness of the speaker's voice.

18.  T F    People in the U.S. usually talk at a rate between 120 and 150 words per minute.

19.  T F    A faster rate of speech is usually called for when a speaker is explaining complex information.

20.  T F    Vocalized pauses are an effective way to increase a speaker's credibility.

21.  T F    Pauses usually work best in a speech when they are planned in advance.

22.  T F    Most people recognize and understand about the same number of words in reading as occur in spontaneous speech.

23.  T F    Most people recognize and understand about three times as many words in reading as occur in spontaneous speech.

24.  T F    If you say the "s" in Illinois or the "p" in pneumonia, you are making a mistake in articulation.

25.  T F    You can articulate a word sharply and still mispronounce it.

26.  T F    Ways of talking based on ethnic or regional speech patterns are called dialects.

27.  T F    Dialects are usually based on regional or ethnic speech patterns.

28.  T F    Over the years linguists have concluded that no dialect is inherently better or worse than another dialect.

29.  T F    Regional or ethnic dialects are fine in speeches as long as listeners find them acceptable.

30. <u>T</u> F   When a speaker's body language is inconsistent with her or his words, listeners often believe the body language rather than the words.

31. T <u>F</u>   Research has shown that the speaker's personal appearance is an important factor in about 25 percent of speech situations.

32. T <u>F</u>   Research shows that personal appearance will affect the audience's perception of the speaker in about half of all speaking situations.

33. <u>T</u> F   Rehearsing how you behave at the beginning and end of your speech is one of the easiest things you can do to improve your image with an audience.

34. T <u>F</u>   Since most people are nervous about public speaking, it is perfectly acceptable to finish a speech by declaring, "Am I glad that's over!"

35. T <u>F</u>   As your textbook explains, learning how to gesture is one of the first things a beginning public speaker should concentrate on.

36. T <u>F</u>   Frequent gestures are a sure sign of an effective speaker.

37. T <u>F</u>   The human eyeball expresses an intricate array of emotions.

38. <u>T</u> F   You should start to establish eye contact with the audience even before you begin to speak.

39. <u>T</u> F   In the United States, public speakers who establish strong eye contact are usually perceived as more credible than speakers who have weak eye contact.

40. T <u>F</u>   In the United States, public speakers who establish strong eye contact with listeners are usually perceived as less credible than speakers who have weaker eye contact.

41. T <u>F</u>   According to your textbook, the first step in rehearsing a speech is to practice in front of a mirror.

42. <u>T</u> F   According to your textbook, the first step in practicing your speech delivery is to go through your preparation outline aloud to see how it translates into spoken discourse.

43. T <u>F</u>   A single practice session of two or three hours is usually the best way to rehearse your speech.

44. <u>T</u> F   The question-and-answer session can have as much impact on an audience as what a speaker says during the speech itself.

45.  T̲ F    Handling the question-and-answer session well can enhance a speaker's credibility and strengthen the impact of his or her speech.

46.  T F̲    In most cases, the question-and-answer session has little impact on an audience's response to a speech.

47.  T F̲    When preparing for a question-and-answer session, it is unethical to anticipate potential questions and to write out answers ahead of time.

48.  T F̲    When preparing for a question-and-answer session, it is a bad idea to write out answers to possible questions because doing so can decrease the conversational quality of your delivery.

49.  T̲ F    According to your textbook, when preparing for a question-and-answer session, you should anticipate possible questions, write out your answers in full, and practice the delivery of your answers.

50.  T F̲    When answering questions after a speech, you should try to make your answers as long as possible to use up the time allotted.

51.  T F̲    As your textbook explains, you are most likely to be successful in a question-and-answer session if you approach each question as a challenge to your competence and intelligence.

52.  T F̲    If you receive a hostile question during a question-and-answer session, you should respond in a hostile manner.

53.  T̲ F    If you are asked a hostile question during a question-and-answer session, you should avoid sounding hostile in your response.

54.  T̲ F    During a question-and-answer session, you should direct your answers primarily to the audience as a whole rather than solely to the individual questioner.

55.  T̲ F    When conducting a question-and-answer session, you should usually restate or paraphrase each question before you answer it.

56.  T F̲    When faced with an inquiry you can't answer during a question-and-answer session, you should usually try to bluff your way through the answer so as to preserve your credibility on the topic.

57.  T̲ F    Unless there is a moderator, the speaker is responsible for making sure the question-and-answer session stays on track and finishes within the specified time limits.

58.  T̲ F    To keep control of the question-and-answer session, a speaker should usually allow no more than one follow-up question from each questioner.

**Multiple Choice Questions** *(Students are to indicate the <u>best</u> answer for each question by circling the correct letter.)*

59.    Good speech delivery

    a.    is accompanied by frequent gestures.
    b.    requires that the speaker have a strong voice.
  *c.    sounds conversational even though it has been rehearsed.
    d.    draws the attention of the audience away from the message.
    e.    is best achieved by reading from a manuscript.

60.    Good speech delivery

    a.    has a conversational quality.
    b.    does not call attention to itself.
    c.    requires a strong voice.
    d.    all of the above.
  *e.    a and b only.

61.    Communication based on a speaker's body and voice, rather than on the use of words, is called

    a.    implicit communication.
  *b.    nonverbal communication.
    c.    unintentional communication.
    d.    instinctive communication.
    e.    physical communication.

62.    In which situation would a speaker be *most* likely to read from a manuscript?

    a.    a speech accepting an award at a company banquet
    b.    a speech in honor of a retiring employee
  *c.    a speech on international policy at the United Nations
    d.    a speech on the activities of a church social committee
    e.    a speech of welcome to new members of the Rotary Club

63.    A political candidate is running for office and must give a speech that will lay out the details of her platform. The speech will be widely covered by newspapers and television. What kind of delivery is the candidate most likely to use?

  *a.    manuscript
    b.    impromptu
    c.    monotonous
    d.    colloquial
    e.    memorized

64.    When speaking from a manuscript, you should

    a.    practice aloud to make sure the speech sounds natural.
    b.    be certain the final manuscript is legible at a glance.
    c.    work on establishing eye contact with the audience.
 *d.    all of the above.
    e.    a and b only.

65.    According to your textbook, the _____ speaker delivers a speech with little or no immediate preparation.

    a.    colloquial
    b.    extemporaneous
    c.    conversational
 *d.    impromptu
    e.    declamatory

66.    In which situation would a speaker be *most* likely to recite a speech from memory?

 *a.    when making a toast at a wedding
    b.    when responding to questions during a class lecture
    c.    when reporting earnings to the yearly stockholders' meeting
    d.    when presenting a lengthy proposal to the city council
    e.    when rallying a group to work for lower tuition

67.    Which of the following does your textbook mention as an advantage of extemporaneous delivery?

    a.    It requires only a minimal amount of gesturing by the speaker.
    b.    It reduces the likelihood of a speaker making vocalized pauses.
    c.    It improves a speaker's ability to articulate difficult words correctly.
    d.    It requires little or no preparation before the speech is delivered.
 *e.    It allows greater spontaneity than does speaking from a manuscript.

68.    According to your textbook, a speech that sounds spontaneous to the audience no matter how many times it has been rehearsed has a strong _____ quality.

    a.    impromptu
    b.    memorized
 *c.    conversational
    d.    kinesic
    e.    formal

69.    The _____ speaker uses only brief notes or a speaking outline to jog the memory.

    a.    after-dinner
    b.    commemorative
    c.    informative
 *d.    extemporaneous
    e.    persuasive

70. A speech that is fully prepared in advance but that is delivered from a brief set of notes or a speaking outline is called a(n) _____ speech.

    *a. extemporaneous
    b. declamatory
    c. impromptu
    d. manuscript
    e. vocalized

71. Erik is giving a speech in his art history course. He has carefully prepared his presentation and plans to deliver it from a brief set of note cards. What kind of delivery is Erik using?

    a. informal
    b. memorized
    *c. extemporaneous
    d. impromptu
    e. formal

72. Speaking extemporaneously

    a. gives more control over language than does speaking from memory.
    *b. is adaptable to more situations than is speaking from manuscript.
    c. offers more spontaneity and directness than does speaking impromptu.
    d. all of the above.
    e. b and c only.

73. "Conversational quality" in speech delivery means that the

    *a. speech sounds spontaneous even though it has been rehearsed.
    b. speaker is not speaking from memory.
    c. speaker talks the same as she or he would in ordinary conversation.
    d. all of the above.
    e. b and c only.

74. The relative highness or lowness of sounds produced by the human voice is called

    a. rate.
    *b. pitch.
    c. tone.
    d. quality.
    e. volume.

75. According to your textbook, inflection refers to the

    a. dialect of a speaker.
    b. speed at which a person speaks.
    *c. changes in the pitch of a speaker's voice.
    d. clarity of a speaker's articulation.
    e. loudness or softness of a speaker's voice.

76.    Changes in the pitch or tone of a speaker's voice are called

    a.    phonemes.
    b.    polytones.
    c.    enunciations.
\*d.    inflections.
    e.    accents.

77.    It is the _____ of your voice that reveals whether you are asking a question or making a statement, whether you are being sincere or sarcastic.

    a.    spontaneity
    b.    variety
    c.    resonance
\*d.    inflection
    e.    rate

78.    The best rate of speech depends on the

    a.    vocal attributes of the speaker.
    b.    mood the speaker is trying to create.
    c.    composition of the audience.
\*d.    all of the above.
    e.    a and b only.

79.    Which of the following would probably call for a faster speaking rate than normal?

    a.    expressing sadness or contempt
    b.    describing the winning touchdown in last week's game
    c.    summarizing information already familiar to an audience
    d.    all of the above
\*e.    b and c only

80.    If you hoped to convey to your audience the excitement of steering a kayak through a river rapids, you should probably

\*a.    speak at a faster rate.
    b.    use more vocalized pauses.
    c.    break eye contact with your audience.
    d.    gesture less frequently.
    e.    avoid using dialect.

81.    A public speaker who frequently says "uh," "er," or "um" is failing to make effective use of

    a.    vocal variety.
\*b.    pauses.
    c.    pitch.
    d.    rate.
    e.    inflection.

82.    According to your textbook, "uh," "er," "um" and similar expressions in a public
       speech are referred to as

       a.    vocal fillers.
       b.    signposts.
       c.    intonations.
      *d.    vocalized pauses.
       e.    inflections.

83.    Changes in a speaker's rate, pitch, volume, and pauses are referred to as

       a.    vocal direction.
       b.    vocal credibility.
       c.    vocal pronunciation.
       d.    vocal contact.
      *e.    vocal variety.

84.    Forming particular speech sounds crisply and distinctly is called

       a.    verbalization.
      *b.    articulation.
       c.    vocalized pausing.
       d.    pronunciation.
       e.    intonation.

85.    According to your textbook, saying "dunno" instead of "don't know" is an error in

       a.    accent.
      *b.    articulation.
       c.    vocalization.
       d.    intonation.
       e.    emphasis.

86.    According to your textbook, saying "pas-ghetti" instead of "spaghetti" is an error in

       a.    articulation.
       b.    description.
       c.    intonation.
      *d.    pronunciation.
       e.    inflection.

87.    According to your textbook, when people in one region of the country say
       "warter," while people in another region of the country say "water," the difference
       is a matter of

       a.    inflection.
       b.    verbalization.
      *c.    dialect.
       d.    enunciation.
       e.    intonation.

88.    What does your textbook say about speech dialects?

    a.    Most languages have dialects.
    b.    Dialects are usually based on regional or ethnic speech patterns.
    c.    No dialect is inherently better or worse than any other dialect.
 *d.    all of the above
    e.    a and b only

89.    Research has shown that

 *a.    when speakers' nonverbal signals are inconsistent with their words, listeners often believe the nonverbal signals rather than the words.
    b.    the best rate for effective speechmaking is 170 words per minute.
    c.    smooth, graceful gestures are vital to effective speechmaking.
    d.    listeners usually find a somewhat slower than normal speaking rate to be more credible than a slightly faster than normal rate.
    e.    some dialects are inherently better than others.

90.    What does your textbook advise regarding the use of gestures in a speech?

    a.    Gestures should be suited to the audience and occasion.
    b.    Speakers should have a vast number of graceful gestures.
    c.    Gestures should appear natural and spontaneous.
    d.    all of the above
 *e.    a and c only

91.    The study of bodily motion and gestures is part of a subject called

    a.    cybernetics.
    b.    kinetics.
    c.    cryogenics.
 *d.    kinesics.
    e.    cryonics.

92.    Ivory will be giving a presentation for her company to a group of prospective customers at an international trade show, and she is deciding what to wear. According to your textbook, which of the following statements about the role of personal appearance in speechmaking should she keep in mind when making her decision?

 *a.    A speaker's personal appearance should be in keeping with the occasion of the speech.
    b.    Research has shown that bright-colored clothing has a more favorable impact on listeners.
    c.    In most cases, listeners' attitudes are not influenced by the way a speaker is dressed.
    d.    all of the above
    e.    a and b only

93. In which of the following situations will the personal appearance of the speaker have an impact on the audience?

  a. a politician presenting a campaign speech
  b. a business executive giving a financial report
  c. a professor giving a lecture
 *d. all of the above
  e. a and b only

94. What does your textbook say about eye contact for public speakers who address audiences in the United States?

  a. To appear credible and trustworthy, a speaker should gaze intently at one section of the audience.
  b. In classroom speeches, it is most important to maintain steady eye contact with the instructor.
 *c. Speakers should look at the audience about 80 to 90 percent of the time they are talking.
  d. Speakers who establish strong eye contact with the audience lose credibility as a result.
  e. Even with a large audience, engaging the eyes of each person is preferable to scanning the audience in general.

95. During her speech on malpractice insurance, the head of the local branch of the American Medical Association consistently avoided making eye contact with her audience. According to research on the role of nonverbal communication in public speaking, the audience was likely to perceive her as

 *a. insincere.
  b. trustworthy.
  c. inexperienced.
  d. credible.
  e. inconsistent.

96. What does your textbook recommend regarding the *last* step of practicing delivery for a speech?

  a. Listen to a tape of the speech and make last-minute changes in it.
  b. Practice the speech in front of a mirror to check your body language.
  c. Prepare your speaking outline so it is brief and easy to read at a glance.
 *d. Rehearse under conditions as close as possible to the actual speech situation.
  e. Time yourself as you practice the speech out loud and as you use visual aids.

97. What does your textbook recommend as the *first* step of practicing delivery?

  a. Record your speech and listen to it so you can refine your delivery.
  b. Prepare your speaking outline so it is brief and easy to read at a glance.
 *c. Go through your preparation outline aloud to see if what is written works orally.
  d. Rehearse your speech in front of a mirror to check your body language.
  e. Do a dress rehearsal in the room where you will present the speech.

98.    When approaching the lectern and beginning your speech, you should

    a.    start immediately so your audience does not become impatient.
    b.    create a bond with the audience by acknowledging your nervousness.
  *c.    establish eye contact with the audience before you start to speak.
    d.    all of the above.
    e.    a and b only.

99.    As your textbook explains, when preparing for a question-and-answer session, you should

    a.    anticipate possible questions.
    b.    write out your answers in full.
    c.    practice the delivery of your answers.
  *d.    all of the above.
    e.    a and c only.

100.    Which of the following are mentioned by your textbook as guidelines for managing a question-and-answer session?

    a.    direct answers to the entire audience
    b.    be honest and straightforward
    c.    stay on track
  *d.    all of the above
    e.    a and b only

101.    When conducting a question-and-answer session, you should

    a.    allow each questioner to ask as many follow-up questions as they wish.
    b.    try to bluff your way through when faced with a question you can't answer.
  *c.    direct your answers primarily to the audience as a whole.
    d.    all of the above.
    e.    a and b only.

102.    When conducting a question-and-answer session, you should

  *a.    view the session as one more opportunity to communicate your ideas.
    b.    respond to hostile questions in a defensive and argumentative manner.
    c.    allow each questioner to ask as many follow-up questions as they wish.
    d.    all of the above.
    e.    a and c only.

103.    The Dean of Students is introducing a new campus policy on alcohol use. After the presentation, he will respond to questions from students, local residents, and reporters. To prepare for this question-and-answer session, the Dean should

    a.    ask his staff to anticipate potential questions.
    b.    write out answers to potential questions.
    c.    practice the delivery of his answers.
  *d.    all of the above.
    e.    a and b only.

## Short Answer Questions

104.  Communication based on a person's voice and body, rather than on the use of words, is called _____nonverbal_____ communication.

105.  A speech delivered without any immediate preparation is called a(n) _____impromptu_____ speech.

106.  A speech that is fully prepared in advance but delivered from a brief set of notes or a speaking outline is called a(n) _____extemporaneous_____ speech.

107.  When a speech must be delivered word for word a speaker will likely use _____manuscript_____ delivery.

108.  The relative highness or lowness of speech sounds is called _____pitch_____.

109.  _____Rate_____ refers to the speed at which a person speaks.

110.  Mark Twain said, "The right word might be effective, but no word was ever as effective as a rightly timed _____pause_____."

111.  Changes in a speaker's pitch, rate, volume, and pauses are referred to as _____vocal variety_____.

112.  Sloppy _____articulation_____ is the failure to form particular speech sounds crisply and distinctly.

113.  _____Pronunciation_____ is the ability to say a word as indicated in a dictionary, while _____articulation_____ is the ability to form individual speech sounds distinctly.

114.  How we use eye contact, body movement, gestures, and other physical motions to communicate is the subject of an area of study known as _____kinesics_____.

115.  Because they send such revealing nonverbal messages, we think of the _____eyes_____ as "the windows of the soul."

116.  Ways of speaking based on regional or ethnic speech patterns are known as _____dialects_____.

## Essay Questions

117.  Explain the following statement: "Good delivery does not call attention to itself."

118.  In a well-developed essay, compare and contrast the four basic methods of speech delivery.

119.    What are the advantages and disadvantages of speaking extemporaneously compared with speaking from a manuscript?

120.    Explain three steps you should take to deliver a speech effectively from a manuscript.

121.    What does your textbook suggest you should do when you are called upon to present an impromptu speech?

122.    Define *five* of the following eight aspects of vocal delivery and explain their importance to effective public speaking:

    a.   volume

    b.   pitch

    c.   rate

    d.   pauses

    e.   vocal variety

    f.   articulation

    g.   pronunciation

    h.   dialect

123.    Explain the importance to effective public speaking of each of the following aspects of physical delivery:

    a.   personal appearance

    b.   movement

    c.   gestures

    d.   eye contact

124.    What should you do physically to make a favorable impression on listeners just before you begin a speech and just after you finish speaking?

125.    Identify and explain the five steps provided in your textbook for practicing speech delivery.

126.    Explain the steps you should take to prepare for a question-and-answer session.

127.    Explain each of the following aspects of conducting a question-and-answer session:

    a.   Approach questions with a positive attitude.

    b.   Direct answers to the entire audience.

    c.   Stay on track.

---

# Chapter 13 Using Visual Aids

## True-False Questions

1. <u>T</u> F    Research has shown that an average speaker who uses visual aids will come across as more credible and better prepared than a speaker who does not use visual aids.

2. T <u>F</u>    One of the reasons to use visual aids in a speech is that you can break eye contact with the audience while discussing the aids.

3. T <u>F</u>    One of the advantages of using visual aids in a speech is that their meaning is instantly clear to the audience.

4. <u>T</u> F    Research has shown that visual aids can increase both the clarity and the persuasiveness of a speaker's message.

5. <u>T</u> F    Research has shown that using visual aids can increase the audience's retention of a speaker's message.

6. <u>T</u> F    Using visual aids can help combat stage fright.

7. T <u>F</u>    If the object you want to speak about is too large, too small, or unavailable to use as a visual aid, you have little choice but to change the topic of your speech.

8. T <u>F</u>    Models are the best type of visual aid for presenting statistical information.

9. T <u>F</u>    Because a picture is worth a thousand words, it is a good idea to pass photographs among the audience in order to illustrate your point.

10. T <u>F</u>    According to your textbook, it is usually a good idea to write or draw on an overhead transparency while you are speaking.

11. <u>T</u> F    Despite advances in technology it is still necessary for a speaker who is using an overhead projector to work with the projector when practicing the speech.

12.  T <u>F</u>    If you were giving a speech about how to lift weights, the most effective visual aid would probably be a drawing.

13.  <u>T</u> F    If you were summarizing statistical trends in a speech, the best visual aid to use would probably be a graph.

14.  <u>T</u> F    A speech that combines several kinds of visual and audio aids in the same talk is known as a multimedia presentation.

15.  <u>T</u> F    If you wanted to summarize the steps of a process in a speech, the best kind of visual aid to use would probably be a chart.

16.  T <u>F</u>    If you were summarizing statistical trends in a speech, the best visual aid to use would probably be a chart.

17.  T <u>F</u>    One of the advantages of multimedia presentations is that they take less time to prepare than do other kinds of visual aids.

18.  <u>T</u> F    You can be your own visual aid.

19.  <u>T</u> F    One advantage to doing a demonstration during your speech is that it reduces nervousness by providing an outlet for extra adrenaline.

20.  <u>T</u> F    One advantage of preparing your visual aids well in advance is that doing so allows you to use them while practicing your speech.

21.  <u>T</u> F    You should include in a visual aid only what you need to make your point.

22.  <u>T</u> F    When you design a visual aid, you should keep in mind the size of the room in which you will be speaking.

23.  T <u>F</u>    Printing your visual aid in ALL CAPITAL letters is a good way to make sure it will be easy for the audience to read.

24.  T <u>F</u>    In most circumstances it is an excellent idea to present visual aids by drawing or writing on the chalkboard.

25.  <u>T</u> F    In most circumstances you should avoid presenting visual aids by drawing or writing on the chalkboard.

26.  T <u>F</u>    Visual aids should usually be displayed from the left side of the lectern.

27.  T <u>F</u>    Visual aids should usually be displayed from the right side of the lectern.

28.  T <u>F</u>    Passing visual aids among the audience during a speech is helpful to a speaker because it allows listeners to inspect the aids at their own pace.

29.  <u>T</u> F    In most circumstances a speaker should avoid passing visual aids among the audience.

30. <u>T</u> F    A visual aid is only as useful as the explanation that goes with it.

31. T <u>F</u>    Visual aids usually should be used only in informative speeches.

32. T <u>F</u>    When you are going to give an audience material to take home from a speech, you should usually distribute the material at the beginning of the speech.

33. T <u>F</u>    When you are giving an audience material to take home from a speech, you should usually distribute the material in the middle of your speech.

34. <u>T</u> F    When you are going to give an audience material to take home from a speech, you should usually distribute the material after you are finished speaking.

35. T <u>F</u>    In most circumstances you should keep your visual aids on display throughout your speech.

36. <u>T</u> F    It is important to maintain strong eye contact with your audience when you are presenting a visual aid.

## Multiple Choice Questions *(Students are to indicate the <u>best</u> answer for each question by circling the correct letter.)*

37.   Which of the following does your textbook mention as an advantage of using visual aids in a public speech?

   a.   Using visual aids enhances the clarity of the speaker's message.
   b.   Using visual aids reduces the need for eye contact with the audience.
   c.   Using visual aids can help combat the speaker's stage fright.
   d.   all of the above
 *e.   a and c only

38.   Visual aids can be very useful to a speaker because they

   a.   often take the place of statistics.
 *b.   enhance the clarity of a speaker's ideas.
   c.   can be passed among members of the audience.
   d.   do not require a great deal of explanation.
   e.   all of the above.

39.   According to your textbook, which of the following is an advantage of using visual aids in a speech?

   a.   Using visual aids can increase the clarity of a speaker's message.
   b.   Using visual aids can increase the audience's retention of a speaker's message.
   c.   Using visual aids can increase the persuasiveness of a speaker's message.
 *d.   all of the above
   e.   a and b only

40.    Which of the following does your textbook present as a guideline for preparing visual aids?

   *a.   keep visual aids simple
    b.   include a minimum of three fonts
    c.   write words in all capital letters
    d.   all of the above
    e.   a and c only

41.    Visual aids are often helpful to a speaker because they can

    a.   enhance the clarity of a speaker's ideas.
    b.   make information more interesting to listeners.
    c.   help listeners retain a speaker's ideas.
   *d.   all of the above.
    e.   a and b only.

42.    If the object you want to use as a visual aid is not available, the next best option ideally is a

   *a.   model.
    b.   chart.
    c.   slide.
    d.   photograph.
    e.   drawing.

43.    If you wanted to compare the military spending of the United States to that of eight other nations, what type of visual aid should you probably use?

    a.   a map
   *b.   a chart
    c.   a line graph
    d.   a pie graph
    e.   a diagram

44.    According to your textbook, when using color in a visual aid, you should

    a.   include at least four colors.
   *b.   utilize color to highlight key points.
    c.   use color only in multimedia presentations.
    d.   limit overhead transparencies to one color.
    e.   display major ideas in red or green.

45.    When making a multimedia presentation, you should

    a.   limit yourself to showing charts, graphs, photographs, and drawings.
   *b.   be prepared to give your speech even if the equipment malfunctions.
    c.   use a different set of fonts for each chart to keep the audience interested.
    d.   reduce the number of main points to make sure you do not run out of time.
    e.   tell your audience which software program you are using for the speech.

46.    As your textbook explains, if you plan to use a photograph as a visual aid in a speech, you should

   *a.   convert it to a transparency and show it with an overhead projector.
    b.   pass the photograph among the audience so everyone can look at it.
    c.   use a photograph in an oversize book and hold it where it can be seen.
    d.   all of the above.
    e.   b and c only.

47.    To be used effectively as visual aids, photographs should be

    a.   supplemented with drawings.
    b.   in color, not black and white.
   *c.   bigger than ordinary enlargements.
    d.   passed among the audience.
    e.   explained with a chart.

48.    As your textbook explains, you can use a photograph as a visual aid by

    a.   creating an enlargement of at least 18 by 24 inches.
    b.   converting the image to a transparency and showing it with an overhead projector.
    c.   displaying it with a multimedia program.
   *d.   all of the above.
    e.   a and c only.

49.    _____ are especially valuable for showing an audience statistical trends and patterns.

    a.   Models
    b.   Diagrams
    c.   Transparencies
    d.   Blueprints
   *e.   Graphs

50.    If you were discussing statistical trends in a speech, what kind of visual aid would probably work best to clarify the trends for listeners?

    a.   a chart
    b.   a map
    c.   a diagram
   *d.   a graph
    e.   a model

51.    Which of the following would probably be the best kind of visual aid to demonstrate the five major areas of spending in the federal budget?

   *a.   a pie graph
    b.   a diagram
    c.   a line graph
    d.   a chart
    e.   a photograph

52.    A _____ graph is best suited for illustrating simple distribution patterns.

    *a.   pie
     b.   line
     c.   parallel
     d.   ratio
     e.   bar

53.    Which of the following would probably be the best visual aid to demonstrate the distribution of grades for a class?

    *a.   a pie graph
     b.   a quota graph
     c.   a longitudinal graph
     d.   a partition graph
     e.   a line graph

54.    A _____ graph is best suited for showing comparisons between two or more items.

     a.   picture
     b.   parallel
     c.   distributive
     d.   ratio
    *e.   bar

55.    If you wanted to demonstrate the comparative spending of the United States and Canada on four different kinds of social services, which type of visual aid should you probably use?

    *a.   a bar graph
     b.   a drawing
     c.   a line graph
     d.   a chart
     e.   a pie graph

56.    Which of the following would probably be the best kind of visual aid to summarize the major types of agricultural crops grown in the United States?

    *a.   a chart
     b.   a model
     c.   a photograph
     d.   a drawing
     e.   a map

57. If you wanted to summarize the steps of a process in a speech, the best kind of visual aid to use would probably be a

    a. model.
    *b. chart.
    c. diagram.
    d. photograph.
    e. graph.

58. According to your textbook, charts are especially useful as visual aids when a speaker needs to

    a. summarize the steps in a process.
    b. present information the audience might want to write down.
    c. include more categories than can be presented in a pie or bar graph.
    *d. all of the above.
    e. a and c only.

59. A _____ graph is best suited for showing changes in statistics over time or space.

    a. pie
    *b. line
    c. distributive
    d. parallel
    e. ratio

60. According to your textbook, when giving a multimedia presentation, you should

    a. give yourself plenty of time to prepare your slides and to rehearse the delivery of your presentation.
    b. double check your equipment before the audience arrives to make sure the equipment is working properly.
    c. be prepared to give your speech effectively even if all the multimedia equipment were to malfunction.
    *d. all of the above.
    e. a and b only.

61. When used as a visual aid in a speech, a video

    a. should be carefully edited to show exactly what the speaker wants.
    b. can distract attention from the speaker if it is not used properly.
    c. needs to be skillfully integrated into the speaker's presentation.
    *d. all of the above.
    e. b and c only.

62.    According to your textbook, when selecting fonts for a visual aid you should usually use

    a.    a wide variety of fonts.
    b.    decorative fonts.
    c.    a different font for each line.
    d.    italicized fonts.
  *e.    no more than two fonts.

63.    When selecting fonts for a visual aid, you should usually use

    a.    a minimum of four fonts to provide visual variety.
    b.    decorative fonts because they will make the aid more interesting.
    c.    all capital letters so the lettering will be easy to read.
    d.    all of the above.
  *e.    none of the above.

64.    According to your textbook, when using an overhead transparency as a visual aid, you should

    a.    make sure letters and numbers on the transparency are at least 1/4 inch high.
    b.    practice using the transparency on the overhead projector before you speak.
    c.    write on the transparency while you are talking to the audience.
    d.    all of the above.
  *e.    a and b only.

65.    What does your textbook say you should do when presenting visual aids in a speech?

    a.    pass visual aids through the audience
    b.    include visual aids only in informative speeches
    c.    darken the room when presenting overhead transparencies
  *d.    avoid using the chalkboard to present visual aids
    e.    display each visual aid for an equal amount of time

66.    When using visual aids in a speech, you should

    a.    set up visual aids to the left of the lectern.
    b.    not worry about keeping eye contact with the audience.
    c.    try to pass visual aids among the audience.
    d.    keep visual aids on display throughout the speech.
  *e.    avoid drawing visual aids on the chalkboard.

67.    According to your textbook, when using visual aids in a speech you should

    a.    draw pictures or charts directly on the chalkboard.
  *b.    practice with the visual aid when you rehearse your speech.
    c.    keep the visual aid on display through the speech.
    d.    all of the above.
    e.    b and c only.

68.     When using a visual aid in a speech, you should display the aid

        a.    on the left side of the lectern.
    *b.    so everyone in the room can see it.
        c.    throughout the speech.
        d.    all of the above.
        e.    a and b only.


69.     When using visual aids in a speech, you should

        a.    draw graphs and charts on the chalkboard.
        b.    set up visual aids to the right of the lectern.
        c.    not worry about keeping eye contact with the audience.
    *d.    avoid passing visual aids among the audience.
        e.    keep the aids on display throughout the speech.


70.     When using visual aids in a speech, you should

        a.    display visual aids only while discussing them.
        b.    maintain eye contact with listeners when showing visual aids.
        c.    avoid passing visual aids among the audience.
    *d.    all of the above.
        e.    a and c only.


71.     Wei gave his informative speech on meteorology. As part of the speech, he
        displayed an excellent three-color drawing to indicate the different temperatures in
        various layers of the atmosphere. When he got to the visual aid, he said, "As you
        can see, each layer has a different temperature," covered up the drawing, and
        quickly moved on. What should Wei have done to present his visual aid more
        effectively?

    *a.    He should have explained the visual aid more fully.
        b.    He should have shown the drawing with an overhead projector.
        c.    He should have created a handout and passed it among the audience.
        d.    He should have avoided using more than two colors in the drawing.
        e.    He should have displayed a photograph instead of a drawing.


72.     During her speech about sailboats, Diane gave each member of her audience a copy
        of an intricate drawing showing the different parts of a sailboat. Did Diane follow
        the guidelines for visual aids presented in your textbook?

        a.    No. The drawing could have been boring to many members of the audience.
        b.    Yes. Giving the audience a handout during the speech is usually a good idea.
        c.    No. Diane should have reproduced the drawing on the chalkboard instead.
        d.    Yes. The detail of the drawing probably heightened the audience's interest.
    *e.    No. Diane risked losing attention by passing out the drawing during the speech.

73.     The morning of his classroom speech, Robert felt he needed more visual interest in the speech. On his way to class, he bought poster board and a marker and wrote down his main points for the audience to see. Did Robert follow the guidelines for visual aids presented in your textbook?

    a.     Yes. Robert showed quick thinking under pressure by deciding to make the chart.
    b.     No. Robert should have prepared more visual aids than a single chart.
  *c.     No. Robert should have prepared the chart ahead of time and rehearsed with it.
    d.     Yes. Visual aids always heighten the audience's interest and attention.
    e.     No. The chart will distract the audience's attention from Robert's main points.

74.     Rosalie will be giving a persuasive speech on organ donation and wants to distribute organ-donor cards to her listeners. When should she distribute the cards?

    a.     before she starts the speech
    b.     after she reveals her topic in the introduction
    c.     while telling how organ-donor cards work during the body of the speech
    d.     while urging her audience to take action during the conclusion of the speech
  *e.     after she has finished speaking

75.     Elisa is giving a speech on women's athletics and has brought a petition for her listeners to sign. When should she circulate the petition?

    a.     before she begins her speech
    b.     after she reveals the topic of her speech
    c.     after explaining the problems faced by women's athletic teams
    d.     while urging her audience to take action during the conclusion of the speech
  *e.     after she has finished speaking

76.     When you are going to give an audience material to take home from a speech, you should distribute the material

    a.     as the audience arrives for the speech.
    b.     at the beginning of the speech.
    c.     at the time you discuss it during the speech.
    d.     during the conclusion of the speech.
  *e.     after the speech.

77.     As your textbook explains, visual aids are most effective when they are displayed

    a.     throughout the speech.
    b.     during the introduction of a speech.
    c.     on an easel where they are visible to everyone.
  *d.     only while the speaker is discussing them.
    e.     from the right side of the lectern.

78.   At the start of her informative speech, Neva placed a drawing of the major regions of Egypt on an easel to the left of the lectern so it would be easy for her classmates to see throughout the speech. Did Neva follow the guidelines for visual aids presented in your textbook?

   a.   No. Visual aids should be displayed from the right side of the lectern.
   b.   Yes. It is important to display visual aids where everyone can see them.
   c.   No. A photograph would have been a much better choice of visual aid.
   d.   Yes. Drawing a map is an excellent visual aid for a classroom speech.
 *e.   No. Visual aids should be displayed only while they are being discussed.

79.   When using visual aids in a speech, you should

 *a.   display visual aids only while discussing them.
   b.   draw graphs and charts on the chalkboard.
   c.   pass aids among the audience at the start of the speech.
   d.   not worry about maintaining eye contact with the audience.
   e.   display visual aids to the left of the lectern.

80.   According to your textbook, visual aids are most effective when they are

 *a.   explained clearly.
   b.   circulated among the audience.
   c.   presented early in the speech.
   d.   all of the above.
   e.   a and c only.

81.   Visual aids are most effective when they are

   a.   integrated with the rest of the speech.
   b.   explained clearly.
   c.   passed among the audience.
   d.   all of the above.
 *e.   a and b only.

82.   Visual aids are most effective when they are

 *a.   part of a speaker's rehearsal process.
   b.   shown in the introduction of a speech.
   c.   shown in the conclusion of a speech.
   d.   shown throughout the speech.
   e.   circulated among the audience.

## Short Answer Questions

83.    If the object you want to use as a visual aid is not available to you, the next best option ideally is a ____model____.

84.    A(n) ____graph____ is usually the best kind of visual aid for clarifying statistics.

85.    If you wanted to illustrate the increase in the number of people in the U.S. with college degrees since 1900, the best kind of visual aid would probably be a(n) ____graph____.

86.    While a ____pie____ graph is best for illustrating simple distribution patterns, a ____bar____ graph is best for showing comparisons between two or more items.

87.    If you wanted to summarize the steps involved in making cigars, the best kind of visual aid to use would probably be a ____chart____.

88.    If you wanted to list the steps of a process to help your audience remember them better, the best kind of visual aid to use would probably be a ____chart____.

89.    If you wanted to summarize the steps involved in combating frostbite, the best kind of visual aid would probably be a ____chart____.

90.    If you wanted to combine several kinds of visual and audio aids in the same talk, you should probably give a ____multimedia____ presentation.

## Essay Questions

91.    Explain the major advantages of using visual aids in a speech.

92.    If a picture is worth a thousand words, why should a speaker worry about explaining visual aids to the audience?

93.    What are the advantages and disadvantages of using photographs as visual aids in a speech?

94.    In what ways are drawings superior to photographs as visual aids?

95.    What are the three kinds of graphs discussed in your textbook? Give an example of each.

96.    If you are preparing a drawing, a graph, or a chart for use as a visual aid, what steps should you take to make sure the aid will be easy for all your listeners to see?

97. If you are planning to use a video as a visual aid in your speech, what steps should you take to make sure the video will enhance the speech?

98. What kind of visual aid would probably be most effective for explaining each of the following? Explain your choice of visual aid in each case.

    a. the basic equipment and techniques of scuba diving
    b. the increase in the United States national debt since 1920
    c. the markings on different species of tropical fish
    d. where to write for information about career opportunities available to college graduates with degrees in engineering

99. Explain each of the following guidelines for using visual aids in a speech:

    a. Avoid using the chalkboard for visual aids.
    b. Prepare visual aids in advance.
    c. Do not pass visual aids among the audience.
    d. Practice with visual aids when rehearsing the speech.

100. Below are two examples of charts for a speech on the steps in treating a sprain. Which chart best follows the guidelines for visual aids discussed in your textbook? Explain your answer by referring to specific guidelines.

# Chapter **14** Speaking to Inform

## True-False Questions

1. <u>T</u> F    Your textbook discusses four kinds of informative speeches—speeches about objects, speeches about concepts, speeches about processes, and speeches about events.

2. T <u>F</u>    A lawyer urging a jury to acquit her client is an example of informative speaking.

3. <u>T</u> F    When giving an informative speech that explains a process, you will most likely arrange your main points in chronological order.

4. <u>T</u> F    Informative speeches about processes are usually arranged in chronological order.

5. T <u>F</u>    Informative speeches are seldom organized in topical order.

6. <u>T</u> F    "To inform my audience how to create their own Web pages" is a specific purpose statement for an informative speech about a process.

7. <u>T</u> F    If the specific purpose of your informative speech is to recount the history of an event, you will usually arrange the speech in chronological order.

8. T <u>F</u>    An informative speech about a process that has as many as ten or twelve steps is one of the few times it is acceptable to have more than five main points.

9. T <u>F</u>    Informative speeches about concepts are usually arranged in spatial order.

10. T <u>F</u>    Informative speeches about concepts are usually arranged in causal order.

11. <u>T</u> F    Informative speeches about concepts are usually arranged in topical order.

12. T <u>F</u>    Research suggests that connectives are less important in speeches to inform than in speeches to persuade.

13. T <u>F</u>    Clear organization is less important in speeches about processes than in other kinds of informative speeches.

14. T <u>F</u>    A summary is seldom necessary in the conclusion of an informative speech.

15. <u>T</u> F    One of the major barriers to effective informative speaking is overestimating what the audience knows about the topic.

16. T <u>F</u>    As your textbook explains, when you give an informative speech, it is usually a good idea to assume that the audience already knows a lot about your topic.

17. <u>T</u> F    The more you assume your audience knows about your speech topic, the greater are your chances of being misunderstood.

18. <u>T</u> F    Informative speakers need to work as hard as persuasive speakers at relating the topic directly to the audience.

19. <u>T</u> F    When giving an informative speech, you should think about ways to relate your topic to the audience in the body of the speech as well as in the introduction.

20. T <u>F</u>    A public speaker should avoid direct references to the audience in the body of an informative speech.

21. T <u>F</u>    One of the biggest barriers to effective informative speaking is using language that is too simple for the audience.

22. T <u>F</u>    As your textbook explains, technical language is especially helpful for explaining ideas in informative speeches.

23. T <u>F</u>    Abstractions are especially helpful for clarifying ideas in informative speeches.

24. <u>T</u> F    Your textbook recommends comparison and contrast as ways to avoid abstractions in an informative speech.

25. T <u>F</u>    Your textbook recommends using description as a way to personalize ideas in an informative speech.

26. <u>T</u> F    One reason to use clear and straightforward language even when talking about complex ideas is that listeners must understand your message in the time it takes you to say it.

27.  T  F̲    Using jargon in an informative speech is useful since it demonstrates your expertise on the topic.

28.  T  F̲    Informative speakers should avoid explaining ideas in personal terms.

29.  T  F̲    Personal examples are inappropriate for informative speeches on technical topics.

30.  T̲  F    Your textbook recommends using words such as "you" and "your" to help get the audience involved in an informative speech.

31.  T̲  F    Although essay writers are often urged to avoid personal references such as "I," "you," and "we," you should usually try to include such references in an informative speech.

32.  T̲  F    Whenever possible, you should try to enliven your informative speeches by expressing ideas in personal terms.

**Multiple Choice Questions** (*Students are to indicate the best answer for each question by circling the correct letter.*)

33.    Which of the following is an instance of informative speaking?

   a.   a student urging an instructor to reconsider the due date for an assignment
 *b.   a student sharing ideas about leadership based on a book she has read
   c.   a student on stage telling jokes during the intermission of a play
   d.   all of the above
   e.   a and b only

34.    Which of the following is an instance of informative speaking?

   a.   a teacher praising parents for contributing to the school carnival
   b.   a teacher arguing that phonics is a successful method for teaching reading
 *c.   a teacher explaining the requirements for an assignment
   d.   all of the above
   e.   b and c only

35.    Which of the following is an instance of informative speaking?

   a.   an ambassador urging changes in international adoption laws
 *b.   a social worker explaining adoption laws to potential parents
   c.   a scientist convincing colleagues to change their research focus
   d.   all of the above
   e.   b and c only

36.    Which of the following is an instance of informative speaking?

    a.    a business manager reporting on next year's budget
    b.    a pastor urging parishioners to give to a building fund
    c.    a teacher lecturing about methods of speech organization
    d.    all of the above
 *e.    a and c only

37.    Which of the following is an instance of informative speaking?

    a.    a lawyer exhorting a jury not to convict her client
    b.    a teacher urging colleagues to adopt a new curriculum
 *c.    a banker explaining how the stock market operates
    d.    all of the above
    e.    a and c only

38.    Which of the following is an instance of informative speaking?

 *a.    a doctor explaining how antioxidants affect the body
    b.    a vitamin distributor urging listeners to buy antioxidants
    c.    a scientist arguing that antioxidants have minimal health benefits
    d.    all of the above
    e.    a and c only

39.    In an informative speech, the speaker acts as a(n)

    a.    advocate.
    b.    entertainer.
 *c.    teacher.
    d.    motivator.
    e.    evaluator.

40.    According to your textbook, the aims of an informative speech include

    a.    communicating the speaker's information clearly.
    b.    communicating the speaker's information accurately.
    c.    making the speaker's information meaningful to the audience.
 *d.    all of the above.
    e.    a and b only.

41.    "To inform my audience about the major achievements of Ronald Reagan" is a specific purpose statement for an informative speech about a(n)

 *a.    object.
    b.    process.
    c.    event.
    d.    concept.
    e.    function.

42.    "To inform my audience about the different notions of intellectual property in eastern and western cultures" is an example of a specific purpose statement for an informative speech about a(n)

    a.    object.
    b.    event.
   *c.    concept.
    d.    operation.
    e.    process.

43.    "To inform my audience about the major principles of Keynesian economic theory" is a specific purpose statement for a speech about a(n)

    a.    object.
    b.    policy.
    c.    technique.
   *d.    concept.
    e.    process.

44.    "To inform my audience about the internment of Japanese Americans during World War II" is an example of a specific purpose statement for an informative speech about a(n)

   *a.    event.
    b.    narrative.
    c.    condition.
    d.    concept.
    e.    function.

45.    "To inform my audience about the major parts of a 35-millimeter camera" is a specific purpose statement for an informative speech about a(n)

    a.    concept.
    b.    event.
    c.    process.
   *d.    object.
    e.    function.

46.    "To inform my audience how to prepare for a backpacking expedition" is a specific purpose statement for a speech about a(n)

    a.    object.
   *b.    process.
    c.    function.
    d.    concept.
    e.    policy.

47.    A _____ is a systematic series of actions that leads to a specific result or product.

    a.    function
    b.    project
    c.    demonstration
    *d.    process
    e.    custom

48.    "To inform my audience how to make genuine French croissants" is a specific purpose statement for a speech about a(n)

    a.    object.
    *b.    process.
    c.    function.
    d.    event.
    e.    concept.

49.    "To inform my audience how to add memory to a computer" is a specific purpose statement for an informative speech about a(n)

    a.    operation.
    b.    function.
    c.    event.
    d.    concept.
    *e.    process.

50.    "To inform my audience about the three stages in a job interview" is a specific purpose statement for an informative speech about a(n)

    a.    concept.
    b.    object.
    *c.    process.
    d.    function.
    e.    policy.

51.    "To inform my audience about the removal of the Cherokee Indians from their native lands" is an example of a specific purpose statement for a speech about a(n)

    a.    function.
    *b.    event.
    c.    condition.
    d.    object.
    e.    concept.

52.   "To inform my audience about the causes of the American Revolution" is a specific purpose statement for an informative speech about a(n)

    a.   object.
    b.   function.
    c.   institution.
    d.   concept.
*e.   event.

53.   "To inform my audience about the history of Halloween observances" is a specific purpose statement for an informative speech about a(n)

    a.   object.
*b.   event.
    c.   process.
    d.   concept.
    e.   situation.

54.   "To inform my audience about the scientific theories of Stephen Hawking" is a specific purpose statement for a speech about a(n)

*a.   concept.
    b.   object.
    c.   process.
    d.   function.
    e.   event.

55.   "To inform my audience of the major theories about the Bermuda Triangle" is a specific purpose statement for an informative speech about a(n)

    a.   object.
    b.   process.
    c.   event.
*d.   concept.
    e.   function.

56.   "To inform my audience about the pillars of faith in Islam" is an example of a specific purpose statement for an informative speech about a(n)

*a.   concept.
    b.   event.
    c.   function.
    d.   process.
    e.   object.

57.   Speeches about _____ are often more complex than other types of informative speeches.

   a.   objects
   b.   events
   c.   processes
   d.   functions
 *e.   concepts

58.   If your specific purpose statement were "To inform my audience about the three major types of pet lizards," you would probably organize your speech in _____ order.

   a.   spatial
 *b.   topical
   c.   chronological
   d.   comparative
   e.   causal

59.   If your specific purpose statement were "To inform my audience about the three major types of sleep disorders," you would probably organize your speech in _____ order.

 *a.   topical
   b.   chronological
   c.   spatial
   d.   comparative
   e.   causal

60.   If your specific purpose statement were "To inform my audience about the major kinds of dog breeds," you would probably organize your speech in _____ order.

   a.   chronological
   b.   spatial
   c.   descriptive
 *d.   topical
   e.   causal

61.   If your specific purpose statement were "To inform my audience how to make authentic South American empanadas," you would probably organize your speech in _____ order.

   a.   illustrative
 *b.   chronological
   c.   spatial
   d.   comparative
   e.   causal

62.    If your specific purpose were "To inform my audience of the major steps in an effective job interview," you would probably organize your speech in _____ order.

    a.    comparative
    b.    spatial
 *c.    chronological
    d.    causal
    e.    illustrative

63.    If you were giving an informative speech describing the different parts of the Forbidden City in China, you would probably arrange the speech in _____ order.

    a.    illustrative
    b.    causal
    c.    chronological
 *d.    spatial
    e.    comparative

64.    If your specific purpose statement were "To inform my audience about the different layers of the atmosphere," you would probably organize your speech in _____ order.

    a.    topical
    b.    chronological
 *c.    spatial
    d.    comparative
    e.    causal

65.    If your specific purpose were "To inform my audience how windows are manufactured," you would probably organize your speech in _____ order.

    a.    analogical or spatial
    b.    comparative or chronological
    c.    process or topical
    d.    causal or comparative
 *e.    chronological or topical

66.    If your specific purpose were "To inform my audience how to buy and sell stock online," you would probably organize your speech in _____ order.

 *a.    chronological or topical
    b.    analogical or spatial
    c.    comparative or chronological
    d.    causal or functional
    e.    spatial or topical

67.    If your specific purpose statement were "To inform my audience about the major archaeological sites in Central America," you would probably organize your speech in _____ order.

      a.   topical or causal
      b.   spatial or comparative
      c.   comparative or chronological
      d.   chronological or causal
   *e.   spatial or topical

68.    Informative speeches about processes are usually arranged in _____ order.

      a.   causal or spatial
      b.   topical or spatial
      c.   causal or topical
      d.   spatial or chronological
   *e.   chronological or topical

69.    Informative speeches about concepts are usually arranged in _____ order.

      a.   chronological
   *b.   topical
      c.   spatial
      d.   causal
      e.   illustrative

70.    Which of the following is mentioned in your textbook as a guideline for effective informative speaking?

      a.   Relate the subject directly to the audience.
      b.   Don't be too technical.
      c.   Personalize your ideas.
   *d.   all of the above
      e.   a and b only

71.    Which of the following is mentioned in your textbook as one of the five major guidelines for effective informative speaking?

      a.   Use multimedia visual aids.
   *b.   Relate the subject directly to the audience.
      c.   Leave time for questions after the speech.
      d.   Be highly technical in your discussion.
      e.   Rely primarily on abstract language.

72.    Each of the following is mentioned in your textbook as a guideline for effective informative speaking *except*

    a.    personalize your ideas.
    b.    don't overestimate what the audience knows.
  *c.    involve the audience with a call to action.
    d.    relate the subject directly to the audience.
    e.    don't be too technical.

73.    Which of the following is mentioned in your textbook as a guideline for effective informative speaking?

    a.    Avoid talking about your personal experiences.
    b.    Use chronological organization whenever possible.
    c.    Relate to the audience by speaking in technical terms.
    d.    Use abstract language to clarify complex ideas.
  *e.    Don't overestimate what the audience knows.

74.    When giving an informative speech to a general audience, you should take special care to

    a.    state your ideas in abstract terms.
    b.    establish goodwill with the audience in the introduction.
  *c.    avoid being too technical.
    d.    all of the above.
    e.    a and b only.

75.    When giving an informative speech, you should take special care to

  *a.    translate technical information into everyday language.
    b.    state your ideas in abstract terms.
    c.    establish goodwill with the audience in your introduction.
    d.    avoid speaking about complex topics.
    e.    prepare your introduction before the body of your speech.

76.    Which of the following are among the methods recommended in your textbook for avoiding too many abstractions in an informative speech?

    a.    use statistics and testimony
    b.    use narration and dialogue
    c.    use testimony and examples
  *d.    use comparison and contrast
    e.    use data and technical language

77.    Which of the following is presented in your textbook as a guideline for effective informative speaking?

    a.    Use technical language to enhance your credibility.
    b.    Avoid personal words such as "I," "we," "you," and "our."
  *c.    Relate the topic directly and personally to your audience.
    d.    all of the above
    e.    a and c only

78.     Your textbook recommends using _____ in your informative speeches
        as a way to keep your ideas from being overly abstract.

        a.   contrast
        b.   description
        c.   comparison
    *d.   all of the above
        e.   a and c only

79.     Which of the following does your textbook recommend for relating the subject
        directly to your audience in an informative speech?

    *a.   Speak in personal terms such as "you" and "your."
        b.   Take care to establish your credibility in the introduction.
        c.   Devote an equal amount of time to each main point.
        d.   all of the above
        e.   a and b only

80.     What does your textbook mean when it recommends that you "personalize your
        ideas" in an informative speech?

    *a.   Bring information to life by using examples and illustrations.
        b.   Use dramatic statistics for a personal effect.
        c.   Use true-to-life examples rather than hypothetical examples.
        d.   Use slang and jargon to give the speech a personal tone.
        e.   Avoid concrete language because it makes ideas vague and impersonal.

## Short Answer Questions

81.     "To inform my audience about the different sections of a medieval cathedral" is a
        specific purpose statement for an informative speech about a(n) ____object____,
        while "To inform my audience about the beliefs of major Christian sects during the
        middle ages" is a specific purpose statement for an informative speech about a(n)
        ____concept____.

82.     If you were giving an informative speech about the major stages in building
        the Great Wall of China, you would probably organize your speech in
        ____chronological____ order.

83.     If you were giving an informative speech describing the different regions of Ireland,
        you would probably arrange the speech in ____spatial____ order.

84.     A(n) ____process____ is a systematic series of actions that leads to a specific
        result or product.

85.    "To inform my audience how to arrange flowers like a professional florist" is a specific purpose statement for an informative speech about a(n) ___process___.

86.    "To inform my audience how to improve their golf game" is a specific purpose statement for an informative speech about a(n) ___process___. "To inform my audience about the origins of golf in the British Isles" is a specific purpose statement for an informative speech about a(n) ___event___.

87.    Informative speeches about processes are usually arranged in either ___chronological___ or ___topical___ order.

88.    There are many ways to organize informative speeches about events. If your goal is to recount the history of an event, you would most likely arrange the speech in ___chronological___ order.

89.    Informative speeches about concepts are usually arranged in ___topical___ order.

90.    List the five guidelines given in your textbook for effective informative speaking.

___Don't overestimate what the audience knows.___

___Relate the subject directly to the audience.___

___Don't be too technical.___

___Personalize your ideas.___

___Avoid abstractions.___

## Essay Questions

91.    What are the four types of informative speeches discussed in your textbook? Give an example of an effective specific purpose statement for each type.

92.    Informative speeches can be classified into four types: speeches about objects, speeches about processes, speeches about events, and speeches about concepts. Into which category would you place each of the following? Explain your answer in each case.

   a.    a speech recounting the battle of Gettysburg
   b.    a speech describing the surviving texts of Lincoln's Gettysburg Address
   c.    a speech discussing the meaning of the Gettysburg Address
   d.    a speech explaining how to write an effective commemorative address

93.    What are the two types of informative speeches about processes? Give an example of a specific purpose statement for each type.

94.    Explain each of the following guidelines for effective informative speaking:

   a.    Don't overestimate what the audience knows.
   b.    Relate the subject directly to the audience.
   c.    Don't be too technical.
   d.    Avoid abstractions.
   e.    Personalize your ideas.

95.    Explain why informative speakers should be wary of overestimating their audience's knowledge about the topic. What steps should a speaker take when preparing an informative speech to make sure the speech does not go over the heads of the audience?

96.    When preparing an informative speech for a general audience, why is it important to keep in mind that "Nothing interests people more than themselves"?

97.    What does it mean to say an informative speaker should personalize her or his ideas? According to your textbook, what are two major steps a speaker can take to express her or his ideas in personal terms?

98.    Why is it important to avoid technical language when giving an informative speech to a general audience? Provide a brief example illustrating how the use of technical language could reduce the effectiveness of an informative speech.

99.    Below are excerpts from two speeches with the specific purpose "To inform my audience about the effects of Alzheimer's disease." In a well-developed essay, explain which excerpt does a better job implementing the guidelines for informative speaking discussed in Chapter 14 of your textbook. Support your answer with reference to specific passages in each speech.

   **Excerpt 1**

   Alzheimer's disease is a degenerative brain disorder whose initial symptoms are short-term memory loss and impaired concentration. As the disease progresses, its manifestations include dysfunctions of speech, personality, muscle coordination, and mental processes. Eventually, the victim will become incontinent and totally incapacitated. A comatose state is common, and ultimately, the victim's bodily functions cease entirely. The duration of the disease is variable.

**Excerpt 2**

Of all the diseases that can strike us as we age, Alzheimer's may be the cruelest, for it kills its victims twice. If you get Alzheimer's, it first will kill your mind. The simplest tasks—tying a shoe, cooking a hamburger, making a bed—will become impossible because you can no longer remember how to perform them. Names, dates, places—the mental scrapbook of your life—will fade away like aging photographs. If you suffer the most tragic of Alzheimer's symptoms, you will forget your own name and will no longer recognize your loved ones.

Then Alzheimer's will kill your body. No longer able to walk or to control your bodily functions, you will lie curled up in a fetal position, gradually sinking into a coma and then death. Like most Alzheimer's victims, you may survive for six to eight years after the disease begins; like some, you may suffer in this debilitating state for as long as 20 years.

---

# Chapter 15 Speaking to Persuade

## True-False Questions

1. <u>T</u> F     Persuasion is the process of creating, reinforcing, or changing people's beliefs or actions.

2. T <u>F</u>     Because everyone knows that a persuasive speaker's goal is to influence the audience's beliefs or actions, questions of ethics are less important in persuasive speaking than in other kinds of speaking.

3. <u>T</u> F     Even though a persuasive speaker's goal is to influence the audience's beliefs or actions, she or he still has an ethical obligation to present evidence fairly and accurately.

4. <u>T</u> F     One way for a persuasive speaker to uphold the ethical obligations of speechmaking is to learn about all sides of an issue.

5. <u>T</u> F     Of all the kinds of public speaking, persuasion is the most complex and the most challenging.

6. <u>T</u> F     Persuasion is a psychological process in which listeners engage in a mental dialogue with the speaker.

7. <u>T</u> F     Research indicates that audiences often engage in a mental give-and-take with the speaker as they listen to a persuasive speech.

8. <u>T</u> F     When speaking to persuade, you need to think of your speech as a kind of mental dialogue with your audience.

9. T <u>F</u>     Audience analysis and adaptation are less challenging in persuasive speaking than in speaking to inform.

10.   T <u>F</u>   When trying to persuade a hostile audience, you should usually be wary of even mentioning the audience's objections to your point of view.

11.   <u>T</u> F   The target audience is that portion of the whole audience that the speaker most wants to persuade.

12.   T <u>F</u>   Concentrating on a target audience means that a persuasive speaker can ignore the rest of her or his listeners.

13.   <u>T</u> F   Moving listeners from being strongly opposed to a speaker's position to being only moderately opposed would be a sign of a successful persuasive speech.

14.   T <u>F</u>   As your textbook explains, persuasion takes place only if the audience is strongly in favor of the speaker's position by the end of the speech.

15.   <u>T</u> F   When faced with an audience that strongly opposes your point of view, you can consider your persuasive speech a success if it leads even a few listeners to reexamine their views.

16.   T <u>F</u>   A persuasive speech on a question of fact is essentially the same as an informative speech.

17.   T <u>F</u>   Questions of fact are easy subjects for persuasive speeches because they almost always have clear-cut answers.

18.   T <u>F</u>   Questions of fact deal only with events that have already happened.

19.   T <u>F</u>   Questions of fact usually include the word "should."

20.   <u>T</u> F   Persuasive speeches on questions of fact are usually organized in topical order.

21.   T <u>F</u>   Persuasive speeches on questions of fact are usually organized in problem-solution order.

22.   <u>T</u> F   "To persuade my audience that genetically altered crops pose serious hazards to human health" is a specific purpose statement for a persuasive speech on a question of fact.

23.   T <u>F</u>   "To persuade my audience to support the construction of a new convention center" is a specific purpose statement for a question of fact.

24.   <u>T</u> F   "To persuade my audience that Lee Harvey Oswald was the sole assassin of President John F. Kennedy" is a specific purpose statement for a persuasive speech on a question of fact.

25.  <u>T</u> F    When dealing with a question of value, a public speaker needs to justify his or her value judgment on the basis of some set of standards or criteria.

26.  <u>T</u> F    Persuasive speeches on questions of value are almost always arranged in topical order.

27.  T <u>F</u>    Persuasive speeches on questions of value usually argue directly for or against particular courses of action.

28.  <u>T</u> F    "To persuade my audience that *Citizen Kane* is the greatest movie of all time" is a specific purpose statement for a persuasive speech on a question of value.

29.  <u>T</u> F    "To persuade my audience that cloning human beings is morally unjustifiable" is a specific purpose statement for a persuasive speech on a question of value.

30.  T <u>F</u>    "To persuade my audience that college athletic coaches should automatically lose their jobs whenever they are found guilty of recruiting violations" is a specific purpose statement for a persuasive speech on a question of value.

31.  <u>T</u> F    "To persuade my audience that electronic voting is more accurate than punch card voting" is a specific purpose statement for a persuasive speech on a question of fact.

32.  <u>T</u> F    Questions of policy inevitably incorporate questions of fact.

33.  <u>T</u> F    Questions of policy deal with whether something should or should not be done.

34.  <u>T</u> F    Questions of policy usually include the word "should."

35.  <u>T</u> F    "To persuade my audience that the federal government should ban all advertising for tobacco products" is a specific purpose statement for a persuasive speech on a question of policy.

36.  <u>T</u> F    "To persuade my audience that the United States should adopt a national sales tax to help fund additional social programs" is a specific purpose statement for a persuasive speech on a question of policy.

37.  T <u>F</u>    "To persuade my audience that capital punishment does not deter people from committing crimes such as murder" is a specific purpose statement for a persuasive speech on a question of policy.

38.  T <u>F</u>    "To persuade my audience that capital punishment is unjust" is a specific purpose statement for a persuasive speech on a question of fact.

39.   T F    "To persuade my audience that capital punishment is unjust" is a specific purpose statement for a persuasive speech on a question of value.

40.   T F    "To persuade my audience that capital punishment is unjust" is a specific purpose statement for a persuasive speech on a question of policy.

41.   T F    "To persuade my audience that video games are a major cause of youth violence" is a specific purpose statement for a persuasive speech on a question of policy.

42.   T F    When you give a persuasive speech on a question of policy, you can seek either passive agreement or immediate action from your audience.

43.   T F    "To persuade my audience that our community should adopt tougher measures to deal with the problem of noise pollution" is a specific purpose statement for a persuasive speech on a question of policy whose aim is passive agreement.

44.   T F    "To persuade my audience to contribute to the campus blood drive" is a specific purpose statement for a persuasive speech on a question of policy whose aim is passive agreement.

45.   T F    "To persuade my audience to become volunteers for the Special Olympics" is a specific purpose statement for a persuasive speech on a question of policy whose aim is immediate action.

46.   T F    "To persuade my audience that Congress should ban the exportation of dangerous pesticides" is a specific purpose statement for a persuasive speech on a question of policy whose aim is immediate action.

47.   T F    When trying to persuade listeners that are skeptical about your position, you need to deal directly with the reasons for their skepticism.

48.   T F    As your textbook makes clear, when speaking to persuade, it is easier to evoke passive agreement from an audience than to gain immediate action.

49.   T F    According to your textbook, when speaking to persuade, it is easier to gain immediate action from an audience than to evoke passive agreement.

50.   T F    As your textbook explains, speakers who give persuasive speeches seeking immediate action should make their call for action as general as possible.

51.   T F    When trying to persuade listeners to take action, you should usually be specific about the action you want them to take.

52. <u>T</u> F     Research indicates that once a listener takes action in support of a speaker's position, she or he is more likely to support that speaker's position in the future.

53. T <u>F</u>     The burden of proof rests with the persuasive speaker who opposes change.

54. <u>T</u> F     The burden of proof rests with the persuasive speaker who advocates change.

55. T <u>F</u>     When you discuss a question of policy, you must deal with three basic issues—attention, plan, and action.

56. <u>T</u> F     When you discuss a question of policy, you must deal with three basic issues—need, plan, and practicality.

57. T <u>F</u>     If you advocate a new policy in a persuasive speech, your main points will usually fall naturally into topical order.

58. T <u>F</u>     Comparative-advantages order is used most often in organizing persuasive speeches on questions of value.

59. T <u>F</u>     Monroe's motivated sequence is most appropriate for persuasive speeches on questions of value.

60. T <u>F</u>     Monroe's motivated sequence is another name for problem-cause-solution order.

61. <u>T</u> F     Monroe's motivated sequence is most appropriate for speeches that try to persuade listeners to take immediate action.

62. T <u>F</u>     The *first* step in Monroe's motivated sequence is to convince the audience that there is a need for action.

63. <u>T</u> F     The *first* step in Monroe's motivated sequence is to get the attention of the audience.

64. T <u>F</u>     When a speaker uses Monroe's motivated sequence, the need step is usually presented in the introduction.

65. T <u>F</u>     When a speaker uses Monroe's motivated sequence, the satisfaction step is usually presented in the conclusion.

66. T <u>F</u>     The *final* step in Monroe's motivated sequence is to visualize how much better things will be if the speaker's plan is adopted.

67. <u>T</u> F     The *final* step in Monroe's motivated sequence is to call for action by the audience in support of the speaker's plan.

**Multiple Choice Questions** *(Students are to indicate the <u>best</u> answer for each question by circling the correct letter.)*

68.  Of all the kinds of speechmaking, _____ speaking is the most complex and the most challenging.

  \*a.  persuasive
    b.  after-dinner
    c.  ceremonial
    d.  informative
    e.  commemorative

69.  Which of the following is an instance of persuasive speaking?

    a.  A coach reviewing the offensive plays for next week's game.
    b.  A lawyer explaining the details of a plea bargaining agreement to her client.
  \*c.  An architectural firm recommending adoption of its building plan.
    d.  A botanist reporting the discovery of a new species.
    e.  An activist honoring past leaders of the labor movement.

70.  Which of the following is an instance of persuasive speaking?

    a.  A president of a company presenting an award to an outstanding employee.
    b.  A marketing manager explaining a new product to the company's sales force.
    c.  A personnel manager defining employee benefits at a meeting of workers.
  \*d.  A union representative urging management to avoid a strike by raising wages.
    e.  A finance officer reporting sales figures to the board of directors.

71.  Which of the following is an instance of persuasive speaking?

    a.  A United States President praising World War II veterans.
    b.  A history professor lecturing on the rise of industrialism.
    c.  A judge explaining the rules of evidence during a criminal trail.
  \*d.  A developer urging the city council to build a new convention center.
    e.  A geneticist reporting her research to a professional meeting.

72.  According to your textbook, persuasion is a psychological process in which listeners engage in a _____ with the speaker.

  \*a.  mental dialogue
    b.  situational disagreement
    c.  cognitive restructuring
    d.  feedback loop
    e.  logical debate

73.  According to your textbook, you should think of your persuasive speech as

    a.  essentially the same as a commemorative speech.
  \*b.  a kind of mental dialogue with the audience.
    c.  less challenging than speaking to inform.
    d.  all of the above.
    e.  b and c only.

74.    The _____ is that portion of the whole audience that the speaker most wants to persuade.

      a.  core audience
    *b.  target audience
      c.  projected audience
      d.  intended audience
      e.  focus audience

75.    That part of the audience a speaker most wants to persuade is called the

      a.  specific audience.
      b.  designated audience.
      c.  central audience.
      d.  special audience.
    *e.  target audience.

76.    Marta circulated a questionnaire to gauge her classmates' attitudes toward adopting a citywide ban on smoking in all public buildings. She discovered that 5 audience members already agreed there should be a ban, 6 were firmly opposed, and 10 were undecided. From these results, Marta decided that the 10 undecided class members were the _____ for her speech.

      a.  projected audience
      b.  majority audience
      c.  focus audience
      d.  central audience
    *e.  target audience

77.    If you want to persuade a skeptical audience, which of the following is it *most* important for you to do in your speech?

      a.  Define unclear terms in the introduction.
      b.  Organize the speech in problem-solution order.
      c.  Focus the speech on questions of value.
    *d.  Answer the reasons for the audience's skepticism.
      e.  Include a call for action in the conclusion.

78.    As your textbook explains, if you want to persuade a skeptical audience, you need to

      a.  Organize the speech in Monroe's motivated sequence.
      b.  Urge the audience to take immediate action.
      c.  Circulate an audience-analysis questionnaire.
    *d.  Answer the reasons for the audience's skepticism.
      e.  Focus your speech on questions of practicality.

79.   "To persuade my audience that long-term exposure to electromagnetic fields can cause serious health problems" is a specific purpose statement for a persuasive speech on a question of

    a.   value.
    b.   opinion.
    c.   attitude.
    d.   policy.
 *e.   fact.

80.   "To persuade my audience that the use of cell phones by car drivers has contributed to a growing number of automobile accidents" is a specific purpose statement for a persuasive speech on a question of

    a.   policy.
    b.   attitude.
 *c.   fact.
    d.   value.
    e.   opinion.

81.   According to your textbook, "To persuade my audience that birds evolved from dinosaurs" is a specific purpose statement for a persuasive speech on a question of

    a.   policy.
 *b.   fact.
    c.   opinion.
    d.   knowledge.
    e.   research.

82.   The three types of questions that give rise to persuasive speeches are questions of

    a.   opinion, fact, and policy.
    b.   problem, cause, and solution.
 *c.   fact, value, and policy.
    d.   opinion, attitude, and value.
    e.   need, plan, and practicality.

83.   "To persuade my audience that another major earthquake will strike Los Angeles before the year 2020" is a specific purpose statement for a persuasive speech on a question of

 *a.   fact.
    b.   attitude.
    c.   value.
    d.   policy.
    e.   opinion.

84.   "To persuade my audience that soccer will become the highest revenue-producing sport in the United States by 2015" is a specific purpose statement for a persuasive speech on a question of

   a.   policy.
   b.   opinion.
   c.   value.
*d.   fact.
   e.   attitude.

85.   "To persuade my audience that preemptive strikes against suspected terrorists is morally justifiable" is a specific purpose statement for a persuasive speech on a question of

   a.   fact.
   b.   opinion.
   c.   strategy.
   d.   attitude.
*e.   value.

86.   "To persuade my audience that it is unethical for politicians to accept trips paid for by lobbyists" is a specific purpose statement for a persuasive speech on a question of

*a.   value.
   b.   policy.
   c.   attitude.
   d.   opinion.
   e.   fact.

87.   According to your textbook, "To persuade my audience that downloading music from the Internet for personal use is ethically wrong" is a specific purpose statement for a persuasive speech on a question of

   a.   policy.
   b.   opinion.
*c.   value.
   d.   legality.
   e.   fact.

88.   According to your textbook, "To persuade my audience that doctor-assisted suicide is morally acceptable" is a specific purpose statement for a persuasive speech on a question of

   a.   fact.
   b.   policy.
   c.   judgment.
   d.   health.
*e.   value.

89.    At which of the following would you be *most* likely to hear a persuasive speech on a question of fact?

    a.    a graduation ceremony
  *b.    a jury trial
    c.    an awards ceremony
    d.    a political convention
    e.    a retirement banquet

90.    Persuasive speeches on questions of fact are usually organized in _____ order.

  *a.    topical
    b.    problem-solution
    c.    comparative advantages
    d.    problem-cause-solution
    e.    descriptive

91.    "To persuade my audience that Ronald Reagan deserves to be rated as a great President" is a specific purpose statement for a persuasive speech on a question of

    a.    fact.
    b.    attitude.
  *c.    value.
    d.    policy.
    e.    opinion.

92.    "To persuade my audience that it is unethical for journalists to invade people's private lives" is a specific purpose statement for a persuasive speech on a question of

    a.    fact.
    b.    attitude.
  *c.    value.
    d.    policy.
    e.    opinion.

93.    As your textbook explains, persuasive speeches on questions of value are most often organized in _____ order.

  *a.    topical
    b.    analytical
    c.    chronological
    d.    deductive
    e.    causal

94.    As your textbook explains, whenever you give a persuasive speech on a question of value, you need to

    a.    concentrate on convincing listeners who already share your view.
    b.    organize the speech according to Monroe's motivated sequence.
    c.    conclude your speech by urging the audience to take immediate action.
    d.    deal with all three basic issues of need, plan, and practicality.
  *e.    justify your value judgment against a set of standards or criteria.

95.   Persuasive speeches on questions of _____ argue for or against particular courses of action.

    a.   need
    b.   value
 *c.   policy
    d.   fact
    e.   plan

96.   According to your textbook, "To persuade my audience that they should adopt a program of regular exercise" is a specific purpose statement for a persuasive speech on a question of

    a.   action.
 *b.   policy.
    c.   attitude.
    d.   value.
    e.   fact.

97.   According to your textbook, "To persuade my audience that they should practice abstinence as a way to protect themselves from sexually transmitted diseases" is a specific purpose statement for a persuasive speech on a question of

    a.   value.
    b.   attitude.
    c.   obligation.
    d.   judgment.
 *e.   policy.

98.   "To persuade my audience to take a class that will teach them CPR" is a specific purpose statement for a persuasive speech on a question of

    a.   fact.
    b.   attitude.
    c.   value.
 *d.   policy.
    e.   opinion.

99.   "To persuade my audience that there should be tougher enforcement of laws to protect the victims of domestic abuse" is a specific purpose statement for a persuasive speech on a question of

    a.   value.
    b.   attitude.
 *c.   policy.
    d.   opinion.
    e.   judgment.

100. "To persuade my audience that local governments should have full power to regulate cable television companies" is a specific purpose statement for a persuasive speech on a question of

   *a.  policy.
    b.  opinion.
    c.  attitude.
    d.  fact.
    e.  value.

101. "To persuade my audience that the United States National Park Service should reduce the number of camp sites in national parks by 50 percent" is a specific purpose statement for a persuasive speech on a question of

    a.  fact.
    b.  attitude.
    c.  value.
   *d.  policy.
    e.  opinion.

102. As your textbook explains, when you give a persuasive speech on a question of _____, you can seek either passive agreement or immediate action from your audience.

    a.  opinion
   *b.  policy
    c.  judgment
    d.  value
    e.  fact

103. As your textbook explains, you must deal with three basic issues whenever you discuss a question of policy. Those issues are need, plan, and

    a.  efficiency.
   *b.  practicality.
    c.  productivity.
    d.  flexibility.
    e.  viability.

104. Which of the following specific purpose statements is from a persuasive speech seeking passive agreement?

    a.  To persuade my audience to sign organ donor cards.
    b.  To persuade my audience to vote in the next local election.
    c.  To persuade my audience to boycott coffee from plantations that damage the rainforests.
   *d.  To persuade my audience that the campus library should be open 24 hours a day.
    e.  To persuade my audience to adopt a regular exercise program.

105.   Which of the following specific purpose statements is from a persuasive speech seeking immediate action?

   a.   To persuade my audience that the federal government should increase funding to provide computers for children in low-income housing.
   b.   To persuade my audience that the state must increase funding for wetland preservation.
   c.   To persuade my audience that federal campaign finance laws must be reformed to preserve the integrity of electoral process.
  *d.   To persuade my audience to decrease the amount of electricity they use during the summer in order to prevent blackouts.
   e.   To persuade my audience that the college administration should increase spending for intramural athletics on campus.

106.   Which of the following specific purpose statements is from a persuasive speech seeking immediate action?

   a.   To persuade my audience that the federal government should establish a committee to study the regulation of genetically engineered food.
  *b.   To persuade my audience to write their U.S. senators and representatives in support of a bill to regulate genetically engineered food.
   c.   To persuade my audience that proposed legislation to regulate genetically engineered food will hurt farmers.
   d.   To persuade my audience that the federal government must take steps to regulate genetically engineered food.
   e.   To persuade my audience that genetically engineered food poses serious health dangers to consumers.

107.   Which of the following specific purpose statements is from a persuasive speech seeking immediate action?

   a.   To persuade my audience that the state legislature should stiffen driver's license requirements for persons over the age of 75.
  *b.   To persuade my audience to write their legislators in support of stiffening driver's license requirements for persons over the age of 75.
   c.   To persuade my audience that the proposed bill to stiffen driver's license requirements for persons over the age of 75 is just and reasonable.
   d.   To persuade my audience that the state legislature has no business stiffening driver's license requirements for persons over the age of 75.
   e.   To persuade my audience that acting now to stiffen driver's license requirements for people over the age of 75 will save lives.

108.   Regardless of whether your aim is to encourage passive agreement or immediate action, you must deal with three basic issues whenever you discuss a question of policy. They are

   a.   cause, effect, and practicality.
   b.   evidence, practicality, and reasoning.
   c.   need, action, and reaction.
   d.   problem, plan, and solution.
  *e.   need, plan, and practicality.

109.    Which of the following statements is most clearly directed at the practicality issue in a persuasive speech on a question of policy?

    a.    My solution has three major steps.
    b.    We can no longer ignore the seriousness of the problem.
    c.    There are three ways to judge the morality of capital punishment.
  *d.    If my plan is adopted, it will be less expensive than the current system.
    e.    If the government knew what it was doing, we wouldn't be in this mess.

110.    If you give a persuasive speech advocating a change in policy, your main points often will fall naturally into _____ order.

  *a.    problem-solution
    b.    chronological
    c.    causal
    d.    comparative advantages
    e.    topical

111.    Nina's persuasive speech contained the following statement:

> The lack of a national law requiring seat belts on school buses is a serious problem in the United States. Last year alone, 437 children were killed and more than 5,000 injured in accidents involving school buses. Given all the advances in automobile safety in recent years, how can we continue to allow our children to ride in unsafe vehicles?

Which of the three basic issues of persuasive speeches on questions of policy did Nina address in this excerpt?

    a.    practicality
  *b.    need
    c.    satisfaction
    d.    plan
    e.    visualization

112.    In a speech seeking to persuade his audience to donate blood, Ian explained how little time the donation process would take from their busy schedules. Which of the three basic issues of persuasive speeches on questions of policy did Ian address in this part of his speech?

    a.    need
    b.    action
    c.    motivation
  *d.    practicality
    e.    fact

113.  While attempting to persuade her audience to volunteer for a community literacy
      program, Terri provided evidence that volunteering takes only two hours a week
      and that employers look for volunteer service on resumés from job applicants.
      Which of the three basic issues of persuasive speeches on questions of policy was
      Terri addressing in this section of her speech?

    a.  need
    b.  relevance
  *c.  practicality
    d.  clarification
    e.  solution

114.  In a speech seeking to persuade her audience to support the city's ban on unlimited
      drink specials at local bars, Jasmine used examples and statistics to demonstrate the
      seriousness of binge drinking as a problem on college campuses. Which of the three
      basic issues of persuasive speeches on questions of policy did Jasmine address in
      this part of her speech?

  *a.  need
    b.  fact
    c.  action
    d.  value
    e.  plan

115.  Li's persuasive speech contained the following statement:

> To solve the problem of decreasing personal privacy due to
> electronic data-gathering by businesses, I propose more stringent
> privacy laws. These laws should impose strict controls on the
> collection of personal information by businesses. These laws
> should also include stiff penalties for anyone who uses personal
> information for unauthorized purposes.

Which of the three basic issues of persuasive speeches on questions of policy did Li
address in this excerpt?

    a.  need
    b.  practicality
    c.  visualization
    d.  problem
  *e.  plan

116.  The burden of _____ always rests with the persuasive speaker who
      advocates change.

    a.  fact
    b.  opinion
    c.  refutation
    d.  strategy
  *e.  proof

117.    Heather gave her persuasive speech on the problem of teenage alcoholism. In her
        first main point, she showed how serious the problem is. In her second main point,
        she explained why the problem had reached its current proportions. In her third
        main point, she presented some ways of coping with the problem. What
        organizational pattern did Heather use in her speech?

    a.    need-plan-practicality
    b.    comparative advantages
    c.    Monroe's motivated sequence
  *d.    problem-cause-solution
    e.    topical

118.    Seth's persuasive speech contained the following statement:

    Will my policy work? Can we institute a law protecting individual
        privacy against electronic data-gathering by businesses? The
        answer is yes. A policy similar to mine has already been
        instituted successfully in most of the countries of Western
        Europe.

        Which of the three basic issues of persuasive speeches on questions of policy did
        Seth address in this excerpt?

    a.    need
    b.    proposal
  *c.    practicality
    d.    strategy
    e.    action

119.    Roberto's persuasive speech on a question of policy contains the following
        transition between the first and second main points:

    As we have seen, excessive caffeine consumption can create
        serious problems for your body's nervous system and immune
        system. We're now ready to look at ways you can start reducing
        your intake of caffeine.

        Roberto's speech is organized according to which pattern of organization?

    a.    causal
  *b.    problem-solution
    c.    comparative advantages
    d.    persuasive sequence
    e.    topical

120.   The following set of main points for a persuasive speech on a question of policy follows which pattern of organization?

     I.   The shortage of nurses has become a serious national problem.

     II.   The problem can be solved by offering nurses better salaries and better working conditions.

   a.   deliberative
*b.   problem-solution
   c.   comparative advantages
   d.   need-plan-practicality
   e.   causal

121.   The following set of main points for a persuasive speech on a question of policy follows which pattern of organization?

     I.   Bacterial meningitis is a deadly disease that can spread easily on college campuses.

     II.   Every college student should be required to get vaccinated against bacterial meningitis.

   a.   causal
   b.   deliberative
   c.   need-plan-practicality
   d.   comparative advantages
*e.   problem-solution

122.   The following set of main points for a persuasive speech on a question of policy follows which pattern of organization?

     I.   Childhood obesity is a serious health crisis in the United States.

     II.   Childhood obesity is caused by a range of factors from poor nutrition to lack of exercise.

     III.   Childhood obesity can be reduced by action from parents, schools, and the fast-food industry.

   a.   comparative advantages
*b.   problem-cause-solution
   c.   Monroe's motivated sequence
   d.   need-plan-practicality
   e.   topical

123.    The following set of main points for a persuasive speech on a question of policy follows which pattern of organization?

    I.   Installing filtering software on computers in homes, schools, and public libraries is a more effective way of controlling children's access to Internet pornography than is parental monitoring.

    II.   Installing filtering software on computers in homes, schools, and public libraries is a more effective way of controlling children's access to Internet pornography than are government regulations.

    a.   need-plan-practicality
    b.   Monroe's motivated sequence
    c.   problem-cause-solution
  *d.   comparative advantages
    e.   causal

124.    As your textbook explains, _____ order is a way to structure a persuasive speech on a question of policy when the audience already agrees that a problem exists but needs to be persuaded that your plan provides the best solution to the problem.

    a.   problem-solution
  *b.   comparative advantages
    c.   problem-cause-solution
    d.   Monroe's motivated sequence
    e.   need-plan-practicality

125.    Alex's persuasive speech on a question of policy includes the following connective between the second and third main points:

First we saw that health complications from obesity are a growing problem among young adults. Then we looked at some of the major factors leading to this problem. Now let's look at the steps we can take to eliminate the problem.

Alex's speech is organized according to which pattern of organization?

    a.   problem-solution
    b.   comparative advantages
  *c.   problem-cause-solution
    d.   persuasive sequence
    e.   none of the above

126.   Because it follows the process of human thinking, _____ is particularly useful for organizing persuasive speeches that seek immediate action.

    a.   Mitchell's strategic progression
    b.   comparative advantages order
  *c.   Monroe's motivated sequence
    d.   problem-cause-solution order
    e.   Morgan's psychological series

127.   Which organizational pattern is especially effective for persuasive speeches that seek immediate action by listeners?

    a.   comparative advantages order
  *b.   Monroe's motivated sequence
    c.   problem-solution order
    d.   reflective-thinking sequence
    e.   psychological process order

128.   What organizational method for persuasive speeches is designed to take the audience through the five steps of attention, need, satisfaction, visualization, and action?

    a.   Maswell's influence model
    b.   reflective-thinking sequence
    c.   Miller's psychological process
    d.   target audience order
  *e.   Monroe's motivated sequence

129.   The *major* reason Monroe's motivated sequence is such an effective way of organizing persuasive speeches that seek action from listeners is because it

    a.   is limited to five steps.
    b.   can be easily adapted to standard outlining form.
  *c.   follows the process of human thinking.
    d.   is more detailed than problem-solution order.
    e.   is often used by advertisers.

130.   Using vivid imagery to help listeners see the benefits of the plan you are advocating is crucial to the _____ step within Monroe's motivated sequence.

    a.   attention
    b.   motivation
    c.   satisfaction
  *d.   visualization
    e.   action

131.    Which of the following is the *first* step in Monroe's motivated sequence?

    a.   need
    b.   judgment
    c.   motivation
  *d.   attention
    e.   plan

132.    Which of the following is the *second* step in Monroe's motivated sequence?

    a.   plan
    b.   satisfaction
    c.   attention
    d.   action
  *e.   need

133.    Which of the following is the *final* step in Monroe's motivated sequence?

  *a.   action
    b.   motivation
    c.   visualization
    d.   practicality
    e.   solution

## Short Answer Questions

134.    The three kinds of questions that give rise to persuasive speeches are questions of _____fact_____, questions of _____value_____, and questions of _____policy_____.

135.    "To persuade my audience that there is convincing evidence of intelligent life in other parts of the solar system" is a specific purpose statement for a persuasive speech on a question of _____fact_____.

136.    "To persuade my audience that aspertame, the active ingredient in Nutrasweet, poses numerous health risks to consumers" is a specific purpose statement for a persuasive speech on a question of _____fact_____.

137.    "To persuade my audience that it is unethical for insurance companies to deny benefits to people with conditions such as AIDS, multiple sclerosis, and hepatitis-C" is a specific purpose statement for a persuasive speech on a question of _____value_____.

138.    "To persuade my audience that businesses have no right using lie detector tests to pry into employees' private lives" is a specific purpose statement for a persuasive speech on a question of _____value_____.

139.    "To persuade my audience that public officials should act now to upgrade the 911 emergency phone system" is a specific purpose statement for a persuasive speech on a question of _____policy_____ .

140.    "To persuade my audience that our state should impose stricter regulations governing the safety of amusement park rides" is a specific purpose statement for a persuasive speech on a question of ____policy____ .

141.    Persuasive speeches on questions of ____policy____ argue for or against particular courses of action.

142.    Questions of ____policy____ usually include the word "should."

143.    "Who is the greatest Impressionist painter?" is a question of ____value____ . "Should public museums be allowed to raise revenue by selling masterpieces to private collectors?" is a question of ____policy____ . "What was the most expensive piece of art sold on the open market in the 20th century?" is a question of ____fact____ .

144.    As your textbook explains, you must deal with three basic issues whenever you discuss a question of policy. Those issues are need, plan, and ____practicality____ .

145.    The three basic issues of persuasive speeches on questions of policy are ____need____ , ____plan____ , and ____practicality____ .

146.    The following main points for a persuasive speech on a question of policy are arranged in _____problem-solution_____ order.

   I.    The shortage of nurses has become a serious national problem.
   II.   The problem can be solved by offering nurses better salaries and working conditions.

147.    The following main points for a persuasive speech on a question of policy are arranged in _____problem-cause-solution_____ order.

   I.    Violent crime on college campuses is a problem throughout the United States.
   II.   There are three major causes of the problem that are specific to college life.
   III.  An effective solution must deal with all three of these causes.

148.    The following main points for a persuasive speech on a question of policy are arranged in _____comparative advantages_____ order.

   I.    Air bags are superior to seat belts because they provide more complete protection in case of a serious automobile crash.
   II.   Air bags are superior to seat belts because they inflate automatically, rather than depending on the driver to "buckle up."

149.   The five steps of Monroe's motivated sequence are:

a.   _____attention_____

b.   _____need_____

c.   _____satisfaction_____

d.   _____visualization_____

e.   _____action_____

## Essay Questions

150.   Identify and discuss three of the ethical obligations of persuasive speakers discussed in your textbook.

151.   Why is speaking to persuade more difficult than speaking to inform?

152.   Explain the following statement: "You should enter a persuasive speaking situation with a realistic sense of what you can hope to accomplish."

153.   Explain the following statement: "A persuasive speaker should think of her or his speech as a kind of mental dialogue with the audience."

154.   What does it mean to say that audiences engage in a "mental dialogue" with the speaker as they listen to a persuasive speech? What implications does this mental dialogue have for a speaker who seeks to persuade skeptical listeners?

155.   What is the target audience for a persuasive speech? Why is determining and analyzing the target audience so important to effective persuasive speaking?

156.   Explain the distinctions among questions of fact, value, and policy. Give an example of a specific purpose statement for a persuasive speech on each question.

157.   Develop three different specific purpose statements for a persuasive speech on the topic of college tuition—one for a speech dealing with a question of fact, one for a speech dealing with a question of value, and one for a speech dealing with a question of policy.

158.   Explain the following statement: "When you give a persuasive speech on a question of value, you should make sure to justify your value judgment against some identifiable standards or criteria."

159.   Identify and explain the three basic issues of persuasive speeches on questions of policy. What determines how much attention you should give to each issue in a specific speech?

160.   Compare and contrast passive agreement and immediate action as goals for a persuasive speech on a question of policy.

161.   Briefly describe the following methods of speech organization. In what circumstances would a speaker be most likely to use each in a persuasive speech on a question of policy?

a.   problem-cause-solution order
b.   comparative advantages order
c.   Monroe's motivated sequence

162.   Identify the five steps of Monroe's motivated sequence and explain what a speaker should do in each step.

———————————————————

# Chapter 16 Methods of Persuasion

## True-False Questions

1. T <u>F</u>    Study of the methods of persuasion began with communication researchers early in the twentieth century.

2. <u>T</u> F    What many teachers refer to as source credibility was called *ethos* by Aristotle.

3. <u>T</u> F    Competence and character are the most important factors affecting a speaker's credibility.

4. T <u>F</u>    Education and status are the most important factors affecting a speaker's credibility.

5. <u>T</u> F    The more favorably listeners view a speaker's competence and character, the more likely they are to accept what the speaker says.

6. T <u>F</u>    The credibility of a speaker before she or he starts to speak is called derived credibility.

7. <u>T</u> F    The credibility of a speaker before she or he starts to speak is called initial credibility.

8. <u>T</u> F    Derived credibility refers to the credibility of the speaker produced by everything she or he says and does during the speech itself.

9. T <u>F</u>    Terminal credibility is the credibility of the speaker at the start of the speech.

10. <u>T</u> F    Terminal credibility is the credibility of the speaker at the end of the speech.

11. T <u>F</u>    Speakers who explain their expertise on the speech topic are likely to reduce their credibility with the audience.

12. <u>T</u> F    A speaker can have high credibility for one audience and low credibility for another audience.

13. T <u>F</u>    Establishing common ground with an audience is especially important in the conclusion of a persuasive speech.

14. <u>T</u> F    Establishing common ground with an audience is especially important in the introduction of a persuasive speech.

15. <u>T</u> F    A speaker's credibility is affected by everything she or he says and does during the speech.

16. <u>T</u> F    Research shows that a speaker's credibility is strongly affected by his or her delivery.

17. T <u>F</u>    Research has shown that speakers with high initial credibility need to use more evidence than speakers with low initial credibility.

18. <u>T</u> F    Studies have shown that speakers with low initial credibility need to use more evidence than speakers with high initial credibility.

19. <u>T</u> F    One of the reasons to use evidence when speaking to persuade is that it can make your listeners more resistant to counterpersuasion.

20. T <u>F</u>    Research indicates that evidence is usually more persuasive when it is stated in general rather than specific terms.

21. <u>T</u> F    Research indicates that evidence is usually more persuasive when it is stated in specific rather than general terms.

22. T <u>F</u>    Research shows that skeptical listeners are more likely to be persuaded by evidence they are already familiar with than by evidence that is new to them.

23. <u>T</u> F    Research indicates that listeners are more likely to be persuaded by evidence that is new to them than by facts and figures they already know.

24. T <u>F</u>    According to your textbook, it is redundant for persuasive speakers to give their evidence and then to state the point the evidence is meant to prove.

25. <u>T</u> F    Reasoning is the process of drawing a conclusion based on evidence.

26. T <u>F</u>    When you reason from specific instances in a speech, you move from a general example to a specific conclusion.

27. <u>T</u> F    Reasoning from specific instances involves progressing from a number of particular facts to a general conclusion.

28. T <u>F</u>    According to your textbook, when reasoning from specific instances in a persuasive speech, a speaker must present the specific instances before stating the conclusion the specific instances are meant to prove.

29. <u>T</u> F    When reasoning from specific instances in a persuasive speech, it is usually a good idea for a speaker to supplement the specific instances with testimony or statistics showing that the instances are not atypical.

30. <u>T</u> F    When reasoning from specific instances in a persuasive speech, you need to make sure your sample of specific instances is large enough to justify your conclusion.

31. T <u>F</u>    A persuasive speaker who argues that capital punishment should be outlawed because it violates the constitutional principle banning cruel and unusual punishment is reasoning from specific instances.

32. <u>T</u> F    A persuasive speaker who contends that America's older bridges are becoming unsafe because several bridges have collapsed in recent years is reasoning from specific instances.

33. T <u>F</u>    When you reason from principle in a speech, you move from a specific principle to a general conclusion.

34. <u>T</u> F    Reasoning from principle moves from a general principle to a specific conclusion.

35. <u>T</u> F    Because it moves from a general principle to a specific conclusion, reasoning from principle is the opposite of reasoning from specific instances.

36. T <u>F</u>    The following statement is an example of reasoning from principle: "Places such as Singapore that allow caning and other forms of corporal punishment have exceedingly low crime rates. If caning were used in the United States, the U.S. would have lower crime rates as well."

37. <u>T</u> F    The following is an example of reasoning from principle: "All infringements on the right of free expression are unconstitutional. Limitations on the lyrics of popular songs are infringements on the right of free expression. Therefore, all limitations on the lyrics of popular songs are unconstitutional."

38. T <u>F</u>    When you use causal reasoning in a persuasive speech, you seek to establish the relationship between a general principle and a specific conclusion.

39. T <u>F</u>    Although causal reasoning is used a great deal in public speeches, it is seldom used in other situations.

40.  T  <u>F</u>    One of the advantages of using causal reasoning in a persuasive speech is that the relationship between causes and effects is usually fairly obvious.

41.  <u>T</u>  F    When using causal reasoning in a persuasive speech, you should take special care to avoid the fallacy of *post hoc, ergo propter hoc*.

42.  <u>T</u>  F    The following statement is an example of reasoning from analogy: "If you can make great tacos, you can make great enchiladas."

43.  T  <u>F</u>    The following statement is an example of reasoning from analogy: "The United Nations charter establishes the right of all people to live free of political oppression. The government of North Korea subjects its people to political oppression. Therefore, the government of North Korea is violating the U.N. charter."

44.  T  <u>F</u>    The most important question to ask when assessing analogical reasoning is whether the general principle of the analogy is valid for the specific case at hand.

45.  <u>T</u>  F    The most important question to ask when assessing analogical reasoning is whether the two cases being compared are essentially alike.

46.  T  <u>F</u>    The either-or fallacy assumes that taking a first step will lead to subsequent steps that cannot be prevented.

47.  <u>T</u>  F    The either-or fallacy forces listeners to choose between two alternatives when more than two alternatives exist.

48.  <u>T</u>  F    The red herring fallacy refers to statements that introduce an irrelevant issue to divert attention from the subject under discussion.

49.  T  <u>F</u>    The red herring fallacy is often known by its Latin name, *post hoc, ergo propter hoc*.

50.  T  <u>F</u>    The red herring fallacy is often referred to as a false dilemma.

51.  T  <u>F</u>    Arguments guilty of the *ad hominem* fallacy argue in a circle without making a clear point.

52.  <u>T</u>  F    Arguments guilty of the *ad hominem* fallacy attack the person rather than dealing with the real issue in dispute.

53.  T  <u>F</u>    The slippery slope fallacy assumes that because something is popular, it is therefore good, correct, or desirable.

54.  <u>T</u>  F    The bandwagon fallacy assumes that because something is popular, it is therefore good, correct, or desirable.

55.  T̲ F   According to your textbook, emotional appeals are usually inappropriate in persuasive speeches on questions of fact.

56.  T̲ F   According to your textbook, emotional appeals are often appropriate in persuasive speeches on questions of policy.

57.  T F̲   As your textbook explains, emotion-laden language is the strongest source of emotional appeal in a persuasive speech.

58.  T F̲   As your textbook explains, it is unethical to use vivid, richly textured examples to generate emotional appeal in a persuasive speech on a question of policy.

59.  T̲ F   The strongest source of emotional appeal in a persuasive speech is the sincerity and conviction of the speaker.

60.  T̲ F   Regardless of whether a persuasive speaker uses emotional appeal, she or he should always build the speech on a firm foundation of facts and logic.

## Multiple Choice Questions *(Students are to indicate the best answer for each question by circling the correct letter.)*

61.  What contemporary researchers term credibility, Aristotle termed

   a.  ethics.
   b.  logos.
  *c.  ethos.
   d.  pathos.
   e.  credos.

62.  According to your textbook, the two most important factors affecting the credibility of a persuasive speaker are

  *a.  competence and character.
   b.  prestige and charisma.
   c.  character and reputation.
   d.  popularity and intelligence.
   e.  charisma and competence.

63.  According to your textbook, the two most important factors affecting the credibility of a persuasive speaker are competence and

   a.  logic.
   b.  charisma.
  *c.  character.
   d.  pathos.
   e.  status.

64.     To create common ground with an audience in the introduction of a persuasive speech, your textbook recommends that you

   *a.    show the audience that you share their values.
    b.    use statistics to show the extent of a problem.
    c.    confront the audience for failing to do the right thing.
    d.    all of the above.
    e.    a and b only.

65.     Efram's audience was persuaded by his speech because they perceived him to be sincere, trustworthy, and to have their best interests at heart. Which factor of credibility influenced Efram's audience?

    a.    dynamism
    b.    charisma
    c.    expertise
   *d.    character
    e.    competence

66.     Which of the following statements about speaker credibility is true?

    a.    A speaker's credibility is based on her or his reputation rather than on what happens during a speech.
    b.    Credibility refers to the speaker's true character and competence, not merely to the audience's perception of the speaker.
    c.    A speaker's credibility is affected by almost every aspect of the speech except delivery.
    d.    Although credibility is an important factor for professional speakers, it does not matter in classroom speeches.
   *e.    The same speaker can have high credibility for one audience and low credibility for another audience.

67.     Which of the following statements about speaker credibility is true?

    a.    A speaker's credibility is affected above all by how the audience perceives the speaker's personal appearance.
   *b.    A speaker's credibility is affected above all by how the audience perceives the speaker's competence and character.
    c.    A speaker's credibility is affected above all by how the audience perceives the speaker's manner of delivery.
    d.    A speaker's credibility is affected above all by how the audience perceives the speaker's personality and reputation.
    e.    A speaker's credibility is affected above all by how the audience perceives the speaker's intelligence and prestige.

68.    A local landlord with a reputation for failing to return security deposits at the end of a lease has been invited to present his viewpoint at a meeting of the local tenants' union. To everyone's surprise, the landlord accepts the invitation despite the fact that he will be facing an audience with a decidedly negative view of his integrity. What factor will the landlord have to overcome if his speech is to have any chance of being persuasive?

   *a.    low initial credibility
    b.    low generated credibility
    c.    low introductory credibility
    d.    low terminal credibility
    e.    low derived credibility

69.    The credibility of a speaker before he or she starts to speak is called _____ credibility.

   *a.    initial
    b.    negative
    c.    derived
    d.    steady
    e.    terminal

70.    According to your textbook, the credibility of a speaker at the end of the speech is called _____ credibility.

    a.    final
    b.    derived
    c.    concluding
   *d.    terminal
    e.    acquired

71.    According to your textbook, the credibility of a speaker produced by everything the speaker says or does during the speech itself is called

    a.    created credibility.
   *b.    derived credibility.
    c.    demonstrated credibility.
    d.    generated credibility.
    e.    terminal credibility.

72.    Which of the following is recommended in your textbook as a way to enhance your credibility in a persuasive speech?

    a.    explain your expertise on the speech topic
    b.    deliver your speeches fluently and expressively
    c.    establish common ground with your audience
   *d.    all of the above
    e.    a and c only

73. Which of the following is recommended in your textbook as a way to enhance your credibility in a persuasive speech?

   *a. establish common ground with your audience
   b. avoid talking about your personal knowledge of the topic
   c. relate the topic to the audience in your introduction
   d. all of the above
   e. a and b only

74. According to your textbook, research has shown that

   a. speakers with low initial credibility do not need to use as much evidence as speakers with high initial credibility.
   b. the credibility of a speaker is determined above all by how the audience perceives the speaker's intelligence and prestige.
   *c. speakers can enhance their credibility by delivering their speeches fluently and expressively.
   d. personal appearance is the most important factor in determining a speaker's derived credibility.
   e. a speaker can begin with low terminal credibility and develop high initial credibility as the speech proceeds.

75. Using evidence is especially critical in a persuasive speech when your target audience

   a. is apathetic about your point of view.
   b. is neutral toward your point of view.
   c. supports your point of view.
   *d. opposes your point of view.
   e. is not sure of your point of view.

76. According to your textbook, using evidence in a persuasive speech can

   a. increase the speaker's credibility.
   b. inoculate listeners against counterpersuasion.
   c. compensate for fallacious reasoning.
   d. all of the above.
   *e. a and b only.

77. When giving a persuasive speech to an audience that opposes your point of view, it is especially important that you use _____ to answer their objections to your views.

   a. visual aids
   b. syllogisms
   c. credibility statements
   d. emotional appeals
   *e. evidence

78.    According to your textbook, it is especially important to use evidence in a persuasive speech to

    a.    reinforce your competence on the topic.
    b.    establish common ground with your audience.
\*c.    answer listeners' objections to your position.
    d.    generate goodwill among your audience.
    e.    reinforce your reasoning.

79.    Studies have found that public speakers will usually be more persuasive when they

    a.    use evidence that is already familiar to the audience.
\*b.    present evidence in specific rather than general terms.
    c.    state evidence without drawing explicit conclusions from it.
    d.    avoid emotional appeals when seeking action from the audience.
    e.    speak slightly slower than normal when delivering the speech.

80.    As your textbook explains, studies have found that public speakers will usually be more persuasive when they

    a.    use specific evidence.
    b.    use evidence from credible sources.
    c.    use evidence that is new to the audience.
\*d.    all of the above.
    e.    a and b only.

81.    According to your textbook, all of the following are tips for using evidence in a persuasive speech *except*

    a.    present evidence in specific rather than general terms.
\*b.    balance the amount of evidence used to support each main point.
    c.    support ideas with evidence that is new to the audience.
    d.    make clear the point your evidence is supposed to prove.
    e.    rely on evidence from competent, credible sources.

82.    According to your textbook, as a persuasive speaker, your two *major* concerns with respect to reasoning are to

    a.    establish credibility and reason correctly.
    b.    make sure your reasoning is clear and credible.
    c.    avoid fallacies and support reasoning with testimony.
    d.    adapt reasoning to both hostile and favorable listeners.
\*e.    make sure your reasoning is sound and convincing.

83.    When reasoning from specific instances in a persuasive speech, you should be especially
       careful to

       a.   avoid the fallacy of *post hoc, ergo propter hoc*.
    *b.   keep from generalizing too hastily.
       c.   state your conclusion before the specific instances that prove it.
       d.   all of the above.
       e.   b and c only.

84.    Which of the following is presented in your textbook as a guideline for reasoning from
       specific instances in a persuasive speech?

       a.   reinforce your argument with statistics and testimony
       b.   include at least one extended example among your specific instances
       c.   avoid generalizing too hastily
       d.   all of the above
    *e.   a and c only

85.    What kind of reasoning is used in the following statement?

            In recent months, newspapers have carried reports of vicious dogs
            attacking people in Los Angeles, St. Louis, Boston, and Orlando. These
            reports show that dog attacks are an increasingly serious problem
            nationwide.

       a.   analogical reasoning
       b.   reasoning from principle
       c.   journalistic reasoning
    *d.   reasoning from specific instances
       e.   causal reasoning

86.    What kind of reasoning is used in the following statement?

            In the 1770s the American colonists boycotted British tea and had a big
            impact on British trade. In 1993 manufacturers in Bangladesh released
            150,000 child laborers as a result of threatened boycotts against their
            products. More recently, Colgate has stopped animal testing for its
            personal care products in response to consumer boycotts. It is clear from
            these examples that boycotts have long been used as an instrument of
            social change.

       a.   circular reasoning
       b.   analogical reasoning
       c.   deductive reasoning
    *d.   reasoning from specific instances
       e.   reasoning from principle

87.   What kind of reasoning is used in the following statement?

The income of male accountants is 20 percent higher than the income of female accountants. There is a similar difference between the income of male and female lawyers. Even among doctors, we find an income gap of 20 percent or more within most medical specialties. It is clear that in many professions women continue to earn less than men.

   a.   reasoning from gender
   b.   reasoning from comparison
*c.   reasoning from specific instances
   d.   reasoning from general cases
   e.   reasoning from principle

88.   Which of the following is presented in your textbook as a guideline for reasoning from specific instances in a persuasive speech?

   a.   Cite specific instances that are familiar to your audience.
   b.   Be sure to state the conclusion before the specific instances that support it.
*c.   Avoid sweeping conclusions not justified by the specific instances.
   d.   Use a hypothetical example to relate the specific instances to the audience.
   e.   Take care that the specific instances being compared are essentially alike.

89.   What kind of reasoning is used in the following statement?

In recent years there have been a number of highly publicized cases of sexual harassment in business, government, and education. Thus we can conclude that sexual harassment continues to be a problem for women in the workplace.

   a.   causal reasoning
   b.   reasoning from principle
*c.   reasoning from specific instances
   d.   emotional reasoning
   e.   analogical reasoning

90.   What error in reasoning is exemplified by the following statement?

French movies are all dull. I saw three of them last semester in my film class and couldn't stay awake through a single one.

   a.   false cause
   b.   faulty deduction
   c.   invalid analogy
*d.   hasty generalization
   e.   circular thinking

91.     What error in reasoning is exemplified by the following statement?

        Both of my roommates drink at least three cans of soda every day and
        neither of them is overweight, so all those studies that link soda
        consumption to obesity must be wrong.

        a.   circular reasoning
      *b.   hasty generalization
        c.   invalid analogy
        d.   false cause
        e.   bandwagon

92.     According to your textbook, when you reason in a persuasive speech from a general
        principle to a specific conclusion, you are using

        a.   analogical reasoning.
      *b.   reasoning from principle.
        c.   reasoning by generalization.
        d.   reasoning from premises.
        e.   universal reasoning.

93.     What kind of reasoning is used in the following statement?

        We should be taking every step we can to protect our health. Getting
        vaccinated against bacterial meningitis will help protect our health.
        Therefore, each of us should get vaccinated against bacterial meningitis.

        a.   reasoning from cause
        b.   reasoning from prudence
        c.   reasoning from specific instances
      *d.   reasoning from principle
        e.   reasoning from safety

94.     In her speech on chewing tobacco, Catherine made the following argument:

        To be effective, laws governing chewing tobacco sales to minors must be
        enforced and must have adequate penalties for people who violate the
        law. My proposal will significantly increase both enforcement provisions
        and penalties for violators. Therefore, my plan will be effective.

        What kind of reasoning did Catherine use?

      *a.   reasoning from principle
        b.   reasoning from analogy
        c.   reasoning from specific instances
        d.   reasoning from expediency
        e.   reasoning from need

95.    As your textbook explains, when reasoning from principle in a persuasive speech, it is particularly important that you

    a.    establish the credibility of your causal premise.
    b.    draw your conclusion from a large and representative sample.
  *c.    assess whether you need to support your general principle with evidence.
    d.    make sure your general principle and minor premise are analogous.
    e.    balance the time spent on your minor premise and causal premise.

96.    What kind of reasoning is exemplified in the following statement?

Politicians who are guilty of corruption do not deserve to be reelected. Last year our U.S. representative was proved to be corrupt by using campaign donations for personal financial gain. Therefore, our U.S. representative does not deserve to be reelected.

    a.    reasoning from specific instances
    b.    causal reasoning
    c.    reasoning by generalization
    d.    analogical reasoning
  *e.    reasoning from principle

97.    What kind of reasoning is exemplified in the following statement?

According to a study by the University of Michigan, married men in the United States earn an average of 31 percent more money than unmarried men. It seems clear, then, that for many men being married is a major cause of financial success.

  *a.    causal reasoning
    b.    analogical reasoning
    c.    reasoning from principle
    d.    statistical reasoning
    e.    deductive reasoning

98.    What kind of reasoning is used in the following statement?

U.S. children raised in two-parent families with incomes below the poverty line have a greater incidence of school absences, lower test scores, and less chance of finishing high school than do children raised in one-parent households with incomes at least 10 percent above the poverty line. We can see, therefore, that it is the economic stability of the family, not its family structure, that determines a child's ability to succeed in school.

    a.    chain reasoning
  *b.    causal reasoning
    c.    deductive reasoning
    d.    analogical reasoning
    e.    practical reasoning

99.     According to your textbook, what error in reasoning should a speaker watch out for when using causal reasoning in a persuasive speech?

    a.   claiming a causal link between two events when they are merely coincidental
    b.   assuming that events have only one cause when there may be multiple causes
    c.   committing the *post nobis* fallacy of using inappropriate causal evidence
    d.   all of the above
 *e.   a and b only

100.    According to your textbook, what kind of reasoning is exemplified in the following statement?

> We do not have to look very far to find reasons for the explosion in the number of violent crimes committed by teenagers in the United States. Not only are guns readily available to teenagers, but today's teenagers have grown up in a culture that glamorizes violence in television and films. The average child in the U.S. has seen more than 20,000 murders on television by the time he or she turns eighteen. Is it any wonder that many of those children are now committing violent crimes themselves?

    a.   analogical reasoning
    b.   reasoning from principle
 *c.   causal reasoning
    d.   reasoning from deduction
    e.   analytical reasoning

101.    What error in reasoning is exemplified by the following statement?

> I always wear my blue sweater when I take an exam, but I couldn't find it yesterday. If I had worn it yesterday, I would not have flunked my accounting exam.

    a.   circular thinking
    b.   hasty generalization
    c.   invalid analogy
 *d.   false cause
    e.   faulty deduction

102.    *Post hoc, ergo propter hoc*, meaning "after this, therefore because of this," is a fallacy associated with _____ reasoning.

    a.   parallel
    b.   deductive
    c.   comparative
    d.   descriptive
 *e.   causal

103.   The following statement is an example of reasoning from _____

This program was implemented in Philadelphia two years ago and has provided housing for more than 2,000 people at little cost to the city. If it can work there, it can work here, too.

   a.   cause.
   b.   validity.
   c.   principle.
 *d.   analogy.
   e.   maxim.

104.   What kind of reasoning is used in the following statement?

Requiring students to sign an honor code has reduced the incidences of cheating at George Mason University. If we adopt such a code at our school, it will help us reduce the amount of cheating as well.

   a.   chain reasoning
   b.   deductive reasoning
   c.   dependent reasoning
   d.   practical reasoning
 *e.   analogical reasoning

105.   What kind of reasoning is used in the following statement?

Local control of the school system is the most effective way to educate our children. Therefore, local control of the health care system is the most effective way to maintain the health of our citizens.

 *a.   analogical reasoning
   b.   practical reasoning
   c.   specific reasoning
   d.   factual reasoning
   e.   dependent reasoning

106.   What kind of reasoning is used in the following passage?

The Amber Alert system has already proved effective in the states where it has been adopted. Because it has helped return kidnapped children to their parents in those states, we can be confident that it will produce similar results once it is passed into law in our state.

   a.   legal reasoning
   b.   comparative reasoning
   c.   functional reasoning
   d.   practical reasoning
 *e.   analogical reasoning

107.    What kind of reasoning is used in the following statement?

> In Germany, female employees can take up to 18 weeks of maternity leave with full pay. If such a plan can work in a prosperous nation such as Germany, surely it can work throughout the United States.

  a.   generalization
  b.   causal
 *c.   analogical
  d.   specific
  e.   descriptive

108.    In her speech arguing for the elimination of pennies from the U.S. money supply, Susan demonstrated that her plan will work by showing that a similar plan worked when the U.S. eliminated the half penny in 1857. What kind of reasoning did Susan use in her argument?

  a.   causal reasoning
 *b.   analogical reasoning
  c.   deductive reasoning
  d.   comparative reasoning
  e.   classical reasoning

109.    When reasoning analogically, you infer that

  a.   a causal relationship can be established between two or more events.
 *b.   what is true in one case will also be true in a similar case.
  c.   a general principle is validated by a question of fact.
  d.   your position is true because it is demonstrated by statistical trends.
  e.   a specific conclusion is true because it is verified by a general principle.

110.    What kind of reasoning is used in the following statement?

> Colorizing old movies such as *Citizen Kane* is like repainting the *Mona Lisa*.

 *a.   analogical
  b.   artistic
  c.   reasoning from principle
  d.   reasoning from specific instances
  e.   causal

111.    According to your textbook, the most important question to ask when assessing analogical reasoning in a persuasive speech is

  a.   whether there are enough analogies to support the general conclusion.
  b.   whether the analogical principle is supported by the major premise.
  c.   whether the analogy avoids the fallacy of *post hoc, ergo propter hoc*.
 *d.   whether the two cases being compared are essentially alike.
  e.   whether the analogy assumes that complex events have only a single cause.

112.    According to your textbook, the following statement is an example of what type of fallacy?

   In high school I didn't have to study at all and I earned good grades in all my classes, so I'm sure I don't need to study to do well in my college classes.

   a.  either-or
   b.  red herring
   *c.  invalid analogy
   d.  hasty deduction
   e.  false cause

113.    A red herring fallacy

   a.  assumes that because two things are related in time, they are causally linked.
   *b.  introduces an irrelevant issue to divert attention from the subject under discussion.
   c.  assumes that because something is popular, it is therefore good, correct, or desirable.
   d.  forces listeners to choose between two alternatives when more than two alternatives exist.
   e.  assumes that taking a first step will inevitably lead to other steps that cannot be prevented.

114.    According to your textbook, the following statement is an example of what type of fallacy?

   How can we be so concerned about shielding children in the U.S. from Internet pornography when millions of children around the world continue to be sold into slavery every year?

   a.  either-or
   *b.  red herring
   c.  false deduction
   d.  *ad hominem*
   e.  invalid analogy

115.    According to your textbook, the following statement is an example of what type of fallacy?

   Why should we be concerned about Siberian tigers becoming extinct when there are more and more homeless people who need our support?

   *a.  red herring
   b.  *ad hominem*
   c.  hasty generalization
   d.  slippery slope
   e.  either-or

116.    According to your textbook, the following statement is an example of what type of fallacy?

We are spending too much time talking about regulating the cable TV industry while other countries are beating us in technological development.

    a.    slippery slope
    b.    bandwagon
    c.    either-or
*d.    red herring
    e.    invalid analogy

117.    An either-or fallacy

    a.    assumes that because two things are related in time, they are causally linked.
    b.    attacks the person rather than dealing with the real issue in dispute.
    c.    introduces an irrelevant issue to divert attention from the subject under discussion.
*d.    forces listeners to choose between two alternatives when more than two alternatives exist.
    e.    assumes that because something is popular, it is therefore good, correct, or desirable.

118.    As your textbook explains, the either-or fallacy is often referred to as a(n)

    a.    red herring.
    b.    invalid analogy.
    c.    hasty generalization.
    d.    faulty deduction.
*e.    false dilemma.

119.    According to your textbook, the following statement is an example of what type of fallacy?

Either we all sign organ donor cards or medical facilities will start cloning people just to sell their body parts.

*a.    either-or
    b.    invalid analogy
    c.    hasty deduction
    d.    false principle
    e.    red herring

120.    According to your textbook, the following statement is an example of what type of fallacy?

We have only two choices. Either we fully support the government's counter-terrorism measures or we become traitors who give comfort to our enemies.

    a.    false cause
    b.    invalid analogy
    c.    hasty generalization
    d.    erroneous principle
*e.    either-or

121.    According to your textbook, the following statement is an example of what type of fallacy?

Representative Thompson's school proposal may be first rate, but don't forget that he never attended college himself.

   a.   bandwagon
*b.   *ad hominem*
   c.   hasty generalization
   d.   *post hoc, ergo propter hoc*
   e.   either-or

122.    According to your textbook, the following statement is an example of what type of fallacy?

Hannah makes a good argument in favor of providing economic benefits for same-sex couples, but what else would you expect from someone who is openly gay?

   a.   invalid analogy
   b.   *post hoc, ergo propter hoc*
   c.   hasty generalization
*d.   *ad hominem*
   e.   either-or

123.    A slippery slope fallacy

*a.   assumes that taking a first step will inevitably lead to other steps that cannot be prevented.
   b.   introduces an irrelevant issue to divert attention from the subject under discussion.
   c.   assumes that because something is popular, it is therefore good, correct, or desirable.
   d.   forces listeners to choose between two alternatives when more than two alternatives exist.
   e.   assumes that because two things are related in time, they are causally linked.

124.    According to your textbook, the following statement is an example of what type of fallacy?

Of course, Senator Davis opposes serious tax reform. Before going into politics, he was a corporate lawyer who defended several companies that have since been implicated in unethical financial dealings.

   a.   bandwagon
   b.   slippery slope
   c.   hasty generalization
   d.   invalid analogy
*e.   *ad hominem*

125. According to your textbook, the following statement is an example of what type of fallacy?

People who oppose the governor's new welfare program are all a bunch of selfish rich people who don't have any concern for those less fortunate than themselves.

    a. bandwagon
    b. invalid analogy
    c. hasty generalization
\*d. *ad hominem*
    e. false cause

126. The *ad hominem* fallacy

\*a. attacks the person rather than dealing with the real issue in dispute.
    b. assumes that complex events have only a single cause.
    c. assumes that because something is popular, it is therefore correct.
    d. all of the above.
    e. b and c only.

127. According to your textbook, the following statement is an example of what type of fallacy?

Everyone runs red lights when they're in a hurry, so there's no reason I shouldn't do it, too.

    a. slippery slope
    b. hasty generalization
    c. false cause
    d. either-or
\*e. bandwagon

128. According to your textbook, the following statement is an example of what type of fallacy?

Eliminating the space shuttle program is clearly the right thing to do. After the last shuttle disaster, several polls showed that 55 to 60 percent of Americans thought we should abolish the program.

\*a. bandwagon
    b. either-or
    c. hasty generalization
    d. false cause
    e. invalid analogy

129.   According to your textbook, the following statement is an example of what type of fallacy?

       If we encourage elementary school students to use computers in the classroom, they will spend less time reading books. As a result, they will fall way behind in developing reading, writing, and thinking skills. Pretty soon we will have a generation of illiterates on our hands.

    a.   invalid analogy
    b.   bandwagon
 *c.   slippery slope
    d.   red herring
    e.   either-or

130.   According to your textbook, the following statement is an example of what type of fallacy?

       More people use Pepcid AC than any other product to control the indigestion caused by acid reflux syndrome. Therefore, you can be sure it is the most effective treatment.

    a.   either-or
    b.   hasty generalization
 *c.   bandwagon
    d.   false cause
    e.   invalid analogy

131.   According to your textbook, the following statement is an example of what type of fallacy?

       More than 31 states now have laws permitting citizens to carry concealed weapons. The popularity of these laws shows that allowing people to carry concealed weapons is a good idea.

    a.   false cause
    b.   red herring
    c.   invalid analogy
    d.   slippery slope
 *e.   bandwagon

132.   According to your textbook, the following statement is an example of what type of fallacy?

       We must either support the governor's plan to reduce spending on education or we will never be able to balance the state budget.

 *a.   either-or
    b.   faulty comparison
    c.   hasty generalization
    d.   invalid analogy
    e.   bandwagon

133.   "The only way to keep our children from becoming involved with drugs and crime is to enforce a strict curfew every night of the week" is an example of which of the following fallacies?

  a.   faulty deduction
  b.   invalid analogy
*c.   either-or
  d.   red herring
  e.   bandwagon

134.   What fallacy is exemplified by the following statement?

  If we approve a construction permit for this home, the next thing you know other people will want to build in our valley. Then they will pave new roads and put in gas stations and other businesses. Before you know it, all of our beautiful land will be turned into a parking lot for a giant shopping mall.

  a.   red herring
  b.   *ad hominem*
  c.   bandwagon
*d.   slippery slope
  e.   either-or

135.   A bandwagon fallacy

  a.   assumes that taking a first step will inevitably lead to other steps that cannot be prevented.
  b.   introduces an irrelevant issue to divert attention from the subject under discussion.
*c.   assumes that because something is popular, it is therefore good, correct, or desirable.
  d.   forces listeners to choose between two alternatives when more than two alternatives exist.
  e.   assumes that because two things are related in time, they are causally linked.

136.   According to your textbook, the following statement is an example of what type of fallacy?

  Every presidential administration in recent memory has engaged in questionable fundraising activities, so I don't see any reason why it is wrong for the current administration to do so.

  a.   red herring
*b.   bandwagon
  c.   slippery slope
  d.   invalid syllogism
  e.   hasty generalization

137.    According to your textbook, which of the following statements is true?

    a.    Emotional appeal is incompatible with ethical public speaking.
    b.    A public speaker should not substitute emotional appeal for evidence and reasoning.
    c.    Emotional appeal is usually inappropriate in a persuasive speech on a question of fact.
    d.    all of the above
 *e.    b and c only

138.    According to your textbook, emotional appeal is

    a.    inappropriate in a persuasive speech on a question of policy.
 *b.    often necessary when a speaker is trying to move an audience to action.
    c.    most effectively generated by using emotionally charged words.
    d.    unethical unless the emotional appeal is combined with causal reasoning.
    e.    seldom used by public speakers in support of honorable causes.

139.    As your textbook explains, emotional appeal is

    a.    seldom used by public speakers in support of honorable causes.
    b.    unethical unless the emotional appeal is combined with reasoning from principle.
 *c.    often necessary when a speaker is trying to move an audience to action.
    d.    all of the above.
    e.    a and b only.

140.    According to your textbook, emotional appeal is inappropriate in a persuasive speech on a question of

 *a.    fact.
    b.    ethics.
    c.    practicality.
    d.    policy.
    e.    value.

141.    According to your textbook, when using emotional appeal in a persuasive speech, you should usually

    a.    use as many emotionally laden words as you can.
 *b.    let emotional appeal grow naturally out of the speech content.
    c.    avoid blurring the lines between reason and emotional appeal.
    d.    restrict emotional appeals to the conclusion of the speech.
    e.    substitute emotional appeals for evidence and reasoning.

142.    As your textbook explains, _____ are usually the most effective supporting materials if you want to increase the emotional appeal of a persuasive speech.

    a.    statistics
    b.    analogies
    c.    research studies
    d.    quotations
 *e.    examples

143. Appeals to audience emotions such as fear, compassion, guilt, or pride are the kinds of appeals that Aristotle referred to as

    a. ethos.
    b. kairos.
 *c. pathos.
    d. demos.
    e. logos.

144. Which of the following is recommended in your textbook as a method for generating emotional appeal in a persuasive speech?

    a. use clear visual aids
    b. develop vivid examples
    c. speak with sincerity and conviction
    d. all of the above
 *e. b and c only

145. Which of the following is recommended by your textbook as a method for generating emotional appeal in a persuasive speech?

 *a. develop vivid examples
    b. increase the rate of your delivery
    c. substitute emotional appeals for evidence
    d. use more denotative language
    e. employ visual aids

146. According to your textbook, the strongest source of emotional appeal in persuasive speaking is

    a. the speaker's integrity and prestige.
    b. true-to-life supporting material.
    c. dramatic, emotionally charged language.
 *d. the speaker's sincerity and conviction.
    e. vivid comparison and contrast.

147. What does your textbook advise regarding the ethical use of emotional appeals in a persuasive speech?

    a. Restrict emotional appeals to the conclusion of the speech.
    b. Use emotional appeals on topics that do not lend themselves to reasoning.
    c. Avoid emotional appeals when speaking on a question of policy.
    d. Limit emotional appeals to speeches using Monroe's motivated sequence.
 *e. Use emotional appeals to supplement your evidence and reasoning.

## Short Answer Questions

148.    What modern scholars of persuasion refer to as credibility, Aristotle referred
        to as ____ethos____.

149.    According to your textbook, the two most important factors affecting the credibility
        of a persuasive speaker are ____competence____ and ____character____.

150.    Above all, a speaker's credibility is affected by two factors: ____competence____
        and ____character____.

151.    ____Initial____ credibility is the credibility of the speaker before she or he begins to
        speak. ____Derived____ credibility is the credibility produced by everything the
        speaker says and does during the speech. ____Terminal____ credibility is the
        credibility of the speaker at the end of the speech.

152.    ____Logos____ was the name used by Aristotle for the logical appeal of a
        speaker.

153.    When used in a persuasive speech, supporting materials such as examples,
        statistics, and testimony are referred to as ____evidence____.

154.    Your textbook presents four tips for using evidence in a persuasive speech. They are:

        a.    ____Use specific evidence.____

        b.    ____Use novel evidence.____

        c.    ____Use evidence from credible sources.____

        d.    ____Make clear the point of your evidence.____

155.    ____Reasoning____ is a process of drawing a conclusion based on evidence.

156.    According to your textbook, the following statement is an example of
        ____causal____ reasoning:

        President John Kennedy was assassinated on November 22, 1963.
        The Beatles hit the top of the charts for the first time less than a
        month later. Can there be any doubt that the Beatles' rise to
        popularity was brought about partly by Kennedy's death, which
        left a void in the hearts of America's youth that was quickly filled
        by the dynamic singing group?

157. According to your textbook, the following statement is an example of the _____slippery slope_____ fallacy:

> You will be sorry if you allow employees to take time off to aid sick family members. First they will want time off to help spouses and children. Then they will skip work to help parents and grandparents. Before you know it, they will be gone for nephews and cousins, and you won't have anyone around to do their jobs.

158. According to your textbook, the following statement is an example of _____analogical_____ reasoning:

> In the state of Texas, high school students cannot compete in extracurricular activities unless they maintain passing grades. If such a plan can work in Texas, it can work in our state, too.

159. According to your textbook, the following statement is an example of the _____red herring_____ fallacy:

> I don't know why we are wasting time debating campaign finance reform when more and more international terrorists are focusing their attacks on the United States.

160. According to your textbook, the following statement is an example of reasoning from _____specific instances_____.

> In Montana an infant's underactive thyroid went undiagnosed for three months because of a medical laboratory testing error. In Louisiana a 26-year-old woman died because a medical laboratory inaccurately analyzed a mole that had been removed from her neck as noncancerous. And in California a teacher lost his life to a rare form of pneumonia when a medical laboratory confused his test results with those of another person. We can see, then, that inaccurate medical lab tests are a problem throughout the United States.

161. According to your textbook, the following statement is an example of the _____either-or_____ fallacy:

> Our company has only two options—either to cut employee benefits or to lay off large numbers of workers.

162. According to your textbook, the following statement is an example of the _____bandwagon_____ fallacy:

> I think the governor has excellent ideas for prison reform. After all, polls show that 70 percent of the state supports his position.

163. _____Pathos_____ was the name used by Aristotle for the emotional appeal of the speaker.

164. Your textbook discusses three methods of generating emotional appeal in a persuasive speech. The three methods are:

    a. _____Use emotional language._____

    b. _____Develop vivid examples._____

    c. _____Speak with sincerity and conviction._____

## Essay Questions

165. What role does the speaker's credibility play in the success or failure of a persuasive speech? Identify and explain two specific steps a speaker can take to boost her or his credibility when speaking to persuade.

166. What are the two factors of speaker credibility discussed in your text? How does each affect the success of a persuasive speech?

167. Identify and explain the three types of credibility discussed in your textbook.

168. Explain the following statement: "When you use evidence in a persuasive speech, you should think of yourself as engaged in a mental dialogue with the audience."

169. Explain each of the following guidelines for using evidence in a persuasive speech.

    a. Use specific evidence.
    b. Use novel evidence.
    c. Use evidence from credible sources.
    d. Make clear the point of your evidence.

170. What is reasoning from specific instances? Explain three guidelines you should follow when you reason from specific instances in a persuasive speech.

171. What is the difference between reasoning from principle and reasoning from specific instances? Give an example of your own choosing of both kinds of reasoning.

172. What is causal reasoning? Explain two errors in causal reasoning speakers should avoid in their speeches.

173. What is analogical reasoning? How do you judge the validity of an analogy?

174. Why is analogical reasoning frequently used when a speaker is dealing with the practicality issue in a persuasive speech on a question of policy?

175. Explain and give an example of each of the following fallacies:

    a. hasty generalization
    b. *post hoc, ergo propter hoc*
    c. invalid analogy
    d. red herring

176. Explain and give an example of each of the following fallacies:

    a. either-or
    b. *ad hominem*
    c. slippery slope
    d. bandwagon

177. In what circumstances is it ethical for public speakers to use emotional appeals when speaking to persuade? Are there any kinds of persuasive speeches in which emotional appeals are inappropriate? Explain your answer.

178. Explain the following statement: "When persuasion is the end, passion also must be engaged."

--------------------------------------------------

# Chapter 17 Speaking on Special Occasions

## True-False Questions

1. T <u>F</u>    The primary purpose of a special occasion speech is to convey information to an audience.

2. <u>T</u> F    A graduation address and a toast at a wedding are both examples of speeches for special occasions.

3. T <u>F</u>    The purpose of a speech of introduction is to introduce the person receiving an award or an honor.

4. <u>T</u> F    The purpose of a speech of introduction is to introduce the main speaker to the audience.

5. T <u>F</u>    One major purpose of a speech of introduction is to focus attention on the person making the introduction.

6. <u>T</u> F    One major purpose of a speech of introduction is to build enthusiasm for the upcoming speaker.

7. T <u>F</u>    As your textbook explains, speeches of introduction usually should be 8 to 10 minutes long.

8. T <u>F</u>    When giving a speech of introduction, you should be sure to praise the speaking skills of the main speaker.

9. <u>T</u> F    One major purpose of a speech of introduction is to establish a welcoming climate that will boost the credibility of the main speaker.

10. T <u>F</u>  If you are introducing the same speaker to an audience of college students for a morning presentation and to the city chamber of commerce for an afternoon presentation, you should use the same speech for each occasion.

11. T <u>F</u>  When giving a speech of introduction, you should state the name of the main speaker as soon as possible to avoid confusion among members of the audience.

12. <u>T</u> F  When giving a speech of introduction, you should usually save the name of the main speaker until the final moment, even when the audience already knows who he or she is.

13. <u>T</u> F  As defined in your textbook, a speech of presentation is a speech that presents someone a gift, an award, or some other form of public recognition.

14. <u>T</u> F  Speeches of presentation are given when someone is receiving publicly a gift or an award.

15. T <u>F</u>  The main purpose of a speech of presentation is to provide a biography of the speaker being presented to the audience.

16. T <u>F</u>  One of the main purposes of a speech of presentation is to build the credibility of the main speaker.

17. T <u>F</u>  The purpose of a speech of presentation is to present the main speaker to the audience.

18. <u>T</u> F  When giving a speech of presentation, you should usually explain why the recipient is being given his or her award.

19. T <u>F</u>  It is almost always in poor taste to mention the losers of an award in a speech of presentation.

20. <u>T</u> F  The basic purpose of an acceptance speech is to give thanks for a gift or an award.

21. <u>T</u> F  The three major traits of a good acceptance speech are brevity, humility, and graciousness.

22. T <u>F</u>  A speech accepting an award is an example of a commemorative speech.

23. <u>T</u> F  The purpose of a commemorative speech is to pay tribute to a person, a group of people, an institution, or an idea.

24. <u>T</u> F  The fundamental purpose of a commemorative speech is to inspire your listeners.

25. T <u>F</u>   The fundamental purpose of a commemorative speech is to convey information about the subject being commemorated.

26. T <u>F</u>   A speech urging Congress to construct a memorial in Washington, D.C., to recognize women's contributions to the American Revolution is an example of a commemorative speech.

27. T <u>F</u>   A speech presenting an award to a professor for outstanding teaching is an example of a commemorative speech.

28. <u>T</u> F   A speech praising the bravery of the firefighters killed in New York on September 11, 2001, is an example of a commemorative speech.

29. <u>T</u> F   A speech honoring the astronauts who gave their lives on the space shuttle *Columbia* is an example of a commemorative speech.

30. T <u>F</u>   A commemorative speech honoring a person is essentially a biography of that person.

31. T <u>F</u>   Effective commemorative speeches depend above all on the speaker's use of reasoning.

32. <u>T</u> F   Effective commemorative speeches depend above all on the speaker's use of language.

33. T <u>F</u>   A commemorative speech is the one kind of speech in which clichés and trite sentiments are appropriate.

34. T <u>F</u>   An after-dinner speech is basically the same as a commemorative speech.

35. <u>T</u> F   An after-dinner speech is best thought of as a kind of speech to entertain.

36. T <u>F</u>   An after-dinner speech is best thought of as a kind of speech to inform.

37. <u>T</u> F   After-dinner speeches as a formal type of speech developed in England during the early 1800s.

38. <u>T</u> F   As your textbook explains, after-dinner speeches can be given at breakfast or lunch gatherings as well as after dinner.

39. <u>T</u> F   Even though humor is an important element of an after-dinner speech, the speaker should still strive to provide special insight into the topic.

40. <u>T</u> F   The main difference between an after-dinner speech and a speech to inform or to persuade is less the choice of topic than how the topic is developed.

41. T <u>F</u>   The supporting materials for an after-dinner speech should be chosen primarily for their persuasive force.

42.   T  F      The supporting materials for an after-dinner speech should be chosen primarily for their entertainment value.

43.   T  F      Like other kinds of speeches, after-dinner speeches require careful organization.

44.   T  F      "To inform my audience about the different methods used by meteorologists to predict the weather" is an appropriate specific purpose statement for an after-dinner speech.

45.   T  F      "To persuade my audience that William Shakespeare did not write the plays attributed to him" is an example of a specific purpose statement for an after-dinner speech.

46.   T  F      "Television commercials I have known and hated" is an appropriate topic for an after-dinner speech.

47.   T  F      "To entertain my audience by telling them about the typical mishaps that happen during family vacations" is an appropriate specific purpose statement for an after-dinner speech.

## Multiple Choice Questions *(Students are to indicate the best answer for each question by circling the correct letter.)*

48.   Which of the following is an example of a speech for a special occasion?

   *a.   a speech presenting an award to a retiring newspaper editor
    b.   a presentation on marketing strategy at a sales meeting
    c.   a talk to new college students about how to register for classes
    d.   a campaign speech by a candidate for the U.S. Senate
    e.   a lecture by a visiting professor in a college class

49.   One main purpose of a speech of introduction is to

    a.   explain why the person being introduced is receiving her or his award.
    b.   inspire the audience with a sense of the significance of the occasion.
   *c.   create a welcoming climate to build enthusiasm for the main speaker.
    d.   explain why listeners should pay tribute to a person, idea, or institution.
    e.   enhance the credibility of the speaker who is making the introduction.

50.   Which of the following is recommended by your textbook as a guideline for a speech of introduction?

    a.   Prepare your speech so it will last between 15 and 20 minutes.
    b.   Use a quotation at the beginning to secure the attention of the audience.
   *c.   Make sure your remarks about the main speaker are completely accurate.
    d.   Generate humor with an embarrassing story about the main speaker.
    e.   Assume that the audience knows nothing about the main speaker.

51.     According to your textbook, the best way to create a sense of anticipation and drama in a speech of introduction is to

   *a.    save the name of the main speaker for last.
    b.    tell the audience that the main speaker is an excellent orator.
    c.    use an overhead projector to highlight the main speaker's accomplishments.
    d.    deliver the speech word for word from a written manuscript.
    e.    give a detailed biography of the main speaker.

52.     A speaker introducing the president of a university to an audience of prospective students and their families will *best* accomplish this goal by

    a.    praising the president as the finest public speaker on campus.
    b.    presenting a detailed biography of the president's entire life.
    c.    discussing the history of the university and its tradition of excellent athletic teams.
   *d.    summarizing the president's major accomplishments at the university.
    e.    defending the changes in graduation requirements instituted by the president.

53.     All of the following are presented in your textbook as guidelines for a speech of introduction *except*

    a.    be brief.
    b.    adapt your remarks to the occasion.
   *c.    bring the speech to life by using a hypothetical example.
    d.    try to create a sense of anticipation and drama.
    e.    make sure your remarks are completely accurate.

54.     One method recommended in your textbook for creating a sense of drama and anticipation in a speech of introduction is to

    a.    present a brief biography of the main speaker.
   *b.    save the name of the main speaker until the final moment.
    c.    use visual aids that focus attention on the main speaker.
    d.    praise the speaking skills of the main speaker.
    e.    make sure the introduction is completely accurate.

55.     Before presenting the college's Athlete of the Year award, the athletic director made a point of praising the two athletes who were runners up in this year's competition. According to your textbook, was this choice appropriate for a speech of presentation?

    a.    No. It is almost always in poor taste to mention the losers.
    b.    Yes. Identifying the losers makes the winner look even better.
    c.    No. Naming anyone other than the winner usually irritates the audience.
   *d.    Yes. It is often appropriate to praise the losers of a competition.
    e.    No. Mentioning the losers diminishes the value of an award.

56. As your textbook explains, when you give a speech of introduction you should be sure to adapt your remarks to the

    a.   occasion.
    b.   audience.
    c.   main speaker.
 *d.   all of the above.
    e.   a and b only.

57. What does it mean to say that a speech of introduction should be "adapted to the main speaker"?

    a.   The speech should preview what the main speaker's points will be.
    b.   The speech should be given in the same style as the person being introduced.
 *c.   The speech should avoid creating discomfort for the main speaker.
    d.   all of the above
    e.   a and c only

58. According to your textbook, the main purpose of a speech of presentation is to present

    a.   the main speaker to the audience.
    b.   thanks for a gift or an award.
    c.   the reasons why a person deserves commendation.
    d.   information about the importance of the occasion.
 *e.   a gift or an award to the recipient.

59. When giving a speech of presentation, you should usually

 *a.   tell why the recipient is receiving her or his award.
    b.   present the main speaker briefly and accurately.
    c.   avoid mentioning the losers of the award competition.
    d.   adapt your presentation to the main speaker.
    e.   give a brief biography of the main speaker.

60. Which of the following is an example of a speech of presentation?

    a.   a speech presenting a new reporter to the newspaper staff
    b.   a speech presenting reasons why a new high school needs to be built
    c.   a speech presenting a famous professor who will lecture on economics
 *d.   a speech presenting a certificate of recognition to an outstanding worker
    e.   a speech presenting the annual earnings report to stockholders

61. Which of the following is an example of a speech of presentation?

    a.   a speech presenting a main speaker to the audience
    b.   a speech presenting a eulogy at a funeral
    c.   a speech presenting a toast to the bride and groom
    d.   a speech presenting a new manager to her employees
 *e.   a speech presenting an award to an outstanding student

62.    At a comedy awards show, Adam Sandler gave a splendid speech explaining why David Letterman was receiving a special award for his achievements in television comedy. According to your textbook, what kind of special occasion speech did Sandler deliver?

   a.    an after-dinner speech
   b.    a speech of introduction
*c.    a speech of presentation
   d.    a memorial speech
   e.    a celebratory speech

63.    When Carlos Bustamante was presented the Alumni of the Year award at his alma mater's annual award dinner, he gave a speech thanking the school for recognizing his work. What kind of speech did Carlos give?

*a.    an acceptance speech
   b.    a speech of introduction
   c.    a commemorative speech
   d.    a speech of presentation
   e.    an informative speech

64.    According to your textbook, a speech in which an individual gives thanks for a gift or award is termed a(n)

   a.    speech of presentation.
   b.    commemorative speech.
   c.    after-dinner speech.
*d.    acceptance speech.
   e.    speech of introduction.

65.    According to your textbook, in a speech of acceptance a speaker should usually

   a.    thank the people who are bestowing the award.
   b.    praise himself or herself for having the talent to win the award.
   c.    express appreciation for the people who helped him or her gain the award.
   d.    all of the above.
*e.    a and c only.

66.    According to your textbook, the major traits of a good acceptance speech are brevity, humility, and

   a.    humor.
   b.    clarity.
   c.    confidence.
*d.    graciousness.
   e.    fluency.

67.    Which of the following is an example of a commemorative speech?

    a.    a speech to a local history club recounting the major events in the life of the famous architect Frank Lloyd Wright

    b.    a speech urging the city council to use architectural plans by Frank Lloyd Wright as the basis for a new convention center

    c.    a speech explaining the major elements of Frank Lloyd Wright's architectural genius to a class of art history students

  \*d.    a speech praising the architectural accomplishments of Frank Lloyd Wright at the opening of a museum devoted to his work

    e.    a speech telling the audience where they can visit buildings designed by Frank Lloyd Wright

68.    Which of the following is an example of a commemorative speech?

    a.    A speech seeking to convince the school board to keep the schools open for extracurricular activities on Martin Luther King Day.

    b.    A speech to the student government aimed at getting funding for special campus activities on Martin Luther King Day.

    c.    A lecture to a community audience explaining the oratorical techniques used in Martin Luther King's "I Have a Dream."

    d.    A speech analyzing the philosophy of nonviolent protest employed by Martin Luther King during the civil rights movement.

  \*e.    A speech honoring Martin Luther King's life and legacy at the opening event for the campus-wide Martin Luther King Day observances.

69.    According to your textbook, a speech that pays tribute to a person, a group, an institution, or an idea is called a

    a.    dedication speech.

  \*b.    commemorative speech.

    c.    remembrance speech.

    d.    celebratory speech.

    e.    memorial speech.

70.    According to your textbook, when your fundamental purpose in a speech is to inspire the audience, you are most likely going to be giving a(n) _____ speech.

    a.    informative

    b.    persuasive

    c.    after-dinner

  \*d.    commemorative

    e.    acceptance

71.    According to your textbook, the fundamental purpose of a commemorative speech is to

    a.    inform.
    b.    exhort.
    c.    entertain.
    d.    convert.
  *e.    inspire.

72.    As your textbook explains, a successful commemorative speech usually depends on the speaker's ability to

    a.    motivate a passive audience to take action.
  *b.    put into language the thoughts and emotions appropriate to the occasion.
    c.    explain why the recipient is receiving an award.
    d.    all of the above.
    e.    a and b only.

73.    Which of the following is an example of a commemorative speech?

    a.    the President's State of the Union message
    b.    a soccer coach's pre-game pep talk
    c.    a speaker's acceptance of an award
    d.    a teacher's lecture on banking ethics
  *e.    a daughter's eulogy in honor of her father

74.    If you attended the Academy Awards and heard the following speeches, which one would be an example of a commemorative speech?

    a.    A speech accepting the best actor award.
    b.    A speech explaining the history of the Oscar statue.
  *c.    A speech honoring Audrey Hepburn for her lifetime achievements.
    d.    A speech explaining the balloting system and new security measures.
    e.    A speech calling for an end to land mines throughout the world.

75.    As explained in your textbook, when delivering a commemorative speech, you should take special care to

    a.    provide a detailed biography of the person being commemorated.
    b.    heighten appreciation for the person being commemorated.
    c.    use creative language to express feelings and sentiments.
    d.    all of the above.
  *e.    b and c only.

76.    As your textbook explains, perhaps no speech depends more on the creative and subtle use of language than does the

  *a.    commemorative speech.
    b.    speech of presentation.
    c.    persuasive speech.
    d.    speech of introduction.
    e.    informative speech.

77.   As your textbook explains, we continue to find commemorative speeches like the Gettysburg Address meaningful and inspiring primarily because

   a.   they were given by important historical figures.
*b.   of their eloquent use of language.
   c.   they were delivered from memory.
   d.   of the occasions on which they were delivered.
   e.   they motivated people to take heroic action.

78.   After-dinner speeches are best thought of as a kind of speech to

*a.   entertain.
   b.   inform.
   c.   persuade.
   d.   commemorate.
   e.   eulogize.

79.   As a formal type of speech, after-dinner speeches first developed in

   a.   America during the 1920s.
*b.   England during the early 1800s.
   c.   California during World War II.
   d.   Germany during the 1850s.
   e.   Europe during the French Revolution.

80.   Which of the following are characteristic of after-dinner speeches?

   a.   After-dinner speeches can be given any time of day or evening.
   b.   After-dinner speeches are best thought of as speeches to entertain.
   c.   After-dinner speeches are a branch of informative speaking.
   d.   all of the above
*e.   a and b only

81.   Which of the following statements is true regarding after-dinner speaking?

   a.   An after-dinner speech should not be given at a luncheon.
   b.   An after-dinner speech is essentially the same as an informative speech.
*c.   An after-dinner speech can be given at any time of day or evening.
   d.   An after-dinner speech should tell why the recipient is getting an award.
   e.   An after-dinner speech should not strive to make any serious points.

82.   As your textbook explains, the supporting materials in an after-dinner speech should be chosen primarily for their

   a.   emotional appeal.
*b.   entertainment value.
   c.   informative clarity.
   d.   persuasive power.
   e.   historical accuracy.

83.    Although it is always based on materials chosen for their entertainment value, the
_____ speech should strive to make a thoughtful point about its theme.

  \*a.    after-dinner
    b.    presentation
    c.    commemorative
    d.    acceptance
    e.    introductory

84.    Which of the following is an appropriate specific purpose statement for an after-dinner speech?

    a.    To entertain my audience by telling them the lengths parents go to in order to get kids to eat healthy foods.
    b.    To entertain my audience by examining the lighter side of terrorism and insurgency in the Middle East.
    c.    To entertain my audience by discussing the absurd questions people ask when they call for technical support.
    d.    all of the above
  \*e.    a and c only

85.    Which of the following would be *most* appropriate as a specific purpose statement for an after-dinner speech?

    a.    To entertain my audience by explaining how to get the most for their money when buying a home entertainment system.
    b.    To entertain my audience by tracing the development of recent treatments for the AIDS virus.
    c.    To entertain my audience by telling them why they should support spending cuts in Medicare.
  \*d.    To entertain my audience by looking at unusual ways people cope with daily life in our high-tech society.
    e.    To entertain my audience by describing three major theories about the impact of global climate on human history.

86.    Which of the following would be *most* appropriate as a specific purpose statement for an after-dinner speech?

    a.    To entertain my audience by urging them to form a neighborhood association to protect local wetlands.
  \*b.    To entertain my audience by telling them about the thrill and agony of learning how to play golf.
    c.    To entertain my audience by telling them the best kind of clothing to wear to protect themselves from skin cancer.
    d.    To entertain my audience by exploring the humor in both sides of the debate over abortion rights.
    e.    To entertain my audience by explaining to them the state laws governing child custody agreements.

87.    Which of the following would be *most* appropriate as a specific purpose statement for an after-dinner speech?

a.    To entertain my audience by telling them about the two major theories of extraterrestrial intelligence.
b.    To entertain my audience by showing them the humorous side of racial discrimination.
c.    To entertain my audience by showing them why they should support the Special Olympics.
d.    To entertain my audience by telling them how to buy the best used car for the best price.
*e.    To entertain my audience by showing them the trials and tribulations of being a middle-aged college student.

## Short Answer Questions

88.    A speech presenting the main speaker to the audience is called a speech of _____introduction_____.

89.    A speech announcing the winner of an award and giving the award to the recipient is called a speech of _____presentation_____.

90.    A speech that gives thanks for a gift or an award is called a(n) _____acceptance_____ speech.

91.    A speech paying tribute to a person, idea, or institution is called a(n) _____commemorative_____ speech.

92.    A Memorial Day speech honoring U.S. soldiers who have died in defense of their country is an example of a(n) _____commemorative_____ speech.

93.    "To entertain my audience by showing them the unexpected pitfalls of working as a waitress" is a specific purpose statement for a(n) _____after-dinner_____ speech.

## Essay Questions

94.    Define and give an example of each of the following:

a.    speech of introduction
b.    speech of presentation
c.    acceptance speech
d.    commemorative speech
e.    after-dinner speech

95.    Your textbook provides six guidelines for effective speeches of introduction. In a well-developed essay, identify and explain four of these guidelines.

96.    What does it mean to say that a speech of introduction should be adapted to the main speaker?

97.    What is the difference between a speech of presentation and an acceptance speech?

98.    How is a commemorative speech similar to and different from an informative speech?

99.    Explain the following statement: "In some ways a commemorative speech is like an Impressionist painting—a picture with warm colors and texture capturing a mood or a moment."

100.   Explain the similarities and differences between an after-dinner speech and an informative speech in each of the following areas:

   a.   choice of speech topic
   b.   selection of supporting materials
   c.   method of organization

101.   Explain the following statement: "Humor can contribute to a successful after-dinner speech, but it is not essential."

---

# Chapter 18 Speaking in Small Groups

## True-False Questions

1. <u>T</u> F    One of the defining traits of a small group is that its members assemble for a specific purpose.

2. <u>T</u> F    Most experts set the maximum number of members for a small group at seven or eight.

3. <u>T</u> F    There is a great deal of research to show that if members of a small group work well together, they can almost always resolve a problem better than a single person can.

4. <u>T</u> F    To function effectively, a small group needs capable leadership.

5. T <u>F</u>    To function effectively, a small group needs a specific leader.

6. T <u>F</u>    The newest or least experienced member of a small group is usually referred to as the implied leader.

7. <u>T</u> F    A person who by ability, force of personality, or simply by talking the most, takes on a leadership role in a small group is called an emergent leader.

8. <u>T</u> F    A small group that meets for only one session should almost always have a designated leader.

9. <u>T</u> F    Each member of a small group should be prepared to assume a leadership role when necessary.

10. <u>T</u> F    The procedural needs of a small group include such matters as deciding when the group will meet, taking notes during the meeting, and summarizing the group's progress at the end of the meeting.

11. T <u>F</u>    The procedural needs of a small group include such matters as whether members get along with each other and feel good about their roles in the group.

12. T <u>F</u>    The procedural needs of a small group revolve around interpersonal relations among the group's members.

13. T <u>F</u>    Helping the group reach consensus on its final decision is an example of a procedural need in a small group.

14. <u>T</u> F    Deciding when and where the group will meet is an example of a procedural need in a small group.

15. <u>T</u> F    Setting the agenda for each meeting is an example of a procedural need in a small group.

16. T <u>F</u>    According to your textbook, task needs involve the communicative actions necessary to maintain interpersonal relations in a small group.

17. <u>T</u> F    The task needs of a small group include such matters as distributing the workload among group members, keeping the group on track, and helping the group reach consensus.

18. T <u>F</u>    The task needs of a small group include such matters as encouraging full participation in the group, settling interpersonal conflicts, and helping members feel good about their roles in the group.

19. T <u>F</u>    Deciding when and where the group will meet is an example of a task need in a small group.

20. T <u>F</u>    Helping group members get along with each other is an example of a task need in a small group.

21. <u>T</u> F    Collecting information is an example of a task need in a small group.

22. <u>T</u> F    Helping the group reach consensus on its final decision is an example of a task need in a small group.

23. <u>T</u> F    The maintenance needs of a small group include such matters as whether members get along with each other and feel good about their roles in the group.

24. T <u>F</u>    The maintenance needs of a small group include such matters as researching the discussion topic, keeping the group on track, and helping the group reach consensus.

25.  T  F̲   Collecting information about the discussion topic is an example of a maintenance need in a small group.

26.  T̲  F   Helping group members get along with each other is an example of a maintenance need in a small group.

27.  T  F̲   As your textbook explains, hidden agendas are necessary for effective group discussion.

28.  T̲  F   As in other forms of communication, effective listening is vital to communication in small-group discussion.

29.  T  F̲   As your textbook explains, disagreements among members of a small group should be kept on the interpersonal level so they won't interfere with the group's ability to complete its task.

30.  T̲  F   Disagreements among group members should be kept at the task level rather than the interpersonal level.

31.  T  F̲   As your textbook makes clear, personal conflicts are essential if a small group is to function successfully.

32.  T̲  F   Defining the problem is the first step in the reflective-thinking method for small group discussion.

33.  T  F̲   Generating potential solutions is the first step in the reflective-thinking method for small group discussion.

34.  T̲  F   The question for a problem-solving group discussion should usually be phrased as a question of policy.

35.  T  F̲   Questions for problem-solving discussions should usually be phrased so as to allow for yes-or-no answers.

36.  T̲  F   "What steps should be taken to reduce gun violence in the U.S.?" is an example of a well-worded question for a problem-solving group discussion.

37.  T  F̲   "Should our city build a new recreation center?" is an example of a well-worded question for a problem-solving group discussion.

38.  T̲  F   A common failing of problem-solving groups is that they start to discuss solutions before agreeing on criteria for the solutions.

39.  T̲  F   Brainstorming is especially useful when a problem-solving group is trying to generate potential solutions.

40.  T̲  F   According to your textbook, the best approach to brainstorming in a small group is for each member to write down her or his ideas before sharing them with the group.

41. <u>T</u>  F    Brainstorming for potential solutions requires that a small group wait until all potential solutions have been presented to begin evaluating them.

42. T  <u>F</u>    The ideal of small-group discussion is to reach a majority decision on major issues facing the group.

43. <u>T</u>  F    The ideal of small-group discussion is to reach a consensus decision on major issues facing the group.

44. T  <u>F</u>    The best way to reach a consensus decision in a problem-solving group is to take a vote on the issue in dispute.

45. T  <u>F</u>    The work of a problem-solving group ends with the last stage of the reflective-thinking process.

46. <u>T</u>  F    An oral report from a problem-solving small group is usually delivered by one person.

47. <u>T</u>  F    In a symposium, each participant in turn delivers a prepared speech on a different aspect of a common topic.

48. T  <u>F</u>    A symposium is essentially a conversation in front of an audience.

49. <u>T</u>  F    A panel discussion is essentially a conversation in front of an audience.

50. T  <u>F</u>    Because a panel discussion involves speaking impromptu, the best preparation for such a discussion is no preparation at all.

51. T  <u>F</u>    A panel discussion is an especially effective way to present the findings of a problem-solving small group.

## Multiple Choice Questions  *(Students are to indicate the __best__ answer for each question by circling the correct letter.)*

52.    According to your textbook, a dyad is

   *a.    a group of two people.
   b.    a group formed to solve a particular problem.
   c.    a group organized to present a symposium.
   d.    a group formed to plan a social event.
   e.    a group without a leader.

53.    As explained in your textbook, one of the defining traits of a small group is that

   a.    the group has a predetermined leader.
   *b.    members of the group assemble for a specific purpose.
   c.    the group succeeds in brainstorming for potential solutions.
   d.    everyone in the group has a similar frame of reference.
   e.    the group follows the reflective-thinking method.

54.     As explained in your textbook, which of the following is a defining trait of a small group?

    a.   the group assembles for a specific purpose
    b.   the group contains a minimum of three members
    c.   the group has a designated leader
    d.   all of the above
  *e.   a and b only

55.     A group member to whom other members defer because of his or her rank or expertise is called a(n)

  *a.   implied leader.
    b.   specific leader.
    c.   emergent leader.
    d.   designated leader.
    e.   appointed leader.

56.     The person who assumes a leadership role in a small group because of her or his ability, personality, or talkativeness is termed a(n)

    a.   specific leader.
    b.   implied leader.
  *c.   emergent leader.
    d.   insistent leader.
    e.   designated leader.

57.     According to your textbook, a small group that meets for only one session should almost always have a(n) _____ leader.

    a.   implied
  *b.   designated
    c.   elected
    d.   emergent
    e.   dynamic

58.     Miriam is the only member of her small group with professional experience on their subject, so her group naturally looks to her to guide the project. What kind of leader is Miriam?

  *a.   implied leader
    b.   maintenance leader
    c.   emergent leader
    d.   designated leader
    e.   task leader

59.    As the vice president for employee relations, Manuel is the only member of his company's executive team attending informal small group meetings where employees are considering proposals to revise the company's personal leave policies. Beginning at its very first meeting the group looks to Manuel for leadership. What kind of leader is Manuel?

    a.    task leader
    b.    emergent leader
    c.    authoritative leader
    d.    maintenance leader
 *e.    implied leader

60.    Rochelle was appointed by her boss to chair a small committee to draft a policy statement on personal use of the office computers. She called a meeting of the group for 9 A.M. Wednesday morning. According to your textbook, what kind of leader is Rochelle?

    a.    emergent leader
 *b.    designated leader
    c.    implied leader
    d.    dominant leader
    e.    task leader

61.    As chair of the student advisory committee, Brad began the meeting by distributing the agenda and minutes from the last meeting. According to your textbook, what kind of leadership need did Brad's action fulfill?

 *a.    a procedural need
    b.    an informational need
    c.    a maintenance need
    d.    an educational need
    e.    a task need

62.    Randall is talkative and offers his opinions freely during small group meetings. Because he participates more than the other members, he has assumed a leadership role within the group. What kind of leader is Randall?

    a.    task leader
    b.    implied leader
 *c.    emergent leader
    d.    designated leader
    e.    accidental leader

63.    According to your textbook, what are the three kinds of leadership needs faced by all problem-solving small groups?

    a.    agenda needs, task needs, and consensus needs
    b.    decision needs, maintenance needs, and personal needs
    c.    procedural needs, agenda needs, and participation needs
    d.    research needs, schedule needs, and judgment needs
 *e.    task needs, procedural needs, and maintenance needs

64.   As explained in your textbook, the leadership needs faced by all problem-solving small groups include

    a.   task needs.
    b.   maintenance needs.
    c.   procedural needs.
  *d.   all of the above.
    e.   a and c only.

65.   As your textbook explains, all problem-solving small groups face three kinds of leadership needs: procedural needs, task needs, and

    a.   agenda needs.
    b.   consensus needs.
  *c.   maintenance needs.
    d.   judgment needs.
    e.   decision needs.

66.   As your textbook explains, by helping group members deal with interpersonal conflict a leader helps the group fulfill _____ needs.

    a.   task
    b.   personal
  *c.   maintenance
    d.   procedural
    e.   comfort

67.   According to your textbook, which of the following is a task need of a problem-solving small group?

    a.   helping group members get along with each other
  *b.   formulating criteria for judging the best solution
    c.   helping members feel good about their roles in the group
    d.   deciding when and where the group will meet
    e.   taking notes during meetings of the group

68.   Which of the following is a procedural need of a problem-solving small group?

    a.   keeping the group from going off on a tangent
    b.   conducting research to help the group analyze the problem
    c.   maintaining good interpersonal relations among the group
  *d.   reserving a room for the group's next meeting
    e.   helping the group reach consensus on its final decision

69.   The maintenance needs of a problem-solving small group center on

  *a.   interpersonal relations in the group.
    b.   the research requirements of the group.
    c.   determining the agenda of the group.
    d.   presenting the recommendations of the group.
    e.   distributing the work load among the group.

70.   Before meeting with her reading group, Holly collected information about the history of a book that had been recommended to the group. During the group's next meeting, Holly shared her findings as the group discussed whether to add the book to its reading list. What kind of leadership need did Holly's actions fulfill?

    a.   personal
    b.   designated
    c.   maintenance
    d.   procedural
 *e.   task

71.   Stacey is part of a problem-solving small group in her speech class. As the first meeting of the group came to an end, Stacey volunteered her apartment as a place for the group to hold its next meeting. According to your textbook, what kind of leadership need did Stacey's action fulfill?

    a.   a task need
 *b.   a procedural need
    c.   an agenda need
    d.   a consensus need
    e.   a maintenance need

72.   Myenne is part of a problem-solving small group in her speech class. When the group was deciding how best to go about its work, Myenne suggested that group members work in pairs, with each pair tackling one of the main issues facing the group. According to your textbook, what kind of leadership need did Myenne's action fulfill?

    a.   a decision need
    b.   a maintenance need
    c.   a procedural need
 *d.   a task need
    e.   a consensus need

73.   At a meeting of the student government council, Allen and Isabella got into a heated argument about a minor point that was irrelevant to the main subject facing the council. At that point, Jalen said, "I'm certain Allen and Isabella can pursue their discussion at another time, but right now we have to keep focused on our main subject." According to your textbook, what kind of leadership need did Jalen's action fulfill?

 *a.   task
    b.   personal
    c.   procedural
    d.   maintenance
    e.   agenda

74. At a meeting of her breast-cancer survivors group, Susan Huerta presented information on the most recent diet and exercise recommendations for women. According to your textbook, what kind of leadership need did Susan's actions fulfill?

    a. a procedural need
    b. an informational need
    c. a maintenance need
    d. an educational need
 *e. a task need

75. Which of the following is a maintenance need of a problem-solving small group?

 *a. easing interpersonal tensions among group members
    b. using the Internet to research the issue under consideration
    c. ordering lunch for the group during its scheduled break
    d. outlining the major reason for adopting the group's policy
    e. organizing a symposium to present the group's decision

76. Which of the following is a maintenance need of a problem-solving small group?

    a. setting the agenda of each meeting
    b. keeping the discussion on track
    c. helping the group reach consensus on a final decision
    d. presenting an oral report for the group
 *e. reducing interpersonal tension in the group

77. Jovita is part of a problem-solving group in her speech class. By the third meeting of the group, Jovita noticed Dylan seemed unhappy with his role in the group. At the next meeting Jovita made sure to respond thoughtfully to each of Dylan's contributions. By the end of the meeting, it was clear that Dylan felt better about the way the group was working. According to your textbook, what kind of leadership need did Jovita's action fulfill?

    a. interpersonal need
    b. engagement need
 *c. maintenance need
    d. procedural need
    e. task need

78. According to your textbook, each of the following is a procedural need of a small group *except*

 *a. analyzing the issue facing the group.
    b. deciding where the group will meet next.
    c. preparing and distributing handouts for the group's meeting.
    d. summarizing the group's progress at the end of the meeting.
    e. setting the agenda for the group's meeting.

79.   According to your textbook, which of the following is a responsibility of *every* member in a problem-solving small group?

    a.   seek to become the group's designated leader
    b.   reserve a room for the group's meetings
    c.   keep disagreement at the interpersonal level
 *d.   work to keep the group's discussion on track
    e.   serve as the moderator in a panel discussion

80.   According to your textbook, which of the following is a responsibility of *every* member in a problem-solving small group?

 *a.   commit yourself to achieving the goals of the group
    b.   establish hidden agendas to help the group fulfill its objectives
    c.   encourage outgoing individuals to participate in group meetings
    d.   make sure the group takes a formal vote on its major decisions
    e.   keep disagreement in the group at the interpersonal level

81.   According to your textbook, each of the following is a responsibility of every member in a small group *except*

    a.   fulfilling individual assignments.
    b.   encouraging full participation.
    c.   avoiding interpersonal conflicts.
    d.   keeping the discussion on track.
 *e.   setting the agenda for group meetings.

82.   As explained in your textbook, each of the following is a responsibility of every member in a small group *except*

 *a.   calling for a formal vote on major decisions.
    b.   keeping the discussion on track.
    c.   encouraging full participation by group members.
    d.   being committed to the goals of the group.
    e.   fulfilling individual assignments.

83.   Which of the following is mentioned in your textbook as a responsibility of *every* member in a small group?

    a.   reach solutions swiftly
    b.   develop hidden agendas
    c.   call for a vote on major issues
    d.   avoid disagreement at all costs
 *e.   encourage full participation

84.   According to your textbook, when formulating a question for discussion, a problem-solving small group should phrase the question

    a.   to allow for a wide variety of answers.
    b.   to balance the work load among group members.
    c.   as a question of policy.
    d.   all of the above.
 *e.   a and c only.

85.   As explained in your textbook, when formulating a question for discussion, a problem-solving small group should phrase the question

   *a.   as a question of policy.
    b.   so as to allow for a yes-or-no answer.
    c.   in a way that will encourage brainstorming.
    d.   all of the above.
    e.   b and c only.

86.   According to your textbook, when formulating a question for discussion, a problem-solving small group should phrase the question

    a.   so the whole group can answer it.
    b.   so the group can reach a majority decision.
   *c.   so as to allow a wide variety of answers.
    d.   so as to avoid interpersonal conflict in the group.
    e.   all of the above.

87.   In a sense, defining the problem for a problem-solving small group discussion is like choosing the _____ for a speech.

   *a.   specific purpose
    b.   rhetorical question
    c.   central idea
    d.   general purpose
    e.   main points

88.   Which of the following is the *first* step in the reflective-thinking method for small group discussion?

   *a.   define the problem
    b.   set the agenda
    c.   establish criteria for solutions
    d.   analyze the problem
    e.   elect a leader

89.   Once a problem-solving small group has defined the problem, what is the *next* step they should follow in the reflective-thinking method for small group discussion?

    a.   establish criteria for solutions
    b.   select the best solution
    c.   set an agenda for solving the problem
    d.   reach a consensus decision
   *e.   analyze the problem

90.    Once a problem-solving small group has defined the problem and analyzed the problem, what is the *next* step they should follow in the reflective-thinking method for small-group discussion?

    a.    generate potential solutions
    b.    assign members to research the problem
    c.    consider the practicality of various solutions
  *d.    establish criteria for solving the problem
    e.    retrace the decision-making process

91.    Once a problem-solving small group has defined the problem and analyzed the problem, what is the *next* step they should follow in the reflective-thinking method for small group discussion?

    a.    set an agenda for solving the problem
  *b.    establish criteria for solutions to the problem
    c.    reach a consensus on the causes of the problem
    d.    select the best solution to the problem
    e.    reassess the phrasing of the problem

92.    As your textbook explains, a decision that is acceptable to all members of a small group is called a _____ decision.

    a.    prudent
  *b.    consensus
    c.    deliberative
    d.    compromise
    e.    judicious

93.    Amy's group for her speech class was following the reflective-thinking method for problem-solving small groups. When it came time to choose the best solution, the group decided early on to take a vote, with the majority winning out, rather than drag out the discussion until the group could reach a decision that pleased everyone. According to your textbook, was this the best way for Amy's group to proceed?

    a.    Yes. Voting is the recommended procedure for reaching a decision in small groups.
  *b.    No. A small group should try every method to reach consensus before resorting to a vote.
    c.    Yes. Continuing to discuss solutions usually leads to interpersonal conflicts in the group.
    d.    No. Rather than voting, a group should brainstorm about rephrasing the question for discussion.
    e.    Yes. Voting is the most effective way to reach a decision and maintain group harmony.

94.     Having reached consensus on a policy for increasing child safety in the homes of gun owners, Ben's small group decided to have each member deliver a prepared speech on a different aspect of the group's work. According to your textbook, what method of presenting its recommendations did Ben's group use?

        a.   an open forum
        b.   a convocation
        c.   a panel discussion
        d.   an oral report
      *e.   a symposium

95.     The ideal in small group discussion is to reach a _____ decision.

        a.   compromise
        b.   consistent
        c.   communicable
      *d.   consensus
        e.   communal

96.     In a symposium, the participants

        a.   speak briefly, informally, and impromptu.
        b.   talk to each other loudly enough for the audience to hear.
      *c.   deliver prepared speeches on different aspects of the topic.
        d.   frequently interrupt each other to make a point.
        e.   begin by responding to questions from the audience.

97.     According to your textbook, a public presentation in which several people present prepared speeches on different aspects of the same topic is called a(n)

        a.   panel discussion.
        b.   oral report.
        c.   town hall meeting.
        d.   open forum.
      *e.   symposium.

98.     According to your textbook, a(n) _____ is a public presentation in which several people present prepared speeches on different aspects of the same topic.

        a.   oral report
        b.   roundtable
        c.   panel discussion
      *d.   symposium
        e.   open forum

99.    A(n) _____ is essentially a conversation in front of an audience.

    *a.    panel discussion
    b.    oral report
    c.    convocation
    d.    symposium
    e.    open forum

100.    If Max is designated to present the findings and recommendations of his small group's deliberations to a large group of stockholders, he will most likely need to

    *a.    prepare an oral report.
    b.    create a panel discussion.
    c.    give an impromptu presentation.
    d.    plan a town hall meeting.
    e.    moderate a symposium.

101.    A(n) _____ is composed of participants who talk to each other loudly enough for the audience to hear.

    a.    convocation
    b.    oral report
    c.    symposium
    *d.    panel discussion
    e.    open forum

## Short Answer Questions

102.    When one member of a small group has a personal goal that conflicts with the goals of the group as a whole, he or she is said to have a(n) ____hidden____ agenda.

103.    A(n) ____designated____ leader of a small group is appointed or elected when the group is formed.

104.    A group member to whom other members defer because of her or his rank or expertise is known as a(n) ____implied____ leader.

105.    A(n) ____emergent____ leader is someone who takes on a leadership role through her or his ability, force of personality, or simply by talking the most during group meetings.

106.    The ____procedural____ needs of a problem-solving small group include such "housekeeping" requirements as deciding when and where the group is to meet, reserving a room, and taking notes during the meeting.

107. The ____task____ needs of a problem-solving small group include actions necessary to help the group complete its work. Such actions include analyzing the issues facing the group, keeping the group on track, and formulating criteria for the most effective solution.

108. The ____maintenance____ needs of a problem-solving small group include such matters as how well members get along with each other and whether members feel good about their roles in the group.

109. The first step in the reflective-thinking method for discussion in problem-solving groups is ____define the problem____.

110. A(n) ____symposium____ consists of a moderator and several speakers, each of whom presents a prepared speech on a different aspect of the same topic. A(n) ____panel discussion____ also consists of a moderator and several speakers, but rather than presenting formal prepared speeches, the speakers essentially carry on a conversation in front of the audience.

111. The five steps in the reflective-thinking method for discussion in problem-solving small groups are:

   a. ____define the problem____

   b. ____analyze the problem____

   c. ____establish criteria for solutions____

   d. ____generate potential solutions____

   e. ____select the best solution____

## Essay Questions

112. Explain each of the following kinds of leaders for small group discussion:

   a. implied leader
   b. emergent leader
   c. designated leader

113. Explain the following statement: "A small group can function effectively without a specific leader, but never without leadership."

114. Explain the differences among procedural needs, task needs, and maintenance needs in a problem-solving small group. Give an example of each kind of need.

115.    Explain the five major responsibilities of all members of a small group. Why are all five so important that every participant in a small group should take them as personal objectives?

116.    What is a hidden agenda? Why is a hidden agenda a barrier to effective group discussion?

117.    Explain the following statement: "It is not necessary that members of a small group agree all the time, but they should keep disagreement at the task level."

118.    Explain the five stages of the reflective-thinking method for discussion in problem-solving small groups.

119.    Explain the following statement: "In some ways, defining the problem for a small group discussion is similar to determining the specific purpose for a speech."

120.    Define and explain each of the following methods of presenting the recommendations of a problem-solving small group:

   a.    oral report
   b.    symposium
   c.    panel discussion

121.    Identify the flaw(s) in each of the following questions for a problem-solving small group. Rewrite each question so as to eliminate the flaw(s).

   a.    What should be done to eliminate the incredibly dirty and corrupt campaign techniques of modern politicians?

   b.    Should our state pass a new law to combat child abuse?

   c.    What should our school do to offset the loss of student loan money from the federal government and to help students find jobs after they graduate?

122.    Compare and contrast a symposium and a panel discussion. In your answer, be sure to explain the responsibilities of the moderator and the speakers in both kinds of presentations.

# Part Three

# Chapter Quizzes

# Chapter 1 Speaking in Public

## True-False Quiz

*Indicate whether each of the following statements is true or false by <u>circling</u> the appropriate letter.*

1.   T   F   The three major goals of public speaking are to inform, to persuade, and to entertain.

2.   T   F   When you adjust to the situation of a public speech, you are doing on a larger scale what you do everyday in conversation.

3.   T   F   Thinking positively about your ability to give a speech is one way to control your anxiety about speaking.

4.   T   F   Critical thinking is a way of thinking negatively about everything you hear in a speech.

5.   T   F   The nonverbal messages that listeners send back to speakers are called feedback.

6.   T   F   Most of the time the listener's frame of reference is identical with the speaker's frame of reference.

7.   T   F   When you give a speech to your classmates, you are engaged in one-way communication.

8.   T   F   Avoiding ethnocentrism means that you must agree with the values and practices of all groups and cultures.

9.   T   F   As your textbook explains, most of the nervousness public speakers feel internally is not visible to their listeners.

10.  T   F   Although language changes from culture to culture, the meaning of nonverbal signals is consistent across cultures.

# Chapter 1 Speaking in Public

## Multiple Choice Quiz

*Indicate the best answer for each of the following questions by circling the correct letter.*

1.  Everything a speaker says is filtered through a listener's

    a.  frame of reference.
    b.  credibility.
    c.  feedback.
    d.  personal screen.
    e.  psychological field.

2.  Which of the following does your textbook recommend as a way to deal with nervousness in your speeches?

    a.  Concentrate on thinking about your stage fright.
    b.  Work especially hard on your conclusion.
    c.  Avoid making eye contact with your audience.
    d.  Try to generate extra adrenaline as you speak.
    e.  Think of your speech as an act of communication.

3.  Dealing with such matters as the logical relationships among ideas, the soundness of evidence, and the differences between fact and opinion are all part of what your textbook calls

    a.  deduction.
    b.  critical thinking.
    c.  rational communication.
    d.  oral deliberation.
    e.  induction.

4.  According to your textbook, a listener anxious about an upcoming exam, worried about a recent argument with a friend, or distracted by cold air in the classroom would be experiencing

    a.  interference.
    b.  situational cues.
    c.  communication apprehension.
    d.  psychological dissonance.
    e.  feedback.

5.    Public speakers who seek to communicate with listeners from cultures other than their own need to take special care to avoid _____ in their speeches.

   a.   ethnocentrism
   b.   vocalized pauses
   c.   personal statements
   d.   visual aids
   e.    gestures

6.    Which of the following strategies is *least* likely to help you deal with nervousness in your speeches?

   a.   thinking positively
   b.   concentrating on your stage fright
   c.   working especially hard on your introduction
   d.   making eye contact with members of your audience
   e.    using visual aids

7.    According to your textbook, when you employ the power of visualization as a method of controlling stage fright, you should

   a.   decrease the time spent preparing your speech.
   b.   keep your mental pictures from becoming too vivid.
   c.   focus on the positive aspects of your speech.
   d.   all of the above.
   e.   a and b only.

8.    According to your textbook, the three major goals of public speaking are informing, persuading, and

   a.   demonstrating.
   b.   entertaining.
   c.   actuating.
   d.   selling.
   e.    convincing.

9.    _____ lets you know how your message is being received.

   a.   Vocal variety
   b.   Credibility
   c.   Feedback
   d.   Interference
   e.   Audience adaptation

10.   Many of the skills used in public speaking are the same as those used in everyday conversation. These skills include

   a.   organizing your thoughts logically.
   b.   tailoring your message to your audience.
   c.   adapting to listener feedback.
   d.   all of the above.
   e.   b and c only.

# Chapter 2 Ethics and Public Speaking

## True-False Quiz

*Indicate whether each of the following statements is true or false by <u>circling</u> the appropriate letter.*

1.  T  F    The first responsibility of a speaker is to make sure her or his goal is ethically sound.

2.  T  F    As the Roman rhetorician Quintilian noted 2,000 years ago, the ideal of commendable speechmaking is to persuade the audience by any means necessary.

3.  T  F    A speaker's ethical obligations decrease as the size of the audience decreases.

4.  T  F    Ethical decisions need to be justified against a set of standards or criteria.

5.  T  F    One of the best ways to avoid falling into the trap of plagiarism is to start work on your speeches well before they are due.

6.  T  F    Taking someone's entire speech and passing it off as your own is a form of unethical behavior called incremental plagiarism.

7.  T  F    It is necessary for a public speaker to identify his or her source whether the speaker is paraphrasing or quoting verbatim.

8.  T  F    Just as public speakers have ethical responsibilities, so too do the people who listen to a speech.

9.  T  F    Global plagiarism occurs when a speaker patches together several quotations or paraphrases without citing the sources of the statements.

10. T  F    It is possible to disagree entirely with a speaker's ideas but still support the speaker's right to express those ideas.

# Chapter 2 Ethics and Public Speaking

## Multiple Choice Quiz

*Indicate the best answer for each of the following questions by circling the correct letter.*

1.   According to your textbook, _____ plagiarism occurs when the speech as a whole is ethical but the speaker fails to give credit for particular quotations and paraphrases.

   a.   incidental
   b.   informative
   c.   inferential
   d.   invalid
   e.   incremental

2.   In public speaking, sound ethical decisions involve weighing a potential course of action against

   a.   the frame of reference of the audience.
   b.   a set of ethical guidelines or standards.
   c.   the speaker's strategic objectives.
   d.   a specific code of legal rules.
   e.   the personal opinions of the speaker.

3.   According to your textbook, the guidelines for ethical listening in a public speaking situation include

   a.   maintaining the free and open expression of ideas.
   b.   judging the speaker on the basis of her or his prestige.
   c.   taking accurate notes of what the speaker says.
   d.   all of the above.
   e.   a and c only.

4.   As explained in your textbook, public speakers have an ethical obligation to avoid name-calling and other forms of abusive language because such language

   a.   is forbidden by the first amendment to the U.S. Constitution.
   b.   violates current standards of political correctness on college campuses.
   c.   changes meaning based on the frame of reference of the audience.
   d.   is used by speakers who are not fully prepared for their presentations.
   e.   demeans the personal dignity of the groups or individuals being attacked.

5.   As your textbook explains, a speaker who assembles a speech by copying word for word from two or three sources is committing what kind of plagiarism?

   a.   global
   b.   incremental
   c.   scientific
   d.   patchwork
   e.    credible

6.   According to your textbook, _____ plagiarism occurs when a speaker takes a speech entirely from a single source and passes it off as her or his own.

   a.   incremental
   b.   global
   c.   valid
   d.   patchwork
   e.   scientific

7.   All of the following are presented in your textbook as guidelines for ethical speechmaking *except*

   a.   be honest in what you say.
   b.   avoid name-calling and other forms of abusive language.
   c.   be fully prepared for each speech.
   d.   make sure your goals are ethically sound.
   e.   explain your credibility on the speech topic.

8.   Which of the following does your textbook recommend as a way to steer clear of incremental plagiarism?

   a.   Avoid using direct quotations from other people in your speech.
   b.   Only use your original ideas so there is no risk of plagiarism.
   c.   Avoid citing sources that might make someone suspect plagiarism.
   d.   Cite the sources of all quotations and paraphrases in your speech.
   e.   Avoid paraphrasing information from other people in your speech.

9.   Jerome found several excellent sources for his informative speech. He pulled key information from them, blended those ideas into his own perspective, and cited his sources when he presented the speech. Which of the following statements *best* describes this situation?

   a.   Jerome is ethical because he cited his sources and used them to develop his own slant on the topic.
   b.   Jerome is guilty of incremental plagiarism because he used quotations and paraphrases from other people in his speech.
   c.   Jerome is ethical because he did not copy his speech from a single source.
   d.   Jerome is guilty of patchwork plagiarism because he used ideas from several different sources in his speech.
   e.   Jerome is guilty of global plagiarism because he did not develop his speech entirely from his own knowledge and experience.

10.   Because speechmaking is a form of power, we must always be sure to speak

    a.   concisely.
    b.   persuasively.
    c.   ethically.
    d.   forcefully.
    e.   consistently.

# Chapter 3  Listening

## True-False Quiz

*Indicate whether each of the following statements is true or false by <u>circling</u> the appropriate letter.*

1.   T  F   Note taking is usually a barrier to effective listening.

2.   T  F   People need effective listening skills in almost all occupations.

3.   T  F   Listening to provide emotional support for someone is called empathic listening.

4.   T  F   When listening critically for evidence, you should consider primarily how the evidence relates to your personal frame of reference.

5.   T  F   If you disagree with a speaker, you have nothing to gain by listening carefully.

6.   T  F   According to your textbook, listening to understand a classroom lecture is an example of comprehensive listening.

7.   T  F   People spend more time listening than in any other communicative activity.

8.   T  F   Note taking is usually a barrier to effective listening.

9.   T  F   One of the major barriers to effective communication is that the brain can process words much faster than a speaker can talk.

10.  T  F   According to your textbook, when focusing your listening, you should concentrate on a speaker's main points, evidence, and technique.

# Chapter 3 Listening

## Multiple Choice Quiz

*Indicate the best answer for each of the following questions by circling the correct letter.*

1.  In studies about communication skills within businesses, most business managers rank _____ as the skill most crucial to their jobs.

    a.  public speaking
    b.  conversation
    c.  writing
    d.  critical thinking
    e.  listening

2.  Tara's campus organization has invited several travel agents to speak to the group about their best deals on trips for spring break. As Tara listens, she is deciding which travel package is the best one for her. During the presentations, she is engaged in which form of listening?

    a.  critical
    b.  appreciative
    c.  comprehensive
    d.  empathic
    e.  intimate

3.  According to your textbook, when you focus your listening as a means of becoming a better listener, you should listen for

    a.  main points.
    b.  evidence.
    c.  technique.
    d.  all of the above.
    e.  a and b only.

4.  According to your textbook, when you listen to evaluate a speaker's message for purposes of accepting it or rejecting it, what kind of listening is involved?

    a.  critical
    b.  sympathetic
    c.  appreciative
    d.  empathic
    e.  comprehensive

5. When listening for a speaker's evidence, you should keep an ear out for its

    a. sufficiency.
    b. accuracy.
    c. objectivity.
    d. relevance.
    e. all of the above.

6. Lance is enjoying Chris Rock's stand-up comedy routine at the Civic Center. According to your textbook, Lance is engaged in _____ listening.

    a. critical
    b. appreciative
    c. comprehensive
    d. empathic
    e. intimate

7. Ted is listening to the introduction of Janine's speech when he thinks to himself, "Man, this is really going to be boring." What aspect of poor listening identified in your textbook is Ted exhibiting in this example?

    a. listening too hard
    b  jumping to conclusions
    c. rejecting the speaker's frame of reference
    d. giving in to distractions
    e. not listening comprehensively

8. Sarah is listening to her roommate to provide emotional support in a time of distress. According to your textbook, Sarah is engaged in _____ listening.

    a. critical
    b. appreciative
    c. empathic
    d. personal
    e. comprehensive

9. Which of the following is included among the four major causes of poor listening discussed in your textbook?

    a. trying to remember everything the speaker says
    b. jumping to conclusions about the speaker's ideas
    c. taking written notes while the speech is in progress
    d. all of the above
    e. a and b only

10. Your textbook recommends _____ as the most effective method of note taking for listening to a speech.

    a. trying to write down everything a speaker says
    b. creating a keyword outline
    c. writing down a speaker's most interesting ideas
    d. creating a full-sentence outline
    e. using the Harvard listening system

# Chapter 4 Selecting a Topic and a Purpose

## True-False Quiz

*Indicate whether each of the following statements is true or false by <u>circling</u> the appropriate letter.*

1.   T  F   The first step in speechmaking is choosing a topic for your speech.

2.   T  F   Most often, a speaker's general purpose will fall into one of two categories—to inform or to demonstrate.

3.   T  F   The central idea indicates precisely what the speaker hopes to accomplish in a speech.

4.   T  F   "To inform my audience of the major steps in responding to a medical emergency" is an example of an effective specific purpose statement for an informative speech.

5.   T  F   The specific purpose of a speech usually "sums up" the main points to be developed in the body of the speech.

6.   T  F   The central idea of a speech should be stated as a full sentence.

7.   T  F   "The three major expenses for people traveling abroad are transportation, food, and lodging" is an example of a well-worded central idea for a speech.

8.   T  F   The specific purpose statement should usually be phrased as a question.

9.   T  F   "To inform my audience about the origins of martial arts and how to perform yoga" is an example of an effective specific purpose statement for an informative speech.

10.  T  F   The central idea reveals more about the content of a speech than does the specific purpose.

# Chapter 4   Selecting a Topic and a Purpose

## Multiple Choice Quiz

*Indicate the <u>best</u> answer for each of the following questions by circling the correct letter.*

1.   According to your textbook, brainstorming is especially helpful when you are having trouble

   a.   choosing a speech topic.
   b.   determining the general purpose.
   c.   determining the specific purpose.
   d.   phrasing the central idea.
   e.   analyzing the audience.

2.   Which of the following is out of place in a speech to inform?

   a.   advocating
   b.   explaining
   c.   reporting
   d.   demonstrating
   e.   telling

3.   "To inform my audience about the three basic steps in preventive medicine" is an example of a

   a.   main point.
   b.   specific purpose.
   c.   thesis statement.
   d.   central idea.
   e.   general purpose.

4.   According to your textbook, what is the *most important* early step in the process of developing a successful speech?

   a.   phrasing the general purpose
   b.   researching for speech materials
   c.   formulating the specific purpose
   d.   brainstorming for a central idea
   e.   selecting the residual message

5.  As a specific purpose statement, "To inform my audience about computer technology" is too

    a.  figurative.
    b.  broad.
    c.  trivial.
    d.  technical.
    e.  detailed.

6.  Which of the following is appropriate in a speech to persuade?

    a.  advocating
    b.  exhorting
    c.  convincing
    d.  all of the above
    e.  a and c only

7.  "To inform about saving for retirement" is a poorly phrased specific purpose statement because it

    a.  is too specific.
    b.  contains figurative language.
    c.  is written as a statement instead of a question.
    d.  does not include a reference to the audience.
    e.  is too trivial.

8.  The central idea of a speech should

    a.  avoid figurative language.
    b.  be written as a full sentence.
    c.  be phrased as a question.
    d.  all of the above.
    e.  a and b only.

9.  According to your textbook, "Getting an internship at a major corporation requires a great deal of work, but the rewards are well worth the effort" is an example of a(n)

    a.  speech proposal.
    b.  specific purpose.
    c.  informative thesis.
    d.  topic statement.
    e.  central idea.

10. "To persuade my audience that continuing to spend money on the space program is like throwing good money after bad" is a poorly phrased specific purpose statement for a speech because it is

    a.  expressed in figurative language.
    b.  written as a declarative sentence rather than a question.
    c.  too technical.
    d.  all of the above.
    e.  a and c only.

# Chapter 5  Analyzing the Audience

## True-False Quiz

*Indicate whether each of the following statements is true or false by <u>circling</u> the appropriate letter.*

1.  T  F    Adapting to audiences is one of the easiest tasks facing beginning speakers.

2.  T  F    Audience analysis first comes into play after a speaker has chosen a specific purpose.

3.  T  F    Even when listeners pay close attention, they don't process a speaker's message exactly as the speaker intended.

4.  T  F    Gender, sexual orientation, age, race, ethnicity, and group membership are all factors to consider when conducting a demographic audience analysis.

5.  T  F    As a general rule, the larger your audience the less formal your speech presentation should be.

6.  T  F    Knowing how the physical setting might affect your listeners' receptivity to your ideas is an important factor in situational audience analysis.

7.  T  F    Interest, knowledge, and attitude are the three most important factors to consider when determining an audience's disposition toward a speaker's topic.

8.  T  F    No matter what the occasion, listeners will have fairly definite expectations about the kinds of speeches appropriate for the occasion.

9.  T  F    Egocentrism means that audiences typically approach speeches by asking "Why is this important for me?"

10. T  F    The process of audience adaptation is over by the time a speaker starts delivering the speech.

# Chapter 5 Analyzing the Audience

## Multiple Choice Quiz

*Indicate the <u>best</u> answer for each of the following questions by circling the correct letter.*

1.    Audience analysis is an important factor in which of the following?

    a.    selecting a topic
    b.    organizing the speech
    c.    choosing supporting materials
    d.    all of the above
    e.    a and c only

2.    The *primary* purpose of speechmaking is to

    a.    gain a desired response from listeners.
    b.    please the majority of the audience.
    c.    display the speaker's research skills.
    d.    practice getting up in front of an audience.
    e.    test new ideas through audience feedback.

3.    Dimitri plans to give a speech to his classmates about the principles of physics behind the design of hybrid automobiles. The most important factor for Dimitri to consider when analyzing his audience is probably its

    a.    age.
    b.    group membership.
    c.    attitude toward the speaker.
    d.    knowledge about the topic.
    e.    size.

4.    The process by which a speaker seeks to create a bond with listeners by emphasizing common values, goals, and experiences is referred to as _____ by communication scholars.

    a.    framing
    b.    identification
    c.    egocentrism
    d.    structuring
    e.    affiliation

5. According to your textbook, which of the following is a factor in situational audience analysis?

   a. the audience's cultural background
   b. the audience's religious beliefs
   c. the audience's group membership
   d. the audience's gender
   e. the audience's attitude toward the topic

6. Which of the following is a demographic characteristic of a speech audience?

   a. age
   b. interest
   c. size
   d. attitude
   e. knowledge

7. Which of the following is a demographic characteristic of a speech audience?

   a. age
   b. interest
   c. size
   d. attitude
   e. knowledge

8. To say that people usually want to hear about things that are meaningful to them is to say that people are

   a. empathic.
   b. eclectic.
   c. egotistic.
   d. egalitarian.
   e. egocentric.

9. Which of the following elements usually has the greatest impact on the length a speech should be?

   a. the audience's disposition toward the topic
   b. the physical setting for the speech
   c. the audience's attitudes toward the speaker
   d. the occasion for the speech
   e. the group membership of the audience

10. As the size of your audience increases, your presentation should usually become more

   a. formal.
   b. flexible.
   c. extemporaneous.
   d. punctual.
   e. informal.

# Chapter 6 Gathering Materials

## True-False Quiz

*Indicate whether each of the following statements is true or false by <u>circling</u> the appropriate letter.*

1.   T  F   If you use a tape recorder in a research interview, you should keep it secret from the person being interviewed.

2.   T  F   Periodical databases help you locate magazine and journal articles.

3.   T  F   Because the Internet is such a vast source of information, your textbook recommends using it to replace library research when preparing your speeches.

4.   T  F   You can almost always count on the reliability of Internet research materials found through major search engines such as Google and Yahoo.

5.   T  F   One of the great strengths of the Internet as a research tool is the access it provides to government documents and publications.

6.   T  F   According to your textbook, the three major criteria against which to test documents that you locate on the Internet are authorship, sponsorship, and recency.

7.   T  F   When taking research notes, it is important to distinguish between direct quotations, paraphrases, and your own ideas.

8.   T  F   The only way you can use a search engine to find information on the Internet is by conducting a keyword search.

9.   T  F   One advantage of using virtual libraries for speech research is that they contain only material that has been screened for accuracy and reliability.

10.  T  F   Your most important task before conducting a research interview is to work out the questions you will ask during the interview.

# Chapter 6 Gathering Materials

## Multiple Choice Quiz

*Indicate the best answer for each of the following questions by circling the correct letter.*

1. The most important task when preparing to conduct a research interview is

    a. devising questions to ask during the interview.
    b. deciding whether or not to use a tape recorder.
    c. choosing what to wear during the interview.
    d. selecting an appropriate interviewing style.
    e. deciding whether or not to take notes during the interview.

2. The best source for numerical data about life in the United States is

    a. *Who's Who.*
    b. *Encyclopedia Americana.*
    c. *World Almanac and Book of Facts.*
    d. *New York Times Index.*
    e. *Statistical Abstract of the United States.*

3. A(n) _____ is a research aid that catalogues articles from a large number of journals or magazines.

    a. abstract
    b. biographical aid
    c. reference work
    d. periodical database
    e. keyword index

4. The _____ is the key to finding information in the library.

    a. general index
    b. catalogue
    c. periodicals guide
    d. encyclopedia
    e. browser

5. When taking research notes, you should

    a. put all notes from each source on a single index card or sheet of paper.
    b. record notes only when you're sure you'll use the information in your speech.
    c. take all notes as direct quotations.
    d. all of the above.
    e. none of the above.

6.   According to your textbook, the three criteria for judging the reliability of documents located on the Internet are recency, authorship, and

   a.   indexing.
   b.   sponsorship.
   c.   interactivity.
   d.   graphics.
   e.   creativity.

7.   If you can't identify the author of a document on the World Wide Web, your textbook recommends that you

   a.   look up the year the document was published.
   b.   bookmark the document and return to it later.
   c.   try to determine the sponsoring organization for the document.
   d.   double check the accuracy of the document's URL.
   e.   search for the document in the library.

8.   As your textbook explains, the best kind of search aid for locating reliable, high quality information on the Internet is a(n)

   a.   search engine.
   b.   electronic catalogue.
   c.   metasearch engine.
   d.   research pilot.
   e.   virtual library.

9.   The part of the library that contains encyclopedias, yearbooks, dictionaries, biographical aids, atlases, and indexes is usually called the

   a.   research room.
   b.   periodical room.
   c.   reference section.
   d.   circulation section.
   e.   information room.

10.   According to your textbook, when citing an Internet document in a speech bibliography, you should include the

   a.   date on which you accessed the document.
   b.   organization responsible for the document if the author's name is not known.
   c.   URL of the document.
   d.   all of the above.
   e.   b and c only.

# Chapter 7 Supporting Your Ideas

## True-False Quiz

*Indicate whether each of the following statements is true or false by <u>circling</u> the appropriate letter.*

1.    T   F    One of the main reasons to use examples in a speech is that they put abstract ideas into concrete terms that listeners can easily understand.

2.    T   F    Brief examples can be used either to illustrate a point or to introduce a topic.

3.    T   F    Whenever you use a hypothetical example in a speech, it is usually a good idea to follow it with statistics or testimony to show that the example is not unrealistic.

4.    T   F    It is seldom necessary to cite the source of statistics in a speech.

5.    T   F    Research has shown that the more statistics you use, the more effective your speech is likely to be.

6.    T   F    Unlike testimony, which can easily be quoted out of context, statistics are difficult to manipulate for biased purposes.

7.    T   F    Acceptable testimony can include either statements from recognized experts or from ordinary people with special expertise on the topic.

8.    T   F    You should almost always round off statistics in a speech.

9.    T   F    Using strong, credible testimony is the best way to add human interest to a speech.

10.   T   F    Examples and testimony are most effective in persuasive speeches, while statistics work best in informative speeches.

# Chapter 7 Supporting Your Ideas

## Multiple Choice Quiz

*Indicate the best answer for each of the following questions by circling the correct letter.*

1.    The best way to add human interest to your speech is to use

    a.    examples.
    b.    quotations.
    c.    graphs.
    d.    statistics.
    e.    metaphors.

2.    The main value of using statistics in a speech is to

    a.    lend realism to the speech.
    b.    enhance the speaker's credibility.
    c.    make the speech more vivid.
    d.    avoid relying on testimony.
    e.    quantify the speaker's ideas.

3.    According to your textbook, if you quoted your cousin about her experience digging for dinosaur bones last summer, you would be using _____ testimony.

    a.    peer
    b.    personal
    c.    paraphrased
    d.    ordinary
    e.    direct

4.    To give the gist of someone's statement in your own words is to

    a.    paraphrase.
    b.    hypothesize.
    c.    corroborate.
    d.    testify.
    e.    quote.

5.    Which of the following is recommended by your textbook as a way to enhance the effectiveness of your examples?

    a.    Practice delivery to enhance your extended examples.
    b.    Avoid using examples drawn from your personal experience.
    c.    Make your examples vivid and richly textured.
    d.    all of the above
    e.    a and c only

6.    When using statistics in a speech, you should usually

    a.    manipulate the statistics to make your point.
    b.    cite exact numbers rather than rounding off.
    c.    increase your speaking rate when giving statistics.
    d.    avoid using too many statistics.
    e.    conceal the source of the statistics.

7.    According to your textbook, if you quoted Harvard business professor John B. Matthews on the strengths and weaknesses of U.S. business schools, you would be using _____ testimony.

    a.    peer
    b.    professional
    c.    expert
    d.    unbiased
    e.    valid

8.    The more _____ your examples, the greater impact they are likely to have.

    a.    hypothetical
    b.    complex
    c.    unusual
    d.    expert
    e.    vivid

9.    According to your textbook, a good way to clarify statistical trends is to

    a.    increase your speaking rate when giving statistics.
    b.    consult the *Guinness Book of World Records*.
    c.    use exact numbers rather than rounding off.
    d.    use visual aids when presenting statistics.
    e.    make sure the statistics are from unbiased sources.

10.    The main value of using expert testimony in a speech is to

    a.    enhance the vividness of the speaker's ideas.
    b.    gain attention in the introduction of the speech.
    c.    build the credibility of speakers who are not experts on their topics.
    d.    keep the audience's attention throughout the body of the speech.
    e.    relate the speaker's ideas directly to the audience.

# Chapter 8 Organizing the Body of the Speech

## True-False Quiz

*Indicate whether each of the following statements is true or false by <u>circling</u> the appropriate letter.*

1.  T  F    Clear organization is usually less important in speaking than in writing.

2.  T  F    Audiences find well-organized speakers to be more credible than poorly organized speakers.

3.  T  F    According to your textbook, the introduction of a speech usually should be prepared before the body.

4.  T  F    According to your textbook, most speeches should contain from five to eight main points.

5.  T  F    Chronological organization is used primarily for informative speeches.

6.  T  F    Speeches arranged in causal order usually have three main points.

7.  T  F    Problem-solution order is used most often in persuasive speeches.

8.  T  F    In topical order the main points proceed from top to bottom, left to right, front to back, east to west, or some similar route.

9.  T  F    "The most important point to remember about . . ." is an example of a signpost.

10. T  F    According to your textbook, transitions state both the idea the speaker is leaving and the one the speaker is coming to.

# Chapter 8 Organizing the Body of the Speech

## Multiple Choice Quiz

*Indicate the best answer for each of the following questions by circling the correct letter.*

1.  What organizational pattern would probably be most effective for arranging the main points of a speech with the specific purpose "To inform my audience about three major ways to block junk mail from their e-mail system"?

    a.  topical
    b.  logistical
    c.  chronological
    d.  technical
    e.  causal

2.  Here are the main points for a speech about the major steps involved in a successful job interview:

    I.  The first step is preparing for the interview before it takes place.
    II. The second step is presenting yourself well during the interview itself.
    III. The third step is following up after the interview.

    These main points are arranged in _____ order.

    a.  topical
    b.  spatial
    c.  chronological
    d.  informative
    e.  causal

3.  According to your textbook, if the following statement occurred in the body of a speech, it would be an example of what kind of connective?

    > In discussing the problem of childhood asthma, we shall look at the symptoms of the disease, its causes, and current treatments.

    a.  signpost
    b   internal preview
    c.  transition
    d.  internal summary
    e.   bridge

4.  When main ideas follow a directional pattern, they are organized in

    a.  geographical order.
    b.  topical order.
    c.  spatial order.
    d.  causal order.
    e.  chronological order.

5.  Which pattern of organization would probably be most effective for arranging the main points of a speech with the specific purpose "To persuade my audience that high school and college football programs should act now to reduce the incidents of serious injuries in their sport."

    a.  spatial
    b.  causal
    c.  problem-solution
    d.  chronological
    e.  topical

6.  A speech about the causes and effects of domestic violence would most likely be organized in _____ order.

    a.  causal
    b.  problem-solution
    c.  topical
    d.  informative
    e.  scientific

7.  The most effective order of main points in a speech depends above all on your topic, purpose, and

    a.  audience.
    b.  research.
    c.  visual aids.
    d.  credibility.
    e.  delivery.

8.  Problem-solution order is most appropriate for organizing _____ speeches.

    a.  acceptance
    b.  informative
    c.  after-dinner
    d.  commemorative
    e.  persuasive

9.  "Now that we have seen the causes of unrest in central Africa, we shall turn to their effects . . ." is an example of a(n)

    a.  internal preview.
    b.  transition.
    c.  internal summary.
    d.  signpost.
    e.  main point.

10.  Which of the following organizational patterns is used more than any other method of speech organization because of its applicability to almost any subject?

    a.  chronological
    b.  spatial
    c.  problem-solution
    d.  topical
    e.  causal

# Chapter 9 Beginning and Ending the Speech

## True-False Quiz

*Indicate whether each of the following statements is true or false by <u>circling</u> the appropriate letter.*

1.   T  F      Regardless of what other methods you use to gain attention, you should almost always relate the topic to your audience in the introduction of a speech.

2.   T  F      Goodwill is the audience's perception of whether the speaker has the best interests of the audience in mind.

3.   T  F      If your topic is clear in the body of the speech, there is no need to state it in the introduction.

4.   T  F      Establishing credibility is an important function of a speech introduction.

5.   T  F      One function of a preview statement is to signal that the body of the speech is about to begin.

6.   T  F      Under normal circumstances, you should work out the exact wording of your introduction after you have finished preparing the body of your speech.

7.   T  F      The crescendo conclusion is essentially a matter of the speaker getting louder and louder as the speech comes to an end.

8.   T  F      It is overly repetitious to restate the central idea in the conclusion of a speech.

9.   T  F      It is inappropriate for a public speaker to say anything so obvious as "in conclusion."

10.   T  F      One function of a speech conclusion is to reinforce the speaker's central idea.

# Chapter 9   Beginning and Ending the Speech

## Multiple Choice Quiz

*Indicate the best answer for each of the following questions by circling the correct letter.*

1. Which of the following would you *most* likely find in a speech introduction?

   a. a credibility statement
   b. a transition
   c. a causal argument
   d. an internal summary
   e. a call to action

2. Which of the following would you *least* likely find in a speech introduction?

   a. a preview statement
   b. a call to action
   c. a credibility statement
   d. a provocative quotation
   e. a startling statement

3. Which of the following would you *most* likely find in a speech introduction?

   a. a transition
   b. an internal summary
   c. a lengthy quotation
   d. a startling statement
   e. a causal argument

4. In the introduction of his speech on the Special Olympics, Mason mentioned that he had attended the events last year to cheer on a family friend who was competing in some races. Sharing this information with the audience helped Mason achieve which goal of a speech introduction?

   a. relating to the audience
   b. generating emotional appeal
   c. stating the importance of the topic
   d. establishing credibility
   e. previewing the body

5.    Which objective of a good speech introduction is fulfilled by the following statement?

> Today we will explore the three most important forms of intellectual property protection—copyrights, trademarks, and patents.

    a.   preview the body
    b.   establish the speaker's goodwill
    c.   state the importance of the topic
    d.   summarize the introduction
    e.   relate to the audience

6.    According to your textbook, the best time to work out the exact wording of a speech introduction is

    a.   shortly after you determine the central idea.
    b.   before you work out the conclusion.
    c.   when you prepare your speaking outline.
    d.   as you rise to deliver an extemporaneous speech.
    e.   after you prepare the body of the speech.

7.    Which of the following is recommended in your textbook as a way to reinforce the central idea in a speech conclusion?

    a.   end with a quotation
    b.   make a dramatic statement
    c.   refer to the introduction
    d.   all of the above
    e.   a and b only

8.    Which of the following would you be *most* likely to find in a speech conclusion?

    a.   a preview statement
    b.   a restatement of the central idea
    c.   a gesture of goodwill
    d.   a credibility statement
    e.   an announcement of the topic

9.    What does your textbook say about preparing an effective speech conclusion?

    a.   Make your conclusion about 5 to 10 percent of the entire speech.
    b.   Work especially hard on establishing your credibility in the conclusion.
    c.   Keep an eye out for concluding materials as you research the speech.
    d.   all of the above
    e.   a and c only

10.    An appeal to action is most appropriate in the conclusion of a(n) _____ speech.

    a.   informative
    b.   after-dinner
    c.   acceptance
    d.   commemorative
    e.   persuasive

# Chapter 10 Outlining the Speech

## True-False Quiz

*Indicate whether each of the following statements is true or false by <u>circling</u> the appropriate letter.*

1. T F  The preparation outline should be drawn up before a speaker begins research for a speech.

2. T F  In a preparation outline, the specific purpose is usually stated before the introduction.

3. T F  Stating main points in a word or two is usually sufficient for a preparation outline.

4. T F  The speaking outline is a more complete version of the preparation outline.

5. T F  A preparation outline should include transitions and internal summaries.

6. T F  In the most common system of outlining, main points are identified by capital letters.

7. T F  A speaking outline should be written on both sides of an index card or sheet of paper.

8. T F  You should keep your speaking outline as brief as possible.

9. T F  A speaking outline should usually include directions for delivering the speech.

10. T F  A bibliography is necessary in both the preparation outline and the speaking outline.

# Chapter 10 Outlining the Speech

## Multiple Choice Quiz

*Indicate the best answer for each of the following questions by circling the correct letter.*

1. Outlining is an important part of public speaking because

   a. an outline helps the speaker compile an organized preliminary bibliography.
   b. an outline helps ensure that ideas flow clearly from one to another.
   c. an outline helps the speaker choose an interesting, sharply focused topic.
   d. all of the above.
   e. a and b only.

2. Which of the following should be included in a preparation outline?

   a. the central idea
   b. a general purpose statement
   c. the preliminary bibliography
   d. directions for delivering the speech
   e. all of the above

3. When making a preparation outline, you should

   a. label transitions and internal summaries.
   b. indicate the introduction, body, and conclusion with Roman numerals.
   c. state the specific purpose as a separate unit before the outline itself.
   d. all of the above.
   e. a and c only.

4. Arranged in random order below are a main point, two subpoints, and two sub-subpoints from a speech preparation outline. Which is the main point?

   a. Melanoma is the least common but most deadly form of skin cancer.
   b. Each year about 7,400 people die from melanoma in the U.S.
   c. Basal cell carcinoma is the most common type of skin cancer.
   d. Two types of skin cancer are melanoma and basal cell carcinoma.
   e. Of all skin cancers diagnosed in the U.S., only 4 percent are melanoma.

5.    Which of the following is a correctly worded main point for a speech preparation outline?

   a.    Leadership.
   b.    What are the major types of leadership?
   c.    Two major types of leadership.
   d.    There are two major types of leadership.
   e.    Leadership: major types.

6.    Subpoints in a preparation outline are

   a.    listed just before the conclusion.
   b.    written in keywords to job the memory.
   c.    indicated by Roman numerals.
   d.    indented farther to the left than main points.
   e.    written in full sentences.

7.    All of the following are necessary in a preparation outline *except*

   a.    labels for the introduction, body, and conclusion.
   b.    directions for delivering the speech.
   c.    transitions, internal previews, and internal summaries.
   d.    a consistent pattern of indentation and symbolization.
   e.    a specific purpose statement.

8.    A catchy speech title is fine as long as it is

   a.    phrased as a question.
   b.    relevant to the speech.
   c.    written as a full sentence.
   d.    all of the above.
   e.    b and c only.

9.    A speaking outline

   a.    does not contain statistics and quotations.
   b.    uses full sentences to jog the speaker's memory.
   c.    is as brief as possible.
   d.    all of the above.
   e.    a and c only.

10.    When Terrence creates a speaking outline for his informative speech on hockey, he should

   a.    include cues for delivering the speech.
   b.    write out quotations he plans to use in the speech.
   c.    follow the visual framework of the preparation outline.
   d.    all of the above.
   e.    a and b only.

# Chapter **11** Using Language

## True-False Quiz

*Indicate whether each of the following statements is true or false by <u>circling</u> the appropriate letter.*

1.  T  F  The words we use to label an event determine to a great extent how we respond to that event.

2.  T  F  The denotative meaning of a word includes all the feelings, associations, and emotions that the word touches off in different people.

3.  T  F  As your textbook explains, a public speaker needs to use big words to impress the audience.

4.  T  F  "History is a drama with many acts" is an example of metaphor.

5.  T  F  The more abstract a word, the more ambiguous it will be.

6.  T  F  In dealing with technical topics, a speaker has little choice but to use technical language.

7.  T  F  "She darted around the bookstore like a hummingbird in a flower garden" is an example of simile.

8.  T  F  Antithesis and alliteration are excellent ways to enhance the imagery of a speech.

9.  T  F  Avoiding sexist language is important in public speaking both as a matter of audience adaptation and as a matter of accuracy in language.

10.  T  F  The connotative meaning of a word is more variable, figurative, and subjective than its denotative meaning.

# Chapter 11 Using Language

## Multiple Choice Quiz

*Indicate the best answer for each of the following questions by circling the correct letter.*

1. Which of the following is discussed in your textbook as a basic criterion for the effective use of language in public speaking?

   a. use language technically
   b. use language appropriately
   c. use language clearly
   d. all of the above
   e. b and c only

2. Jerome wants his audience to appreciate the harsh reality of life for migrant workers in the United States. In addition to using strong supporting materials, he decides to use words with connotative meanings because he knows they will help him

   a. have stronger delivery.
   b. appear as impartial as possible.
   c. arouse an emotional response.
   d. add rhythm to his language.
   e. increase his accuracy.

3. To use language vividly your textbook recommends that speakers employ

   a. metaphor and rhyme.
   b. imagery and rhythm.
   c. concrete words and quotations.
   d. testimony and examples.
   e. antithesis and parallelism.

4. Phrases such as "dry as a bone," "clear as a bell," "dark as night," and "smart as a whip" should be avoided in speeches because they are

   a. abstract.
   b. clichés.
   c. similes.
   d. connotative.
   e. figurative.

5. "Just like an iceberg, the most important dimensions of culture are below the surface" is an example of

    a.   simile.
    b.   antithesis.
    c.   repetition.
    d.   alliteration.
    e.   metaphor.

6. When used effectively, repetition in a speech

    a.   unifies a sequence of ideas.
    b.   helps to build a strong cadence.
    c.   reinforces an idea.
    d.   all of the above.
    e.   b and c only.

7. "Let us never negotiate out of fear. But let us never fear to negotiate" is an example of

    a.   imagery.
    b.   antithesis.
    c.   repetition.
    d.   metaphor.
    e.   illustration.

8. Public speakers should strive to avoid sexist language because such language

    a.   may offend people in the audience.
    b.   is not politically correct.
    c.   is often inaccurate in portraying gender roles.
    d.   all of the above.
    e.   a and c only.

9. Which of the following is discussed in your textbook as a way to use language clearly?

    a.   use familiar words
    b.   choose concrete words
    c.   eliminate clutter
    d.   all of the above
    e.   a and b only

10. "Our mission is to right wrong, to do justice, and to serve humanity" is an example of

    a.   simile.
    b.   antithesis.
    c.   metaphor
    d.   imagery.
    e.   parallelism.

# Chapter 12 Delivery

## True-False Quiz

*Indicate whether each of the following statements is true or false by <u>circling</u> the appropriate letter.*

1.  T  F  Good speech delivery conveys a speaker's ideas without calling attention to itself.

2.  T  F  The question-and-answer session can have as much impact on an audience as what a speaker says during the speech itself.

3.  T  F  Pitch is the relative highness or lowness of the speaker's voice.

4.  T  F  "Conversational quality" in a speech means that the speaker talks the same as she or he would in ordinary conversation.

5.  T  F  Vocalized pauses are an effective way to increase a speaker's credibility.

6.  T  F  If you say the "s" in Illinois or the "p" in pneumonia, you are making a mistake in articulation.

7.  T  F  Dialects are usually based on regional or ethnic speech patterns.

8.  T  F  When a speaker's nonverbal communication is inconsistent with his or her words, listeners tend to believe the words rather than the nonverbal communication.

9.  T  F  When conducting a question-and-answer session, you should usually restate or paraphrase each question before you answer it.

10. T  F  You should start to establish eye contact with the audience even before you begin to speak.

# Chapter 12 Delivery

## Multiple Choice Quiz

*Indicate the <u>best</u> answer for each of the following questions by circling the correct letter.*

1.  Good speech delivery

    a.  has a conversational quality.
    b.  does not call attention to itself.
    c.  requires a strong voice.
    d.  all of the above.
    e.  a and b only.

2.  When speaking from a manuscript, you should

    a.  practice aloud to make sure the speech sounds natural.
    b.  be certain the final manuscript is legible at a glance.
    c.  work on establishing eye contact with the audience.
    d.  all of the above.
    e.  a and b only.

3.  The _____ speaker uses only brief notes or a speaking outline to jog the memory.

    a.  after-dinner
    b.  commemorative
    c.  informative
    d.  extemporaneous
    e.  persuasive

4.  "Conversational quality" in speech delivery means that the

    a.  speech sounds spontaneous even though it has been rehearsed.
    b.  speaker is not speaking from memory.
    c.  speaker talks the same as she or he would in ordinary conversation.
    d.  all of the above.
    e.  b and c only.

5.  The relative highness or lowness of sounds produced by the human voice is called

    a.  rate.
    b.  pitch.
    c.  tone.
    d.  quality.
    e.  volume.

6. According to your textbook, when people in one region of the country say "warter," while people in another region of the country say "water," the difference is a matter of

   a. inflection.
   b. verbalization.
   c. dialect.
   d. enunciation.
   e. intonation.

7. A public speaker who frequently says "uh," "er," or "um" is failing to make effective use of

   a. vocal variety.
   b. pauses.
   c. pitch.
   d. rate.
   e. inflection.

8. In which of the following situations will the personal appearance of the speaker have an impact on the audience?

   a. a politician presenting a campaign speech
   b. a business executive giving a financial report
   c. a professor giving a lecture
   d. all of the above
   e. a and b only

9. What does your textbook advise regarding the use of gestures in a speech?

   a. Gestures should be suited to the audience and occasion.
   b. Speakers should have a vast number of graceful gestures.
   c. Gestures should appear natural and spontaneous.
   d. all of the above
   e. a and c only

10. When conducting a question-and-answer session, you should

   a. view the session as one more opportunity to communicate your ideas.
   b. respond to hostile questions in a defensive and argumentative manner.
   c. allow each questioner to ask as many follow-up questions as they wish.
   d. all of the above.
   e. a and c only.

# Chapter 13 Using Visual Aids

## True-False Quiz

*Indicate whether each of the following statements is true or false by <u>circling</u> the appropriate letter.*

1.   T  F    One of the advantages of using visual aids in a speech is that their meaning is instantly clear to the audience.

2.   T  F    Research has shown that an average speaker who uses visual aids will come across as more credible and better prepared than a speaker who does not use visual aids.

3.   T  F    Because a picture is worth a thousand words, it is a good idea to pass photographs among the audience in order to illustrate your point.

4.   T  F    If you were summarizing statistical trends in a speech, the best visual aid to use would probably be a graph.

5.   T  F    In most circumstances it is an excellent idea to present visual aids by drawing or writing on the chalkboard.

6.   T  F    It is important to maintain eye contact with your audience when you are presenting a visual aid.

7.   T  F    When making a multimedia presentation, you should always be prepared to give your speech even if the equipment malfunctions.

8.   T  F    If you wanted to summarize the steps of a process in a speech, the best kind of visual aid to use would probably be a chart.

9.   T  F    In most circumstances you should keep your visual aids on display throughout your speech.

10.  T  F    When you are going to give an audience material to take home from a speech, you should usually distribute the material after you are finished speaking.

# Chapter 13 Using Visual Aids

## Multiple Choice Quiz

*Indicate the <u>best</u> answer for each of the following questions by circling the correct letter.*

1. According to your textbook, which of the following is an advantage of using visual aids in a speech?

   a. Using visual aids can increase the clarity of a speaker's message.
   b. Using visual aids can increase the audience's retention of a speaker's message.
   c. Using visual aids can increase the persuasiveness of a speaker's message.
   d. all of the above
   e. a and b only

2. If the object you want to use as a visual aid is not available, the next best option ideally is a

   a. model.
   b. chart.
   c. slide.
   d. photograph.
   e. drawing.

3. Which of the following would probably be the best kind of visual aid to demonstrate the five major areas of spending in the federal budget?

   a. a pie graph
   b. a diagram
   c. a line graph
   d. a chart
   e. a photograph

4. According to your textbook, charts are especially useful as visual aids when a speaker needs to

   a. summarize the steps in a process.
   b. present information the audience might want to write down.
   c. include more categories than can be presented in a pie or bar graph.
   d. all of the above.
   e. a and c only.

5.      Visual aids are most effective when they are

    a.   integrated with the rest of the speech.
    b.   explained clearly.
    c.   passed among the audience.
    d.   all of the above.
    e.   a and b only.

6.      According to your textbook, when using visual aids in a speech, you should

    a.   avoid drawing visual aids on the chalkboard.
    b.   not worry about keeping eye contact with the audience.
    c.   try to pass visual aids among the audience.
    d.   keep visual aids on display throughout the speech.
    e.   set up visual aids to the left of the lectern.

7.      _____ are clear sheets of acetate that can be used to present a variety of visual aids.

    a.   Graphs
    b.   Transparencies
    c.   Slides
    d.   Videotapes
    e.   Charts

8.      Elisa is giving a speech on women's athletics and has brought a petition for her listeners to sign. When should she circulate the petition?

    a.   before she begins her speech
    b.   after she reveals the topic of her speech
    c.   after explaining the problems faced by women's athletic teams
    d.   while urging her audience to take action during the conclusion of the speech
    e.   after she has finished speaking

9.      According to your textbook, when giving a multimedia presentation, you should

    a.   give yourself plenty of time to prepare your slides and to rehearse the delivery of your presentation.
    b.   double check your equipment before the audience arrives to make sure the equipment is working properly.
    c.   be prepared to give your speech effectively even if all the multimedia equipment were to malfunction.
    d.   all of the above.
    e.   a and b only.

10.     When selecting fonts for a visual aid, you should usually use

    a.   a minimum of four fonts to provide visual variety.
    b.   decorative fonts because they will make the aid more interesting.
    c.   all capital letters so the lettering will be easy to read.
    d.   all of the above.
    e.   none of the above.

# Chapter 14 Speaking to Inform

## True-False Quiz

*Indicate whether each of the following statements is true or false by <u>circling</u> the appropriate letter.*

1.  T  F   An informative speech about a process that has as many as ten or twelve steps is one of the few times it is acceptable to have more than five main points.

2.  T  F   When giving an informative speech that explains a process, you will most likely arrange your main points in chronological order.

3.  T  F   One reason to use clear and straightforward language even when talking about complex ideas is that listeners must understand your message in the time it takes you to say it.

4.  T  F   A summary is seldom necessary in the conclusion of an informative speech.

5.  T  F   Informative speeches are seldom organized in topical order.

6.  T  F   The more you assume your audience knows about your speech topic, the greater are your chances of being misunderstood.

7.  T  F   One of the biggest barriers to effective informative speaking is using language that is too simple for the audience.

8.  T  F   Your textbook recommends comparison and contrast as ways to avoid abstractions in an informative speech.

9.  T  F   Although essay writers are often urged to avoid personal references such as "I," "you," and "we," you should usually try to include such references in an informative speech.

10. T  F   Informative speakers need to work as hard as persuasive speakers at relating the topic directly to the audience.

# Chapter 14 Speaking to Inform

## Multiple Choice Quiz

*Indicate the best answer for each of the following questions by circling the correct letter.*

1.  Which of the following is an instance of informative speaking?

    a.  a student urging an instructor to reconsider the due date for an assignment
    b.  a student sharing ideas about leadership based on a book she has read
    c.  a student on stage telling jokes during the intermission of a play
    d.  all of the above
    e.  a and b only

2.  "To inform my audience how to add memory to a computer" is a specific purpose statement for an informative speech about a(n)

    a.  operation.
    b.  function.
    c.  event.
    d.  concept.
    e.  process.

3.  If your specific purpose statement were "To inform my audience about the major kinds of dog breeds," you would probably organize your speech in _____ order.

    a.  chronological
    b.  spatial
    c.  descriptive
    d.  topical
    e.  causal

4.  If your specific purpose were "To inform my audience of the major steps in an effective job interview," you would probably organize your speech in _____ order.

    a.  comparative
    b.  spatial
    c.  chronological
    d.  causal
    e.  illustrative

5. "To inform my audience about the removal of the Cherokee Indians from their native lands" is an example of a specific purpose statement for a speech about a(n)

    a. function.
    b. event.
    c. condition.
    d. object.
    e. concept.

6. When giving an informative speech to a general audience, you should take special care to

    a. state your ideas in abstract terms.
    b. establish goodwill with the audience in the introduction.
    c. avoid being too technical.
    d. all of the above.
    e. a and b only.

7. Your textbook recommends using _____ in your informative speeches as a way to keep your ideas from being overly abstract.

    a. contrast
    b. description
    c. comparison
    d. all of the above
    e. a and c only

8. If your specific purpose statement were "To inform my audience about the different layers of the atmosphere," you would probably organize your speech in _____ order.

    a. topical
    b. chronological
    c. spatial
    d. comparative
    e. causal

9. What does your textbook mean when it recommends that you "personalize your ideas" in an informative speech?

    a. Bring information to life by using examples and illustrations.
    b. Use dramatic statistics for a personal effect.
    c. Use true-to-life examples rather than hypothetical examples.
    d. Use slang and jargon to give the speech a personal tone.
    e. Avoid concrete language because it makes ideas vague and impersonal.

10. "To inform my audience about the basic beliefs of Buddhism" is an example of a specific purpose statement for an informative speech about a(n)

    a. concept.
    b. event.
    c. function.
    d. process.
    e. object.

# Chapter 15 Speaking to Persuade

## True-False Quiz

*Indicate whether each of the following statements is true or false by <u>circling</u> the appropriate letter.*

1.   T  F   One way for a persuasive speaker to uphold the ethical obligations of speechmaking is to learn about all sides of an issue.

2.   T  F   A persuasive speech on a question of fact is essentially the same as an informative speech.

3.   T  F   "To persuade my audience that cloning human beings is morally unjustifiable" is a specific purpose statement for a persuasive speech on a question of value.

4.   T  F   "To persuade my audience that video games are a major cause of youth violence" is a specific purpose statement for a persuasive speech on a question of policy.

5.   T  F   Research indicates that audiences often engage in a mental give-and-take with the speaker as they listen to a persuasive speech.

6.   T  F   Audience analysis and adaptation are less challenging in persuasive speaking than in speaking to inform.

7.   T  F   When you give a persuasive speech on a question of policy, you can seek either passive agreement or immediate action from your audience.

8.   T  F   When you discuss a question of policy, you must deal with three basic issues—need, plan, and practicality.

9.   T  F   If you advocate a new policy in a persuasive speech, your main points will usually fall naturally into topical order.

10.  T  F   Monroe's motivated sequence is most appropriate for speeches that try to persuade listeners to take immediate action.

# Chapter 15 Speaking to Persuade

## Multiple Choice Quiz

*Indicate the best answer for each of the following questions by circling the correct letter.*

1.  Which of the following is an instance of persuasive speaking?

    a.  A president of a company presenting an award to an outstanding employee.
    b.  A marketing manager explaining a new product to the company's sales force.
    c.  A personnel manager defining employee benefits at a meeting of workers.
    d.  A union representative urging management to avoid a strike by raising wages.
    e.  A finance officer reporting sales figures to the board of directors.

2.  "To persuade my audience that long-term exposure to electromagnetic fields can cause serious health problems" is a specific purpose statement for a persuasive speech on a question of

    a.  value.
    b.  opinion.
    c.  attitude.
    d.  policy.
    e.  fact.

3.  As your textbook explains, if you want to persuade a skeptical audience, you need to

    a.  Organize the speech in Monroe's motivated sequence.
    b.  Urge the audience to take immediate action.
    c.  Circulate an audience-analysis questionnaire.
    d.  Answer the reasons for the audience's skepticism.
    e.  Focus your speech on questions of practicality.

4.  Which of the following specific purpose statements is from a persuasive speech seeking immediate action?

    a.  To persuade my audience that the federal government should increase funding to provide computers for children in low-income housing.
    b.  To persuade my audience that the state must increase funding for wetland preservation.
    c.  To persuade my audience that federal campaign finance laws must be reformed to preserve the integrity of electoral process.
    d.  To persuade my audience to decrease the amount of electricity they use during the summer in order to prevent blackouts.
    e.  To persuade my audience that the college administration should increase spending for intramural athletics on campus.

5.   That part of the audience a speaker most wants to persuade is called the

   a.   specific audience.
   b.   designated audience.
   c.   central audience.
   d.   special audience.
   e.   target audience.

6.   Persuasive speeches on questions of _____ argue for or against particular courses of action.

   a.   need
   b.   value
   c.   policy
   d.   fact
   e.   plan

7.   Regardless of whether your aim is to encourage passive agreement or immediate action, you must deal with three basic issues whenever you discuss a question of policy. They are

   a.   cause, effect, and practicality.
   b.   evidence, practicality, and reasoning.
   c.   need, action, and reaction.
   d.   problem, plan, and solution.
   e.   need, plan, and practicality.

8.   If you give a persuasive speech advocating a change in policy, your main points often will fall naturally into _____ order.

   a.   problem-solution
   b.   chronological
   c.   causal
   d.   comparative advantages
   e.   topical

9.   According to your textbook, "To persuade my audience that downloading music from the Internet for personal use is ethically wrong" is a specific purpose statement for a persuasive speech on a question of

   a.   policy.
   b.   opinion.
   c.   value.
   d.   legality.
   e.   fact.

10.   Which organizational pattern is especially effective for persuasive speeches that seek immediate action by listeners?

   a.   comparative advantages order
   b.   Monroe's motivated sequence
   c.   problem-solution order
   d.   reflective-thinking sequence
   e.   psychological process order

# Chapter 16 Methods of Persuasion

## True-False Quiz

*Indicate whether each of the following statements is true or false by <u>circling</u> the appropriate letter.*

1.   T  F   Competence and character are the most important factors affecting a speaker's credibility.

2.   T  F   Research shows that a speaker's credibility is strongly affected by his or her delivery.

3.   T  F   Research indicates that evidence is usually more persuasive when it is stated in specific rather than general terms.

4.   T  F   Reasoning from specific instances involves progressing from a number of particular facts to a general conclusion.

5.   T  F   The following statement is an example of reasoning from principle: "Places such as Singapore that allow caning and other forms of corporal punishment have exceedingly low crime rates. If caning were used in the United States, the U.S. would have lower crime rates as well."

6.   T  F   In addition to being illogical, the *ad hominem* fallacy is also unethical.

7.   T  F   The slippery slope fallacy assumes that because something is popular, it is therefore good, correct, or desirable.

8.   T  F   One of the advantages of using causal reasoning in a persuasive speech is that the relationship between causes and effects is usually fairly obvious.

9.   T  F   As your textbook explains, it is unethical to use emotional appeal in a persuasive speech on a question of policy.

10.  T  F   The most important question to ask when assessing analogical reasoning is whether the two cases being compared are essentially alike.

# Chapter 16 Methods of Persuasion

## Multiple Choice Quiz

*Indicate the best answer for each of the following questions by circling the correct letter.*

1.      According to your textbook, the two most important factors affecting the credibility of a persuasive speaker are

   a.   competence and character.
   b.   prestige and charisma.
   c.   character and reputation.
   d.   popularity and intelligence.
   e.   charisma and competence.

2.      According to your textbook, the following statement is an example of what type of fallacy?

   How can we be so concerned about shielding children in the U.S. from Internet pornography when millions of children around the world continue to be sold into slavery every year?

   a.   either-or
   b.   red herring
   c.   false deduction
   d.   *ad hominem*
   e.   invalid analogy

3.      When giving a persuasive speech to an audience that opposes your point of view, it is especially important that you use _____ to answer their objections to your views.

   a.   visual aids
   b.   syllogisms
   c.   credibility statements
   d.   emotional appeals
   e.   evidence

4.      According to your textbook, as a persuasive speaker, your two *major* concerns with respect to reasoning are to

   a.   establish credibility and reason correctly.
   b.   make sure your reasoning is clear and credible.
   c.   avoid fallacies and support reasoning with testimony.
   d.   adapt reasoning to both hostile and favorable listeners.
   e.   make sure your reasoning is sound and persuasive.

5.   Which of the following is presented in your textbook as a guideline for reasoning from specific instances in a persuasive speech?

   a.   reinforce your argument with statistics and testimony
   b.   include at least one extended example among your specific instances
   c.   avoid generalizing too hastily
   d.   all of the above
   e.   a and c only

6.   According to your textbook, emotional appeal is *not* appropriate in which kind of persuasive speech?

   a.   the speech on a question of fact
   b.   the speech on a question of value
   c.   the speech on a question of proof
   d.   the speech on a question of policy
   e.   the speech on a question of ethics

7.   To create common ground with an audience in the introduction of a persuasive speech, your textbook recommends that you

   a.   show the audience that you share their values.
   b.   use statistics to show the extent of a problem.
   c.   confront the audience for failing to do the right thing.
   d.   all of the above.
   e.   a and b only.

8.   According to your textbook, when you reason from principle in a persuasive speech, you should give special attention to

   a.   deciding whether you need to support your general principle with evidence.
   b.   showing that the analogy underlying your general principle is valid.
   c.   establishing your credibility to speak on the matter of principle at hand.
   d.   avoiding the fallacy of *post hoc, ergo proper hoc* in your reasoning.
   e.   balancing the time you spend on your general principle and minor premise.

9.   What error in reasoning is exemplified by the following statement?

   I always wear my blue sweater when I take an exam, but I couldn't find it yesterday. If I had worn it yesterday, I would not have flunked my accounting exam.

   a.   circular thinking
   b.   hasty generalization
   c.   invalid analogy
   d.   false cause
   e.   faulty deduction

10.    When reasoning analogically, you infer that

    a.    a causal relationship can be established between two or more events.
    b.    what is true in one case will also be true in a similar case.
    c.    a general principle is validated by a question of fact.
    d.    your position is true because it is demonstrated by statistical trends.
    e.    a specific conclusion is true because it is verified by a general principle.

# Chapter 17 Speaking on Special Occasions

## True-False Quiz

*Indicate whether each of the following statements is true or false by <u>circling</u> the appropriate letter.*

1. T F The primary purpose of a special occasion speech is to convey information to an audience.

2. T F One major purpose of a speech of introduction is to establish a welcoming climate that will boost the credibility of the main speaker.

3. T F When giving a speech of presentation, you should usually explain why the recipient is being given his or her award.

4. T F The three major traits of a good acceptance speech are brevity, humility, and graciousness.

5. T F The fundamental purpose of a commemorative speech is to inspire your listeners.

6. T F A speech urging Congress to construct a memorial in Washington, D.C., to recognize women's contributions to the American Revolution is an example of a commemorative speech.

7. T F An after-dinner speech is best thought of as a kind of speech to inform.

8. T F "To entertain my audience by telling them about the typical mishaps that happen during family vacations" is an appropriate specific purpose statement for an after-dinner speech.

9. T F A commemorative speech paying tribute to a person is essentially a biography of that person.

10. T F The basic purpose of an acceptance speech is to give thanks for a gift or an award.

# Chapter 17 Speaking on Special Occasions

## Multiple Choice Quiz

*Indicate the **best** answer for each of the following questions by circling the correct letter.*

1. One main purpose of a speech of introduction is to

   a. explain why the person being introduced is receiving her or his award.
   b. inspire the audience with a sense of the significance of the occasion.
   c. create a welcoming climate to build enthusiasm for the main speaker.
   d. explain why listeners should pay tribute to a person, idea, or institution.
   e. enhance the credibility of the speaker who is making the introduction.

2. When giving a speech of presentation, you should usually

   a. tell why the recipient is receiving her or his award.
   b. present the main speaker briefly and accurately.
   c. avoid mentioning the losers of the award competition.
   d. adapt your presentation to the main speaker.
   e. give a brief biography of the main speaker.

3. According to your textbook, when your fundamental purpose in a speech is to inspire the audience, you are most likely going to be giving a(n) _____ speech.

   a. informative
   b. persuasive
   c. after-dinner
   d. commemorative
   e. acceptance

4. Which of the following is an appropriate specific purpose statement for an after-dinner speech?

   a. To entertain my audience by telling them the lengths parents go to in order to get kids to eat healthy foods.
   b. To entertain my audience by examining the lighter side of terrorism and insurgency in the Middle East.
   c. To entertain my audience by discussing the absurd questions people ask when they call for technical support.
   d. all of the above
   e. a and c only

5.   Which of the following is an example of a commemorative speech?

    a.   the President's State of the Union message
    b.   a soccer coach's pep talk
    c.   a speaker's acceptance of an award
    d.   a teacher's lecture on banking ethics
    e.   a daughter's eulogy in honor of her father

6.   All of the following are presented in your textbook as guidelines for a speech of introduction *except*

    a.   be brief.
    b.   adapt your remarks to the occasion.
    c.   bring the speech to life by using a hypothetical example.
    d.   try to create a sense of anticipation and drama.
    e.   make sure your remarks are completely accurate.

7.   According to your textbook, a speech in which an individual gives thanks for a gift or award is termed a(n)

    a.   speech of presentation.
    b.   commemorative speech.
    c.   after-dinner speech.
    d.   acceptance speech.
    e.   speech of introduction.

8.   When giving a speech of presentation, you should usually

    a.   tell why the recipient is receiving her or his award.
    b.   present the main speaker briefly and accurately.
    c.   avoid mentioning the losers of the award competition.
    d.   adapt your presentation to the main speaker.
    e.   give a brief biography of the main speaker.

9.   When delivering a commemorative speech, you should take special care to

    a.   mention all the achievements of the person being commemorated.
    b.   heighten appreciation for the person being commemorated.
    c.   use creative language to express feelings and sentiments.
    d.   all of the above.
    e.   b and c only.

10.   Although it is always based on materials chosen for their entertainment value, the _____ speech should strive to make a thoughtful point about its theme.

    a.   after-dinner
    b.   presentation
    c.   commemorative
    d.   acceptance
    e.   introductory

# Chapter **18** Speaking in Small Groups

## True-False Quiz

*Indicate whether each of the following statements is true or false by <u>circling</u> the appropriate letter.*

1.  T  F    Most experts set the maximum number of members for a small group at seven or eight.

2.  T  F    The newest or least experienced member of a small group is usually referred to as the implied leader.

3.  T  F    The task needs of a small group include such matters as distributing the workload among group members, keeping the group on track, and helping the group reach consensus.

4.  T  F    The procedural needs of a small group include such matters as whether members get along with each other and feel good about their roles in the group.

5.  T  F    Collecting information about the discussion topic is an example of a maintenance need in a small group.

6.  T  F    Hidden agendas are necessary for effective group discussion.

7.  T  F    Disagreements in a small group should be kept at the task level rather than the interpersonal level.

8.  T  F    "What steps should be taken to reduce gun violence in the U.S.?" is an example of a well-worded question for a problem-solving group discussion.

9.  T  F    The best way to reach a consensus decision in a problem-solving group is to take a vote on the issue in dispute.

10. T  F    In a symposium, each participant in turn delivers a prepared speech on a different aspect of a common topic.

# Chapter 18  Speaking in Small Groups

## Multiple Choice Quiz

*Indicate the best answer for each of the following questions by circling the correct letter.*

1.  A group member to whom other members defer because of his or her rank or expertise is called a(n)

    a.  implied leader.
    b.  specific leader.
    c.  emergent leader.
    d.  designated leader.
    e.  appointed leader.

2.  Randall is talkative and offers his opinions freely during small group meetings. Because he participates more than the other members, he has assumed a leadership role within the group. What kind of leader is Randall?

    a.  task leader
    b.  implied leader
    c.  emergent leader
    d.  designated leader
    e.  accidental leader

3.  According to your textbook, what are the three kinds of leadership needs faced by all problem-solving small groups?

    a.  agenda needs, task needs, and consensus needs
    b.  decision needs, maintenance needs, and personal needs
    c.  procedural needs, agenda needs, and participation needs
    d.  research needs, schedule needs, and judgment needs
    e.  task needs, procedural needs, and maintenance needs

4.  According to your textbook, when formulating a question for discussion, a problem-solving small group should phrase the question

    a.  so the whole group can answer it.
    b.  so the group can reach a majority decision.
    c.  so as to allow a wide variety of answers.
    d.  so as to avoid interpersonal conflict in the group.
    e.  all of the above.

5.    Which of the following is mentioned in your textbook as a responsibility of *every* member in a small group?

    a.    reach solutions swiftly
    b.    develop hidden agendas
    c.    call for a vote on major issues
    d.    avoid disagreement at all costs
    e.    encourage full participation

6.    Once a problem-solving small group has defined the problem, what is the *next* step they should follow in the reflective-thinking method for small group discussion?

    a.    establish criteria for solutions
    b.    select the best solution
    c.    set an agenda for solving the problem
    d.    reach a consensus decision
    e.    analyze the problem

7.    As your textbook explains, a decision that is acceptable to all members of a small group is called a _____ decision.

    a.    prudent
    b.    consensus
    c.    deliberative
    d.    compromise
    e.    judicious

8.    If Max is designated to present the findings and recommendations of his small group's deliberations to a large group of stockholders, he will most likely need to

    a.    prepare an oral report.
    b.    create a panel discussion.
    c.    give an impromptu presentation.
    d.    plan a town hall meeting.
    e.    moderate a symposium.

9.    Which of the following is a maintenance need of a problem-solving small group?

    a.    easing interpersonal tensions among group members
    b.    using the Internet to research the issue under consideration
    c.    ordering lunch for the group during its scheduled break
    d.    outlining the major reason for adopting the group's policy
    e.    organizing a symposium to present the group's decision

10.    As explained in your textbook, which of the following is a defining trait of a small group?

    a.    the group assembles for a specific purpose
    b.    the group contains a minimum of three members
    c.    the group has a designated leader
    d.    all of the above
    e.    a and b only

# Part Four

# Answers to

# Chapter Quizzes

# Chapter 1 Speaking in Public

## True-False Quiz

*Indicate whether each of the following statements is true or false by <u>circling</u> the appropriate letter.*

1. <u>T</u> F     The three major goals of public speaking are to inform, to persuade, and to entertain.

2. <u>T</u> F     When you adjust to the situation of a public speech, you are doing on a larger scale what you do everyday in conversation.

3. <u>T</u> F     Thinking positively about your ability to give a speech is one way to control your anxiety about speaking.

4. T <u>F</u>     Critical thinking is a way of thinking negatively about everything you hear in a speech.

5. <u>T</u> F     The nonverbal messages that listeners send back to speakers are called feedback.

6. T <u>F</u>     Most of the time the listener's frame of reference is identical with the speaker's frame of reference.

7. T <u>F</u>     When you give a speech to your classmates, you are engaged in one-way communication.

8. T <u>F</u>     Avoiding ethnocentrism means that you must agree with the values and practices of all groups and cultures.

9. <u>T</u> F     As your textbook explains, most of the nervousness public speakers feel internally is not visible to their listeners.

10. T <u>F</u>     Although language changes from culture to culture, the meaning of nonverbal signals is consistent across cultures.

# Chapter 1 Speaking in Public

## Multiple Choice Quiz

*Indicate the best answer for each of the following questions by circling the correct letter.*

1.    Everything a speaker says is filtered through a listener's

　*a.    frame of reference.
　b.    credibility.
　c.    feedback.
　d.    personal screen.
　e.    psychological field.

2.    Which of the following does your textbook recommend as a way to deal with nervousness in your speeches?

　a.    Concentrate on thinking about your stage fright.
　b.    Work especially hard on your conclusion.
　c.    Avoid making eye contact with your audience.
　d.    Try to generate extra adrenaline as you speak.
　*e.    Think of your speech as an act of communication.

3.    Dealing with such matters as the logical relationships among ideas, the soundness of evidence, and the differences between fact and opinion are all part of what your textbook calls

　a.    deduction.
　*b.    critical thinking.
　c.    rational communication.
　d.    oral deliberation.
　e.    induction.

4.    According to your textbook, a listener anxious about an upcoming exam, worried about a recent argument with a friend, or distracted by cold air in the classroom would be experiencing

　*a.    interference.
　b.    situational cues.
　c.    communication apprehension.
　d.    psychological dissonance.
　e.    feedback.

5.    Public speakers who seek to communicate with listeners from cultures other than their own need to take special care to avoid _____ in their speeches.

&ast;a.   ethnocentrism
   b.   vocalized pauses
   c.   personal statements
   d.   visual aids
   e.    gestures

6.    Which of the following strategies is *least* likely to help you deal with nervousness in your speeches?

   a.   thinking positively
&ast;b.   concentrating on your stage fright
   c.   working especially hard on your introduction
   d.   making eye contact with members of your audience
   e.    using visual aids

7.    According to your textbook, when you employ the power of visualization as a method of controlling stage fright, you should

   a.   decrease the time spent preparing your speech.
   b.   keep your mental pictures from becoming too vivid.
&ast;c.   focus on the positive aspects of your speech.
   d.   all of the above.
   e.   a and b only.

8.    According to your textbook, the three major goals of public speaking are informing, persuading, and

   a.   demonstrating.
&ast;b.   entertaining.
   c.   actuating.
   d.   selling.
   e.    convincing.

9.    _____ lets you know how your message is being received.

   a.   Vocal variety
   b.   Credibility
&ast;c.   Feedback
   d.   Interference
   e.   Audience adaptation

10.    Many of the skills used in public speaking are the same as those used in everyday conversation. These skills include

   a.   organizing your thoughts logically.
   b.   tailoring your message to your audience.
   c.   adapting to listener feedback.
&ast;d.   all of the above.
   e.   b and c only.

# Chapter 2 Ethics and Public Speaking

## True-False Quiz

*Indicate whether each of the following statements is true or false by <u>circling</u> the appropriate letter.*

1. <u>T</u> F  The first responsibility of a speaker is to make sure her or his goal is ethically sound.

2. T <u>F</u>  As the Roman rhetorician Quintilian noted 2,000 years ago, the ideal of commendable speechmaking is to persuade the audience by any means necessary.

3. T <u>F</u>  A speaker's ethical obligations decrease as the size of the audience decreases.

4. <u>T</u> F  Ethical decisions need to be justified against a set of standards or criteria.

5. <u>T</u> F  One of the best ways to avoid falling into the trap of plagiarism is to start work on your speeches well before they are due.

6. T <u>F</u>  Taking someone's entire speech and passing it off as your own is a form of unethical behavior called incremental plagiarism.

7. <u>T</u> F  It is necessary for a public speaker to identify his or her source whether the speaker is paraphrasing or quoting verbatim.

8. <u>T</u> F  Just as public speakers have ethical responsibilities, so too do the people who listen to a speech.

9. T <u>F</u>  Global plagiarism occurs when a speaker patches together several quotations or paraphrases without citing the sources of the statements.

10. <u>T</u> F  It is possible to disagree entirely with a speaker's ideas but still support the speaker's right to express those ideas.

# Chapter 2 Ethics and Public Speaking

## Multiple Choice Quiz

*Indicate the __best__ answer for each of the following questions by circling the correct letter.*

1.    According to your textbook, _____ plagiarism occurs when the speech as a whole is ethical but the speaker fails to give credit for particular quotations and paraphrases.

    a.    incidental
    b.    informative
    c.    inferential
    d.    invalid
 *e.    incremental

2.    In public speaking, sound ethical decisions involve weighing a potential course of action against

    a.    the frame of reference of the audience.
 *b.    a set of ethical guidelines or standards.
    c.    the speaker's strategic objectives.
    d.    a specific code of legal rules.
    e.    the personal opinions of the speaker.

3.    According to your textbook, the guidelines for ethical listening in a public speaking situation include

 *a.    maintaining the free and open expression of ideas.
    b.    judging the speaker on the basis of her or his prestige.
    c.    taking accurate notes of what the speaker says.
    d.    all of the above.
    e.    a and c only.

4.    As explained in your textbook, public speakers have an ethical obligation to avoid name-calling and other forms of abusive language because such language

    a.    is forbidden by the first amendment to the U.S. Constitution.
    b.    violates current standards of political correctness on college campuses.
    c.    changes meaning based on the frame of reference of the audience.
    d.    is used by speakers who are not fully prepared for their presentations.
 *e.    demeans the personal dignity of the groups or individuals being attacked.

5.    As your textbook explains, a speaker who assembles a speech by copying word for word from two or three sources is committing what kind of plagiarism?

    a.    global
    b.    incremental
    c.    scientific
*d.    patchwork
    e.     credible

6.    According to your textbook, _____ plagiarism occurs when a speaker takes a speech entirely from a single source and passes it off as her or his own.

    a.    incremental
*b.    global
    c.    valid
    d.    patchwork
    e.    scientific

7.    All of the following are presented in your textbook as guidelines for ethical speechmaking *except*

    a.    be honest in what you say.
    b.    avoid name-calling and other forms of abusive language.
    c.    be fully prepared for each speech.
    d.    make sure your goals are ethically sound.
*e.    explain your credibility on the speech topic.

8.    Which of the following does your textbook recommend as a way to steer clear of incremental plagiarism?

    a.    Avoid using direct quotations from other people in your speech.
    b.    Only use your original ideas so there is no risk of plagiarism.
    c.    Avoid citing sources that might make someone suspect plagiarism.
*d.    Cite the sources of all quotations and paraphrases in your speech.
    e.    Avoid paraphrasing information from other people in your speech.

9.    Jerome found several excellent sources for his informative speech. He pulled key information from them, blended those ideas into his own perspective, and cited his sources when he presented the speech. Which of the following statements *best* describes this situation?

*a.    Jerome is ethical because he cited his sources and used them to develop his own slant on the topic.
    b.    Jerome is guilty of incremental plagiarism because he used quotations and paraphrases from other people in his speech.
    c.    Jerome is ethical because he did not copy his speech from a single source.
    d.    Jerome is guilty of patchwork plagiarism because he used ideas from several different sources in his speech.
    e.    Jerome is guilty of global plagiarism because he did not develop his speech entirely from his own knowledge and experience.

10.   Because speechmaking is a form of power, we must always be sure to speak

    a.   concisely.
    b.   persuasively.
  *c.   ethically.
    d.   forcefully.
    e.   consistently.

# Chapter 3  Listening

## True-False Quiz

*Indicate whether each of the following statements is true or false by circling the appropriate letter.*

1.  T **F**    Note taking is usually a barrier to effective listening.

2.  **T** F    People need effective listening skills in almost all occupations.

3.  **T** F    Listening to provide emotional support for someone is called empathic listening.

4.  T **F**    When listening critically for evidence, you should consider primarily how the evidence relates to your personal frame of reference.

5.  T **F**    If you disagree with a speaker, you have nothing to gain by listening carefully.

6.  **T** F    According to your textbook, listening to understand a classroom lecture is an example of comprehensive listening.

7.  **T** F    People spend more time listening than in any other communicative activity.

8.  T **F**    Note taking is usually a barrier to effective listening.

9.  **T** F    One of the major barriers to effective communication is that the brain can process words much faster than a speaker can talk.

10. **T** F    According to your textbook, when focusing your listening, you should concentrate on a speaker's main points, evidence, and technique.

# Chapter 3 Listening

## Multiple Choice Quiz

*Indicate the best answer for each of the following questions by circling the correct letter.*

1.    In studies about communication skills within businesses, most business managers rank _____ as the skill most crucial to their jobs.

      a.   public speaking
      b.   conversation
      c.   writing
      d.   critical thinking
    *e.   listening

2.    Tara's campus organization has invited several travel agents to speak to the group about their best deals on trips for spring break. As Tara listens, she is deciding which travel package is the best one for her. During the presentations, she is engaged in which form of listening?

    *a.   critical
      b.   appreciative
      c.   comprehensive
      d.   empathic
      e.   intimate

3.    According to your textbook, when you focus your listening as a means of becoming a better listener, you should listen for

      a.   main points.
      b.   evidence.
      c.   technique.
    *d.   all of the above.
      e.   a and b only.

4.    According to your textbook, when you listen to evaluate a speaker's message for purposes of accepting it or rejecting it, what kind of listening is involved?

    *a.   critical
      b.   sympathetic
      c.   appreciative
      d.   empathic
      e.   comprehensive

5.  When listening for a speaker's evidence, you should keep an ear out for its

    a.  sufficiency.
    b.  accuracy.
    c.  objectivity.
    d.  relevance.
\*e.  all of the above.

6.  Lance is enjoying Chris Rock's stand-up comedy routine at the Civic Center. According to your textbook, Lance is engaged in _____ listening.

    a.  critical
\*b.  appreciative
    c.  comprehensive
    d.  empathic
    e.  intimate

7.  Ted is listening to the introduction of Janine's speech when he thinks to himself, "Man, this is really going to be boring." What aspect of poor listening identified in your textbook is Ted exhibiting in this example?

    a.  listening too hard
\*b  jumping to conclusions
    c.  rejecting the speaker's frame of reference
    d.  giving in to distractions
    e.  not listening comprehensively

8.  Sarah is listening to her roommate to provide emotional support in a time of distress. According to your textbook, Sarah is engaged in _____ listening.

    a.  critical
    b.  appreciative
\*c.  empathic
    d.  personal
    e.  comprehensive

9.  Which of the following is included among the four major causes of poor listening discussed in your textbook?

    a.  trying to remember everything the speaker says
    b.  jumping to conclusions about the speaker's ideas
    c.  taking written notes while the speech is in progress
    d.  all of the above
\*e.  a and b only

10.  Your textbook recommends _____ as the most effective method of note taking for listening to a speech.

    a.  trying to write down everything a speaker says
\*b.  creating a keyword outline
    c.  writing down a speaker's most interesting ideas
    d.  creating a full-sentence outline
    e.  using the Harvard listening system

# Chapter 4 Selecting a Topic and a Purpose

## True-False Quiz

*Indicate whether each of the following statements is true or false by* <u>circling</u> *the appropriate letter.*

1.  <u>T</u> F    The first step in speechmaking is choosing a topic for your speech.

2.  T <u>F</u>    Most often, a speaker's general purpose will fall into one of two categories—to inform or to demonstrate.

3.  T <u>F</u>    The central idea indicates precisely what the speaker hopes to accomplish in a speech.

4.  <u>T</u> F    "To inform my audience of the major steps in responding to a medical emergency" is an example of an effective specific purpose statement for an informative speech.

5.  T <u>F</u>    The specific purpose of a speech usually "sums up" the main points to be developed in the body of the speech.

6.  <u>T</u> F    The central idea of a speech should be stated as a full sentence.

7.  <u>T</u> F    "The three major expenses for people traveling abroad are transportation, food, and lodging" is an example of a well-worded central idea for a speech.

8.  T <u>F</u>    The specific purpose statement should usually be phrased as a question.

9.  T <u>F</u>    "To inform my audience about the origins of martial arts and how to perform yoga" is an example of an effective specific purpose statement for an informative speech.

10.  <u>T</u> F    The central idea reveals more about the content of a speech than does the specific purpose.

# Chapter 4  Selecting a Topic and a Purpose

## Multiple Choice Quiz

*Indicate the best answer for each of the following questions by circling the correct letter.*

1. According to your textbook, brainstorming is especially helpful when you are having trouble

   * a. choosing a speech topic.
   * b. determining the general purpose.
   * c. determining the specific purpose.
   * d. phrasing the central idea.
   * e. analyzing the audience.

2. Which of the following is out of place in a speech to inform?

   * a. advocating
   * b. explaining
   * c. reporting
   * d. demonstrating
   * e. telling

3. "To inform my audience about the three basic steps in preventive medicine" is an example of a

   * a. main point.
   * b. specific purpose.
   * c. thesis statement.
   * d. central idea.
   * e. general purpose.

4. According to your textbook, what is the *most important* early step in the process of developing a successful speech?

   * a. phrasing the general purpose
   * b. researching for speech materials
   * c. formulating the specific purpose
   * d. brainstorming for a central idea
   * e. selecting the residual message

5.    As a specific purpose statement, "To inform my audience about computer technology" is too

    a.    figurative.
\*b.    broad.
    c.    trivial.
    d.    technical.
    e.    detailed.

6.    Which of the following is appropriate in a speech to persuade?

    a.    advocating
    b.    exhorting
    c.    convincing
\*d.    all of the above
    e.    a and c only

7.    "To inform about saving for retirement" is a poorly phrased specific purpose statement because it

    a.    is too specific.
    b.    contains figurative language.
    c.    is written as a statement instead of a question.
\*d.    does not include a reference to the audience.
    e.    is too trivial.

8.    The central idea of a speech should

    a.    avoid figurative language.
    b.    be written as a full sentence.
    c.    be phrased as a question.
    d.    all of the above.
\*e.    a and b only.

9.    According to your textbook, "Getting an internship at a major corporation requires a great deal of work, but the rewards are well worth the effort" is an example of a(n)

    a.    speech proposal.
    b.    specific purpose.
    c.    informative thesis.
    d.    topic statement.
\*e.    central idea.

10.    "To persuade my audience that continuing to spend money on the space program is like throwing good money after bad" is a poorly phrased specific purpose statement for a speech because it is

\*a.    expressed in figurative language.
    b.    written as a declarative sentence rather than a question.
    c.    too technical.
    d.    all of the above.
    e.    a and c only.

# Chapter 5  Analyzing the Audience

## True-False Quiz

*Indicate whether each of the following statements is true or false by <u>circling</u> the appropriate letter.*

1.  T <u>F</u>    Adapting to audiences is one of the easiest tasks facing beginning speakers.

2.  T <u>F</u>    Audience analysis first comes into play after a speaker has chosen a specific purpose.

3.  <u>T</u> F    Even when listeners pay close attention, they don't process a speaker's message exactly as the speaker intended.

4.  <u>T</u> F    Gender, sexual orientation, age, race, ethnicity, and group membership are all factors to consider when conducting a demographic audience analysis.

5.  T <u>F</u>    As a general rule, the larger your audience the less formal your speech presentation should be.

6.  <u>T</u> F    Knowing how the physical setting might affect your listeners' receptivity to your ideas is an important factor in situational audience analysis.

7.  <u>T</u> F    Interest, knowledge, and attitude are the three most important factors to consider when determining an audience's disposition toward a speaker's topic.

8.  <u>T</u> F    No matter what the occasion, listeners will have fairly definite expectations about the kinds of speeches appropriate for the occasion.

9.  <u>T</u> F    Egocentrism means that audiences typically approach speeches by asking "Why is this important for me?"

10. T <u>F</u>    The process of audience adaptation is over by the time a speaker starts delivering the speech.

# Chapter 5   Analyzing the Audience

## Multiple Choice Quiz

*Indicate the best answer for each of the following questions by circling the correct letter.*

1.      Audience analysis is an important factor in which of the following?

     a.   selecting a topic
     b.   organizing the speech
     c.   choosing supporting materials
*d.   all of the above
     e.   a and c only

2.      The *primary* purpose of speechmaking is to

*a.   gain a desired response from listeners.
     b.   please the majority of the audience.
     c.   display the speaker's research skills.
     d.   practice getting up in front of an audience.
     e.   test new ideas through audience feedback.

3.      Dimitri plans to give a speech to his classmates about the principles of physics behind the design of hybrid automobiles. The most important factor for Dimitri to consider when analyzing his audience is probably its

     a.   age.
     b.   group membership.
     c.   attitude toward the speaker.
*d.   knowledge about the topic.
     e.    size.

4.      The process by which a speaker seeks to create a bond with listeners by emphasizing common values, goals, and experiences is referred to as _____ by communication scholars.

     a.   framing
*b.   identification
     c.   egocentrism
     d.   structuring
     e.    affiliation

5.    According to your textbook, which of the following is a factor in situational audience analysis?

    a.    the audience's cultural background
    b.    the audience's religious beliefs
    c.    the audience's group membership
    d.    the audience's gender
\*e.    the audience's attitude toward the topic

6.    Which of the following is a demographic characteristic of a speech audience?

\*a.    age
    b.    interest
    c.    size
    d.    attitude
    e.    knowledge

7.    Which of the following is a demographic characteristic of a speech audience?

\*a.    age
    b.    interest
    c.    size
    d.    attitude
    e.    knowledge

8.    To say that people usually want to hear about things that are meaningful to them is to say that people are

    a.    empathic.
    b.    eclectic.
    c.    egotistic.
    d.    egalitarian.
\*e.    egocentric.

9.    Which of the following elements usually has the greatest impact on the length a speech should be?

    a.    the audience's disposition toward the topic
    b.    the physical setting for the speech
    c.    the audience's attitudes toward the speaker
\*d.    the occasion for the speech
    e.    the group membership of the audience

10.    As the size of your audience increases, your presentation should usually become more

\*a.    formal.
    b.    flexible.
    c.    extemporaneous.
    d.    punctual.
    e.    informal.

# Chapter **6** Gathering Materials

## True-False Quiz

*Indicate whether each of the following statements is true or false by <u>circling</u> the appropriate letter.*

1.  T <u>F</u>   If you use a tape recorder in a research interview, you should keep it secret from the person being interviewed.

2.  <u>T</u> F   Periodical databases help you locate magazine and journal articles.

3.  T <u>F</u>   Because the Internet is such a vast source of information, your textbook recommends using it to replace library research when preparing your speeches.

4.  T <u>F</u>   You can almost always count on the reliability of Internet research materials found through major search engines such as Google and Yahoo.

5.  <u>T</u> F   One of the great strengths of the Internet as a research tool is the access it provides to government documents and publications.

6.  <u>T</u> F   According to your textbook, the three major criteria against which to test documents that you locate on the Internet are authorship, sponsorship, and recency.

7.  <u>T</u> F   When taking research notes, it is important to distinguish between direct quotations, paraphrases, and your own ideas.

8.  T <u>F</u>   The only way you can use a search engine to find information on the Internet is by conducting a keyword search.

9.  <u>T</u> F   One advantage of using virtual libraries for speech research is that they contain only material that has been screened for accuracy and reliability.

10. <u>T</u> F   Your most important task before conducting a research interview is to work out the questions you will ask during the interview.

# Chapter 6 Gathering Materials

## Multiple Choice Quiz

*Indicate the best answer for each of the following questions by circling the correct letter.*

1.    The most important task when preparing to conduct a research interview is

   *a.   devising questions to ask during the interview.
    b.   deciding whether or not to use a tape recorder.
    c.   choosing what to wear during the interview.
    d.   selecting an appropriate interviewing style.
    e.   deciding whether or not to take notes during the interview.

2.    The best source for numerical data about life in the United States is

    a.   *Who's Who.*
    b.   *Encyclopedia Americana.*
    c.   *World Almanac and Book of Facts.*
    d.   *New York Times Index.*
   *e.   *Statistical Abstract of the United States.*

3.    A(n) _____ is a research aid that catalogues articles from a large number of journals or magazines.

    a.   abstract
    b.   biographical aid
    c.   reference work
   *d.   periodical database
    e.   keyword index

4.    The _____ is the key to finding information in the library.

    a.   general index
   *b.   catalogue
    c.   periodicals guide
    d.   encyclopedia
    e.    browser

5.    When taking research notes, you should

    a.   put all notes from each source on a single index card or sheet of paper.
    b.   record notes only when you're sure you'll use the information in your speech.
    c.   take all notes as direct quotations.
    d.   all of the above.
   *  e.   none of the above.

6.      According to your textbook, the three criteria for judging the reliability of documents located on the Internet are recency, authorship, and

    a.   indexing.
\*b.   sponsorship.
    c.   interactivity.
    d.   graphics.
    e.   creativity.

7.      If you can't identify the author of a document on the World Wide Web, your textbook recommends that you

    a.   look up the year the document was published.
    b.   bookmark the document and return to it later.
\*c.   try to determine the sponsoring organization for the document.
    d.   double check the accuracy of the document's URL.
    e.   search for the document in the library.

8.      As your textbook explains, the best kind of search aid for locating reliable, high quality information on the Internet is a(n)

    a.   search engine.
    b.   electronic catalogue.
    c.   metasearch engine.
    d.   research pilot.
\*e.   virtual library.

9.      The part of the library that contains encyclopedias, yearbooks, dictionaries, biographical aids, atlases, and indexes is usually called the

    a.   research room.
    b.   periodical room.
\*c.   reference section.
    d.   circulation section.
    e.   information room.

10.     According to your textbook, when citing an Internet document in a speech bibliography, you should include the

    a.   date on which you accessed the document.
    b.   organization responsible for the document if the author's name is not known.
    c.   URL of the document.
\*d.   all of the above.
    e.   b and c only.

# Chapter 7 Supporting Your Ideas

## True-False Quiz

*Indicate whether each of the following statements is true or false by <u>circling</u> the appropriate letter.*

1.  <u>T</u>  F    One of the main reasons to use examples in a speech is that they put abstract ideas into concrete terms that listeners can easily understand.

2.  <u>T</u>  F    Brief examples can be used either to illustrate a point or to introduce a topic.

3.  <u>T</u>  F    Whenever you use a hypothetical example in a speech, it is usually a good idea to follow it with statistics or testimony to show that the example is not unrealistic.

4.  T  <u>F</u>    It is seldom necessary to cite the source of statistics in a speech.

5.  T  <u>F</u>    Research has shown that the more statistics you use, the more effective your speech is likely to be.

6.  T  <u>F</u>    Unlike testimony, which can easily be quoted out of context, statistics are difficult to manipulate for biased purposes.

7.  <u>T</u>  F    Acceptable testimony can include either statements from recognized experts or from ordinary people with special expertise on the topic.

8.  <u>T</u>  F    You should almost always round off statistics in a speech.

9.  T  <u>F</u>    Using strong, credible testimony is the best way to add human interest to a speech.

10. T  <u>F</u>    Examples and testimony are most effective in persuasive speeches, while statistics work best in informative speeches.

# Chapter 7 Supporting Your Ideas

## Multiple Choice Quiz

*Indicate the best answer for each of the following questions by circling the correct letter.*

1.  The best way to add human interest to your speech is to use

    *a.  examples.
     b.  quotations.
     c.  graphs.
     d.  statistics.
     e.  metaphors.

2.  The main value of using statistics in a speech is to

     a.  lend realism to the speech.
     b.  enhance the speaker's credibility.
     c.  make the speech more vivid.
     d.  avoid relying on testimony.
    *e.  quantify the speaker's ideas.

3.  According to your textbook, if you quoted your cousin about her experience digging for dinosaur bones last summer, you would be using _____ testimony.

    *a.  peer
     b.  personal
     c.  paraphrased
     d.  ordinary
     e.  direct

4.  To give the gist of someone's statement in your own words is to

    *a.  paraphrase.
     b.  hypothesize.
     c.  corroborate.
     d.  testify.
     e.  quote.

5.  Which of the following is recommended by your textbook as a way to enhance the effectiveness of your examples?

     a.  Practice delivery to enhance your extended examples.
     b.  Avoid using examples drawn from your personal experience.
     c.  Make your examples vivid and richly textured.
     d.  all of the above
    *e.  a and c only

6. When using statistics in a speech, you should usually

    a. manipulate the statistics to make your point.
    b. cite exact numbers rather than rounding off.
    c. increase your speaking rate when giving statistics.
*d. avoid using too many statistics.
    e. conceal the source of the statistics.

7. According to your textbook, if you quoted Harvard business professor John B. Matthews on the strengths and weaknesses of U.S. business schools, you would be using _____ testimony.

    a. peer
    b. professional
*c. expert
    d. unbiased
    e. valid

8. The more _____ your examples, the greater impact they are likely to have.

    a. hypothetical
    b. complex
    c. unusual
    d. expert
*e. vivid

9. According to your textbook, a good way to clarify statistical trends is to

    a. increase your speaking rate when giving statistics.
    b. consult the *Guinness Book of World Records*.
    c. use exact numbers rather than rounding off.
*d. use visual aids when presenting statistics.
    e. make sure the statistics are from unbiased sources.

10. The main value of using expert testimony in a speech is to

    a. enhance the vividness of the speaker's ideas.
    b. gain attention in the introduction of the speech.
*c. build the credibility of speakers who are not experts on their topics.
    d. keep the audience's attention throughout the body of the speech.
    e. relate the speaker's ideas directly to the audience.

# Chapter 8 Organizing the Body of the Speech

## True-False Quiz

*Indicate whether each of the following statements is true or false by <u>circling</u> the appropriate letter.*

1.   T <u>F</u>   Clear organization is usually less important in speaking than in writing.

2.   <u>T</u> F   Audiences find well-organized speakers to be more credible than poorly organized speakers.

3.   T <u>F</u>   According to your textbook, the introduction of a speech usually should be prepared before the body.

4.   T <u>F</u>   According to your textbook, most speeches should contain from five to eight main points.

5.   <u>T</u> F   Chronological organization is used primarily for informative speeches.

6.   T <u>F</u>   Speeches arranged in causal order usually have three main points.

7.   <u>T</u> F   Problem-solution order is used most often in persuasive speeches.

8.   T <u>F</u>   In topical order the main points proceed from top to bottom, left to right, front to back, east to west, or some similar route.

9.   <u>T</u> F   "The most important point to remember about . . ." is an example of a signpost.

10.   <u>T</u> F   According to your textbook, transitions state both the idea the speaker is leaving and the one the speaker is coming to.

# Chapter 8 Organizing the Body of the Speech

## Multiple Choice Quiz

*Indicate the best answer for each of the following questions by circling the correct letter.*

1.  What organizational pattern would probably be most effective for arranging the main points of a speech with the specific purpose "To inform my audience about three major ways to block junk mail from their e-mail system"?

    *a.  topical
     b.  logistical
     c.  chronological
     d.  technical
     e.  causal

2.  Here are the main points for a speech about the major steps involved in a successful job interview:

    I.    The first step is preparing for the interview before it takes place.
    II.   The second step is presenting yourself well during the interview itself.
    III.  The third step is following up after the interview.

    These main points are arranged in _____ order.

     a.  topical
     b.  spatial
    *c.  chronological
     d.  informative
     e.  causal

3.  According to your textbook, if the following statement occurred in the body of a speech, it would be an example of what kind of connective?

    In discussing the problem of childhood asthma, we shall look at the symptoms of the disease, its causes, and current treatments.

     a.  signpost
    *b   internal preview
     c.  transition
     d.  internal summary
     e.   bridge

4.    When main ideas follow a directional pattern, they are organized in

    a.   geographical order.
    b.   topical order.
  *c.   spatial order.
    d.   causal order.
    e.   chronological order.

5.    Which pattern of organization would probably be most effective for arranging the main points of a speech with the specific purpose "To persuade my audience that high school and college football programs should act now to reduce the incidents of serious injuries in their sport."

    a.   spatial
    b.   causal
  *c.   problem-solution
    d.   chronological
    e.   topical

6.    A speech about the causes and effects of domestic violence would most likely be organized in _____ order.

  *a.   causal
    b.   problem-solution
    c.   topical
    d.   informative
    e.   scientific

7.    The most effective order of main points in a speech depends above all on your topic, purpose, and

  *a.   audience.
    b.   research.
    c.   visual aids.
    d.   credibility.
    e.   delivery.

8.    Problem-solution order is most appropriate for organizing _____ speeches.

    a.   acceptance
    b.   informative
    c.   after-dinner
    d.   commemorative
  *e.   persuasive

9.    "Now that we have seen the causes of unrest in central Africa, we shall turn to their effects . . ." is an example of a(n)

    a.   internal preview.
  *b.   transition.
    c.   internal summary.
    d.   signpost.
    e.   main point.

10. Which of the following organizational patterns is used more than any other method of speech organization because of its applicability to almost any subject?

    a. chronological
    b. spatial
    c. problem-solution
 *d. topical
    e. causal

# Chapter 9 Beginning and Ending the Speech

## True-False Quiz

*Indicate whether each of the following statements is true or false by <u>circling</u> the appropriate letter.*

1. <u>T</u> F    Regardless of what other methods you use to gain attention, you should almost always relate the topic to your audience in the introduction of a speech.

2. <u>T</u> F    Goodwill is the audience's perception of whether the speaker has the best interests of the audience in mind.

3. T <u>F</u>    If your topic is clear in the body of the speech, there is no need to state it in the introduction.

4. <u>T</u> F    Establishing credibility is an important function of a speech introduction.

5. <u>T</u> F    One function of a preview statement is to signal that the body of the speech is about to begin.

6. <u>T</u> F    Under normal circumstances, you should work out the exact wording of your introduction after you have finished preparing the body of your speech.

7. T <u>F</u>    The crescendo conclusion is essentially a matter of the speaker getting louder and louder as the speech comes to an end.

8. T <u>F</u>    It is overly repetitious to restate the central idea in the conclusion of a speech.

9. T <u>F</u>    It is inappropriate for a public speaker to say anything so obvious as "in conclusion."

10. <u>T</u> F    One function of a speech conclusion is to reinforce the speaker's central idea.

# Chapter 9 Beginning and Ending the Speech

## Multiple Choice Quiz

*Indicate the best answer for each of the following questions by circling the correct letter.*

1.   Which of the following would you *most* likely find in a speech introduction?

   *a.   a credibility statement
   b.   a transition
   c.   a causal argument
   d.   an internal summary
   e.   a call to action

2.   Which of the following would you *least* likely find in a speech introduction?

   a.   a preview statement
   *b.   a call to action
   c.   a credibility statement
   d.   a provocative quotation
   e.   a startling statement

3.   Which of the following would you *most* likely find in a speech introduction?

   a.   a transition
   b.   an internal summary
   c.   a lengthy quotation
   *d.   a startling statement
   e.   a causal argument

4.   In the introduction of his speech on the Special Olympics, Mason mentioned that he had attended the events last year to cheer on a family friend who was competing in some races. Sharing this information with the audience helped Mason achieve which goal of a speech introduction?

   a.   relating to the audience
   b.   generating emotional appeal
   c.   stating the importance of the topic
   *d.   establishing credibility
   e.   previewing the body

5.	Which objective of a good speech introduction is fulfilled by the following statement?

> Today we will explore the three most important forms of intellectual property protection—copyrights, trademarks, and patents.

  *a.	preview the body
   b.	establish the speaker's goodwill
   c.	state the importance of the topic
   d.	summarize the introduction
   e.	relate to the audience

6.	According to your textbook, the best time to work out the exact wording of a speech introduction is

   a.	shortly after you determine the central idea.
   b.	before you work out the conclusion.
   c.	when you prepare your speaking outline.
   d.	as you rise to deliver an extemporaneous speech.
  *e.	after you prepare the body of the speech.

7.	Which of the following is recommended in your textbook as a way to reinforce the central idea in a speech conclusion?

   a.	end with a quotation
   b.	make a dramatic statement
   c.	refer to the introduction
  *d.	all of the above
   e.	a and b only

8.	Which of the following would you be *most* likely to find in a speech conclusion?

   a.	a preview statement
  *b.	a restatement of the central idea
   c.	a gesture of goodwill
   d.	a credibility statement
   e.	an announcement of the topic

9.	What does your textbook say about preparing an effective speech conclusion?

   a.	Make your conclusion about 5 to 10 percent of the entire speech.
   b.	Work especially hard on establishing your credibility in the conclusion.
   c.	Keep an eye out for concluding materials as you research the speech.
   d.	all of the above
  *e.	a and c only

10.	An appeal to action is most appropriate in the conclusion of a(n) _____ speech.

   a.	informative
   b.	after-dinner
   c.	acceptance
   d.	commemorative
  *e.	persuasive

# Chapter **10** Outlining the Speech

## True-False Quiz

*Indicate whether each of the following statements is true or false by <u>circling</u> the appropriate letter.*

1.   T   <u>F</u>   The preparation outline should be drawn up before a speaker begins research for a speech.

2.   <u>T</u>   F   In a preparation outline, the specific purpose is usually stated before the introduction.

3.   T   <u>F</u>   Stating main points in a word or two is usually sufficient for a preparation outline.

4.   T   <u>F</u>   The speaking outline is a more complete version of the preparation outline.

5.   <u>T</u>   F   A preparation outline should include transitions and internal summaries.

6.   T   <u>F</u>   In the most common system of outlining, main points are identified by capital letters.

7.   T   <u>F</u>   A speaking outline should be written on both sides of an index card or sheet of paper.

8.   <u>T</u>   F   You should keep your speaking outline as brief as possible.

9.   <u>T</u>   F   A speaking outline should usually include directions for delivering the speech.

10.   T   <u>F</u>   A bibliography is necessary in both the preparation outline and the speaking outline.

# Chapter 10 Outlining the Speech

## Multiple Choice Quiz

*Indicate the <u>best</u> answer for each of the following questions by circling the correct letter.*

1.   Outlining is an important part of public speaking because

    a.   an outline helps the speaker compile an organized preliminary bibliography.
 *b.   an outline helps ensure that ideas flow clearly from one to another.
    c.   an outline helps the speaker choose an interesting, sharply focused topic.
    d.   all of the above.
    e.   a and b only.

2.   Which of the following should be included in a preparation outline?

 *a.   the central idea
    b.   a general purpose statement
    c.   the preliminary bibliography
    d.   directions for delivering the speech
    e.   all of the above

3.   When making a preparation outline, you should

    a.   label transitions and internal summaries.
    b.   indicate the introduction, body, and conclusion with Roman numerals.
    c.   state the specific purpose as a separate unit before the outline itself.
    d.   all of the above.
 *e.   a and c only.

4.   Arranged in random order below are a main point, two subpoints, and two sub-subpoints from a speech preparation outline. Which is the main point?

    a.   Melanoma is the least common but most deadly form of skin cancer.
    b.   Each year about 7,400 people die from melanoma in the U.S.
    c.   Basal cell carcinoma is the most common type of skin cancer.
 *d.   Two types of skin cancer are melanoma and basal cell carcinoma.
    e.   Of all skin cancers diagnosed in the U.S., only 4 percent are melanoma.

5.      Which of the following is a correctly worded main point for a speech preparation outline?

    a.    Leadership.
    b.    What are the major types of leadership?
    c.    Two major types of leadership.
*d.    There are two major types of leadership.
    e.    Leadership: major types.

6.      Subpoints in a preparation outline are

    a.    listed just before the conclusion.
    b.    written in keywords to job the memory.
    c.    indicated by Roman numerals.
    d.    indented farther to the left than main points.
*e.    written in full sentences.

7.      All of the following are necessary in a preparation outline *except*

    a.    labels for the introduction, body, and conclusion.
*b.    directions for delivering the speech.
    c.    transitions, internal previews, and internal summaries.
    d.    a consistent pattern of indentation and symbolization.
    e.    a specific purpose statement.

8.      A catchy speech title is fine as long as it is

    a.    phrased as a question.
*b.    relevant to the speech.
    c.    written as a full sentence.
    d.    all of the above.
    e.    b and c only.

9.      A speaking outline

    a.    does not contain statistics and quotations.
    b.    uses full sentences to jog the speaker's memory.
*c.    is as brief as possible.
    d.    all of the above.
    e.    a and c only.

10.     When Terrence creates a speaking outline for his informative speech on hockey, he should

    a.    include cues for delivering the speech.
    b.    write out quotations he plans to use in the speech.
    c.    follow the visual framework of the preparation outline.
*d.    all of the above.
    e.    a and b only.

# Chapter 11 Using Language

## True-False Quiz

*Indicate whether each of the following statements is true or false by <u>circling</u> the appropriate letter.*

1. <u>T</u> F    The words we use to label an event determine to a great extent how we respond to that event.

2. T <u>F</u>    The denotative meaning of a word includes all the feelings, associations, and emotions that the word touches off in different people.

3. T <u>F</u>    As your textbook explains, a public speaker needs to use big words to impress the audience.

4. <u>T</u> F    "History is a drama with many acts" is an example of metaphor.

5. <u>T</u> F    The more abstract a word, the more ambiguous it will be.

6. T <u>F</u>    In dealing with technical topics, a speaker has little choice but to use technical language.

7. <u>T</u> F    "She darted around the bookstore like a hummingbird in a flower garden" is an example of simile.

8. T <u>F</u>    Antithesis and alliteration are excellent ways to enhance the imagery of a speech.

9. <u>T</u> F    Avoiding sexist language is important in public speaking both as a matter of audience adaptation and as a matter of accuracy in language.

10. <u>T</u> F    The connotative meaning of a word is more variable, figurative, and subjective than its denotative meaning.

# Chapter **11** Using Language

## Multiple Choice Quiz

*Indicate the best answer for each of the following questions by circling the correct letter.*

1.  Which of the following is discussed in your textbook as a basic criterion for the effective use of language in public speaking?

    a.  use language technically
    b.  use language appropriately
    c.  use language clearly
    d.  all of the above
    *e.  b and c only

2.  Jerome wants his audience to appreciate the harsh reality of life for migrant workers in the United States. In addition to using strong supporting materials, he decides to use words with connotative meanings because he knows they will help him

    a.  have stronger delivery.
    b.  appear as impartial as possible.
    *c.  arouse an emotional response.
    d.  add rhythm to his language.
    e.  increase his accuracy.

3.  To use language vividly your textbook recommends that speakers employ

    a.  metaphor and rhyme.
    *b.  imagery and rhythm.
    c.  concrete words and quotations.
    d.  testimony and examples.
    e.  antithesis and parallelism.

4.  Phrases such as "dry as a bone," "clear as a bell," "dark as night," and "smart as a whip" should be avoided in speeches because they are

    a.  abstract.
    *b.  clichés.
    c.  similes.
    d.  connotative.
    e.  figurative.

5.    "Just like an iceberg, the most important dimensions of culture are below the surface" is an example of

   *a.    simile.
    b.    antithesis.
    c.    repetition.
    d.    alliteration.
    e.    metaphor.

6.    When used effectively, repetition in a speech

    a.    unifies a sequence of ideas.
    b.    helps to build a strong cadence.
    c.    reinforces an idea.
   *d.    all of the above.
    e.    b and c only.

7.    "Let us never negotiate out of fear. But let us never fear to negotiate" is an example of

    a.    imagery.
   *b.    antithesis.
    c.    repetition.
    d.    metaphor.
    e.    illustration.

8.    Public speakers should strive to avoid sexist language because such language

    a.    may offend people in the audience.
    b.    is not politically correct.
    c.    is often inaccurate in portraying gender roles.
    d.    all of the above.
   *e.    a and c only.

9.    Which of the following is discussed in your textbook as a way to use language clearly?

    a.    use familiar words
    b.    choose concrete words
    c.    eliminate clutter
   *d.    all of the above
    e.    a and b only

10.    "Our mission is to right wrong, to do justice, and to serve humanity" is an example of

    a.    simile.
    b.    antithesis.
    c.    metaphor
    d.    imagery.
   *e.    parallelism.

# Chapter 12 Delivery

## True-False Quiz

*Indicate whether each of the following statements is true or false by <u>circling</u> the appropriate letter.*

1. <u>T</u> F  Good speech delivery conveys a speaker's ideas without calling attention to itself.

2. <u>T</u> F  The question-and-answer session can have as much impact on an audience as what a speaker says during the speech itself.

3. <u>T</u> F  Pitch is the relative highness or lowness of the speaker's voice.

4. T <u>F</u>  "Conversational quality" in a speech means that the speaker talks the same as she or he would in ordinary conversation.

5. T <u>F</u>  Vocalized pauses are an effective way to increase a speaker's credibility.

6. T <u>F</u>  If you say the "s" in Illinois or the "p" in pneumonia, you are making a mistake in articulation.

7. <u>T</u> F  Dialects are usually based on regional or ethnic speech patterns.

8. T <u>F</u>  When a speaker's nonverbal communication is inconsistent with his or her words, listeners tend to believe the words rather than the nonverbal communication.

9. <u>T</u> F  When conducting a question-and-answer session, you should usually restate or paraphrase each question before you answer it.

10. <u>T</u> F  You should start to establish eye contact with the audience even before you begin to speak.

# Chapter 12 Delivery

## Multiple Choice Quiz

*Indicate the best answer for each of the following questions by circling the correct letter.*

1. Good speech delivery

   a. has a conversational quality.
   b. does not call attention to itself.
   c. requires a strong voice.
   d. all of the above.
   *e. a and b only.

2. When speaking from a manuscript, you should

   a. practice aloud to make sure the speech sounds natural.
   b. be certain the final manuscript is legible at a glance.
   c. work on establishing eye contact with the audience.
   *d. all of the above.
   e. a and b only.

3. The _____ speaker uses only brief notes or a speaking outline to jog the memory.

   a. after-dinner
   b. commemorative
   c. informative
   *d. extemporaneous
   e. persuasive

4. "Conversational quality" in speech delivery means that the

   *a. speech sounds spontaneous even though it has been rehearsed.
   b. speaker is not speaking from memory.
   c. speaker talks the same as she or he would in ordinary conversation.
   d. all of the above.
   e. b and c only.

5. The relative highness or lowness of sounds produced by the human voice is called

   a. rate.
   *b. pitch.
   c. tone.
   d. quality.
   e. volume.

6.    According to your textbook, when people in one region of the country say "warter," while people in another region of the country say "water," the difference is a matter of

   a.   inflection.
   b.   verbalization.
  *c.   dialect.
   d.   enunciation.
   e.   intonation.

7.    A public speaker who frequently says "uh," "er," or "um" is failing to make effective use of

   a.   vocal variety.
  *b.   pauses.
   c.   pitch.
   d.   rate.
   e.   inflection.

8.    In which of the following situations will the personal appearance of the speaker have an impact on the audience?

   a.   a politician presenting a campaign speech
   b.   a business executive giving a financial report
   c.   a professor giving a lecture
  *d.   all of the above
   e.   a and b only

9.    What does your textbook advise regarding the use of gestures in a speech?

   a.   Gestures should be suited to the audience and occasion.
   b.   Speakers should have a vast number of graceful gestures.
   c.   Gestures should appear natural and spontaneous.
   d.   all of the above
  *e.   a and c only

10.   When conducting a question-and-answer session, you should

  *a.   view the session as one more opportunity to communicate your ideas.
   b.   respond to hostile questions in a defensive and argumentative manner.
   c.   allow each questioner to ask as many follow-up questions as they wish.
   d.   all of the above.
   e.   a and c only.

# Chapter 13 Using Visual Aids

## True-False Quiz

*Indicate whether each of the following statements is true or false by <u>circling</u> the appropriate letter.*

1.   T <u>F</u>   One of the advantages of using visual aids in a speech is that their meaning is instantly clear to the audience.

2.   <u>T</u> F   Research has shown that an average speaker who uses visual aids will come across as more credible and better prepared than a speaker who does not use visual aids.

3.   T <u>F</u>   Because a picture is worth a thousand words, it is a good idea to pass photographs among the audience in order to illustrate your point.

4.   <u>T</u> F   If you were summarizing statistical trends in a speech, the best visual aid to use would probably be a graph.

5.   T <u>F</u>   In most circumstances it is an excellent idea to present visual aids by drawing or writing on the chalkboard.

6.   <u>T</u> F   It is important to maintain eye contact with your audience when you are presenting a visual aid.

7.   <u>T</u> F   When making a multimedia presentation, you should always be prepared to give your speech even if the equipment malfunctions.

8.   <u>T</u> F   If you wanted to summarize the steps of a process in a speech, the best kind of visual aid to use would probably be a chart.

9.   T <u>F</u>   In most circumstances you should keep your visual aids on display throughout your speech.

10.   <u>T</u> F   When you are going to give an audience material to take home from a speech, you should usually distribute the material after you are finished speaking.

# Chapter **13** Using Visual Aids

## Multiple Choice Quiz

*Indicate the best answer for each of the following questions by circling the correct letter.*

1. According to your textbook, which of the following is an advantage of using visual aids in a speech?

   a. Using visual aids can increase the clarity of a speaker's message.
   b. Using visual aids can increase the audience's retention of a speaker's message.
   c. Using visual aids can increase the persuasiveness of a speaker's message.
   *d. all of the above
   e. a and b only

2. If the object you want to use as a visual aid is not available, the next best option ideally is a

   *a. model.
   b. chart.
   c. slide.
   d. photograph.
   e. drawing.

3. Which of the following would probably be the best kind of visual aid to demonstrate the five major areas of spending in the federal budget?

   *a. a pie graph
   b. a diagram
   c. a line graph
   d. a chart
   e. a photograph

4. According to your textbook, charts are especially useful as visual aids when a speaker needs to

   a. summarize the steps in a process.
   b. present information the audience might want to write down.
   c. include more categories than can be presented in a pie or bar graph.
   *d. all of the above.
   e. a and c only.

5.      Visual aids are most effective when they are

   a.   integrated with the rest of the speech.
   b.   explained clearly.
   c.   passed among the audience.
   d.   all of the above.
  *e.   a and b only.

6.      According to your textbook, when using visual aids in a speech, you should

  *a.   avoid drawing visual aids on the chalkboard.
   b.   not worry about keeping eye contact with the audience.
   c.   try to pass visual aids among the audience.
   d.   keep visual aids on display throughout the speech.
   e.   set up visual aids to the left of the lectern.

7.      _____ are clear sheets of acetate that can be used to present a variety of visual aids.

   a.   Graphs
  *b.   Transparencies
   c.   Slides
   d.   Videotapes
   e.   Charts

8.      Elisa is giving a speech on women's athletics and has brought a petition for her listeners to sign. When should she circulate the petition?

   a.   before she begins her speech
   b.   after she reveals the topic of her speech
   c.   after explaining the problems faced by women's athletic teams
   d.   while urging her audience to take action during the conclusion of the speech
  *e.   after she has finished speaking

9.      According to your textbook, when giving a multimedia presentation, you should

   a.   give yourself plenty of time to prepare your slides and to rehearse the delivery of your presentation.
   b.   double check your equipment before the audience arrives to make sure the equipment is working properly.
   c.   be prepared to give your speech effectively even if all the multimedia equipment were to malfunction.
  *d.   all of the above.
   e.   a and b only.

10.     When selecting fonts for a visual aid, you should usually use

   a.   a minimum of four fonts to provide visual variety.
   b.   decorative fonts because they will make the aid more interesting.
   c.   all capital letters so the lettering will be easy to read.
   d.   all of the above.
  *e.   none of the above.

# Chapter 14 Speaking to Inform

## True-False Quiz

*Indicate whether each of the following statements is true or false by <u>circling</u> the appropriate letter.*

1. T <u>F</u>    An informative speech about a process that has as many as ten or twelve steps is one of the few times it is acceptable to have more than five main points.

2. <u>T</u> F    When giving an informative speech that explains a process, you will most likely arrange your main points in chronological order.

3. <u>T</u> F    One reason to use clear and straightforward language even when talking about complex ideas is that listeners must understand your message in the time it takes you to say it.

4. T <u>F</u>    A summary is seldom necessary in the conclusion of an informative speech.

5. T <u>F</u>    Informative speeches are seldom organized in topical order.

6. <u>T</u> F    The more you assume your audience knows about your speech topic, the greater are your chances of being misunderstood.

7. T <u>F</u>    One of the biggest barriers to effective informative speaking is using language that is too simple for the audience.

8. <u>T</u> F    Your textbook recommends comparison and contrast as ways to avoid abstractions in an informative speech.

9. <u>T</u> F    Although essay writers are often urged to avoid personal references such as "I," "you," and "we," you should usually try to include such references in an informative speech.

10. <u>T</u> F    Informative speakers need to work as hard as persuasive speakers at relating the topic directly to the audience.

# Chapter 14 Speaking to Inform

## Multiple Choice Quiz

*Indicate the best answer for each of the following questions by circling the correct letter.*

1.    Which of the following is an instance of informative speaking?

    a.    a student urging an instructor to reconsider the due date for an assignment
 *b.    a student sharing ideas about leadership based on a book she has read
    c.    a student on stage telling jokes during the intermission of a play
    d.    all of the above
    e.    a and b only

2.    "To inform my audience how to add memory to a computer" is a specific purpose statement for an informative speech about a(n)

    a.    operation.
    b.    function.
    c.    event.
    d.    concept.
 *e.    process.

3.    If your specific purpose statement were "To inform my audience about the major kinds of dog breeds," you would probably organize your speech in _____ order.

    a.    chronological
    b.    spatial
    c.    descriptive
 *d.    topical
    e.    causal

4.    If your specific purpose were "To inform my audience of the major steps in an effective job interview," you would probably organize your speech in _____ order.

    a.    comparative
    b.    spatial
 *c.    chronological
    d.    causal
    e.    illustrative

5.    "To inform my audience about the removal of the Cherokee Indians from their native lands" is an example of a specific purpose statement for a speech about a(n)

    a.    function.
  *b.    event.
    c.    condition.
    d.    object.
    e.    concept.

6.    When giving an informative speech to a general audience, you should take special care to

    a.    state your ideas in abstract terms.
    b.    establish goodwill with the audience in the introduction.
  *c.    avoid being too technical.
    d.    all of the above.
    e.    a and b only.

7.    Your textbook recommends using _____ in your informative speeches as a way to keep your ideas from being overly abstract.

    a.    contrast
    b.    description
    c.    comparison
  *d.    all of the above
    e.    a and c only

8.    If your specific purpose statement were "To inform my audience about the different layers of the atmosphere," you would probably organize your speech in _____ order.

    a.    topical
    b.    chronological
  *c.    spatial
    d.    comparative
    e.    causal

9.    What does your textbook mean when it recommends that you "personalize your ideas" in an informative speech?

  *a.    Bring information to life by using examples and illustrations.
    b.    Use dramatic statistics for a personal effect.
    c.    Use true-to-life examples rather than hypothetical examples.
    d.    Use slang and jargon to give the speech a personal tone.
    e.    Avoid concrete language because it makes ideas vague and impersonal.

10.    "To inform my audience about the basic beliefs of Buddhism" is an example of a specific purpose statement for an informative speech about a(n)

  *a.    concept.
    b.    event.
    c.    function.
    d.    process.
    e.    object.

# Chapter 15 Speaking to Persuade

## True-False Quiz

*Indicate whether each of the following statements is true or false by <u>circling</u> the appropriate letter.*

1.  <u>T</u> F    One way for a persuasive speaker to uphold the ethical obligations of speechmaking is to learn about all sides of an issue.

2.  T <u>F</u>    A persuasive speech on a question of fact is essentially the same as an informative speech.

3.  <u>T</u> F    "To persuade my audience that cloning human beings is morally unjustifiable" is a specific purpose statement for a persuasive speech on a question of value.

4.  T <u>F</u>    "To persuade my audience that video games are a major cause of youth violence" is a specific purpose statement for a persuasive speech on a question of policy.

5.  <u>T</u> F    Research indicates that audiences often engage in a mental give-and-take with the speaker as they listen to a persuasive speech.

6.  T <u>F</u>    Audience analysis and adaptation are less challenging in persuasive speaking than in speaking to inform.

7.  <u>T</u> F    When you give a persuasive speech on a question of policy, you can seek either passive agreement or immediate action from your audience.

8.  <u>T</u> F    When you discuss a question of policy, you must deal with three basic issues—need, plan, and practicality.

9.  T <u>F</u>    If you advocate a new policy in a persuasive speech, your main points will usually fall naturally into topical order.

10. <u>T</u> F    Monroe's motivated sequence is most appropriate for speeches that try to persuade listeners to take immediate action.

# Chapter 15 Speaking to Persuade

## Multiple Choice Quiz

*Indicate the best answer for each of the following questions by circling the correct letter.*

1.    Which of the following is an instance of persuasive speaking?

    a.    A president of a company presenting an award to an outstanding employee.
    b.    A marketing manager explaining a new product to the company's sales force.
    c.    A personnel manager defining employee benefits at a meeting of workers.
  *d.    A union representative urging management to avoid a strike by raising wages.
    e.    A finance officer reporting sales figures to the board of directors.

2.    "To persuade my audience that long-term exposure to electromagnetic fields can cause serious health problems" is a specific purpose statement for a persuasive speech on a question of

    a.    value.
    b.    opinion.
    c.    attitude.
    d.    policy.
  *e.    fact.

3.    As your textbook explains, if you want to persuade a skeptical audience, you need to

    a.    Organize the speech in Monroe's motivated sequence.
    b.    Urge the audience to take immediate action.
    c.    Circulate an audience-analysis questionnaire.
  *d.    Answer the reasons for the audience's skepticism.
    e.    Focus your speech on questions of practicality.

4.    Which of the following specific purpose statements is from a persuasive speech seeking immediate action?

    a.    To persuade my audience that the federal government should increase funding to provide computers for children in low-income housing.
    b.    To persuade my audience that the state must increase funding for wetland preservation.
    c.    To persuade my audience that federal campaign finance laws must be reformed to preserve the integrity of electoral process.
  *d.    To persuade my audience to decrease the amount of electricity they use during the summer in order to prevent blackouts.
    e.    To persuade my audience that the college administration should increase spending for intramural athletics on campus.

5.    That part of the audience a speaker most wants to persuade is called the

    a.   specific audience.
    b.   designated audience.
    c.   central audience.
    d.   special audience.
  *e.   target audience.

6.    Persuasive speeches on questions of _____ argue for or against particular courses of action.

    a.   need
    b.   value
  *c.   policy
    d.   fact
    e.   plan

7.    Regardless of whether your aim is to encourage passive agreement or immediate action, you must deal with three basic issues whenever you discuss a question of policy. They are

    a.   cause, effect, and practicality.
    b.   evidence, practicality, and reasoning.
    c.   need, action, and reaction.
    d.   problem, plan, and solution.
  *e.   need, plan, and practicality.

8.    If you give a persuasive speech advocating a change in policy, your main points often will fall naturally into _____ order.

  *a.   problem-solution
    b.   chronological
    c.   causal
    d.   comparative advantages
    e.   topical

9.    According to your textbook, "To persuade my audience that downloading music from the Internet for personal use is ethically wrong" is a specific purpose statement for a persuasive speech on a question of

    a.   policy.
    b.   opinion.
  *c.   value.
    d.   legality.
    e.   fact.

10.    Which organizational pattern is especially effective for persuasive speeches that seek immediate action by listeners?

    a.   comparative advantages order
  *b.   Monroe's motivated sequence
    c.   problem-solution order
    d.   reflective-thinking sequence
    e.   psychological process order

# Chapter 16 Methods of Persuasion

## True-False Quiz

*Indicate whether each of the following statements is true or false by <u>circling</u> the appropriate letter.*

1.   <u>T</u>  F    Competence and character are the most important factors affecting a speaker's credibility.

2.   <u>T</u>  F    Research shows that a speaker's credibility is strongly affected by his or her delivery.

3.   <u>T</u>  F    Research indicates that evidence is usually more persuasive when it is stated in specific rather than general terms.

4.   <u>T</u>  F    Reasoning from specific instances involves progressing from a number of particular facts to a general conclusion.

5.   T  <u>F</u>    The following statement is an example of reasoning from principle: "Places such as Singapore that allow caning and other forms of corporal punishment have exceedingly low crime rates. If caning were used in the United States, the U.S. would have lower crime rates as well."

6.   <u>T</u>  F    In addition to being illogical, the *ad hominem* fallacy is also unethical.

7.   T  <u>F</u>    The slippery slope fallacy assumes that because something is popular, it is therefore good, correct, or desirable.

8.   T  <u>F</u>    One of the advantages of using causal reasoning in a persuasive speech is that the relationship between causes and effects is usually fairly obvious.

9.   T  <u>F</u>    As your textbook explains, it is unethical to use emotional appeal in a persuasive speech on a question of policy.

10.   <u>T</u>  F    The most important question to ask when assessing analogical reasoning is whether the two cases being compared are essentially alike.

# Chapter **16** Methods of Persuasion

## Multiple Choice Quiz

*Indicate the best answer for each of the following questions by circling the correct letter.*

1.    According to your textbook, the two most important factors affecting the credibility of a persuasive speaker are

   \*a.    competence and character.
    b.    prestige and charisma.
    c.    character and reputation.
    d.    popularity and intelligence.
    e.    charisma and competence.

2.    According to your textbook, the following statement is an example of what type of fallacy?

     How can we be so concerned about shielding children in the U.S. from Internet pornography when millions of children around the world continue to be sold into slavery every year?

    a.    either-or
   \*b.    red herring
    c.    false deduction
    d.    *ad hominem*
    e.    invalid analogy

3.    When giving a persuasive speech to an audience that opposes your point of view, it is especially important that you use _____ to answer their objections to your views.

    a.    visual aids
    b.    syllogisms
    c.    credibility statements
    d.    emotional appeals
   \*e.    evidence

4.    According to your textbook, as a persuasive speaker, your two *major* concerns with respect to reasoning are to

    a.    establish credibility and reason correctly.
    b.    make sure your reasoning is clear and credible.
    c.    avoid fallacies and support reasoning with testimony.
    d.    adapt reasoning to both hostile and favorable listeners.
   \*e.    make sure your reasoning is sound and persuasive.

5. Which of the following is presented in your textbook as a guideline for reasoning from specific instances in a persuasive speech?

  a. reinforce your argument with statistics and testimony
  b. include at least one extended example among your specific instances
  c. avoid generalizing too hastily
  d. all of the above
 *e. a and c only

6. According to your textbook, emotional appeal is *not* appropriate in which kind of persuasive speech?

 *a. the speech on a question of fact
  b. the speech on a question of value
  c. the speech on a question of proof
  d. the speech on a question of policy
  e. the speech on a question of ethics

7. To create common ground with an audience in the introduction of a persuasive speech, your textbook recommends that you

 *a. show the audience that you share their values.
  b. use statistics to show the extent of a problem.
  c. confront the audience for failing to do the right thing.
  d. all of the above.
  e. a and b only.

8. According to your textbook, when you reason from principle in a persuasive speech, you should give special attention to

 *a. deciding whether you need to support your general principle with evidence.
  b. showing that the analogy underlying your general principle is valid.
  c. establishing your credibility to speak on the matter of principle at hand.
  d. avoiding the fallacy of *post hoc, ergo proper hoc* in your reasoning.
  e. balancing the time you spend on your general principle and minor premise.

9. What error in reasoning is exemplified by the following statement?

  I always wear my blue sweater when I take an exam, but I couldn't find it yesterday. If I had worn it yesterday, I would not have flunked my accounting exam.

  a. circular thinking
  b. hasty generalization
  c. invalid analogy
 *d. false cause
  e. faulty deduction

10. When reasoning analogically, you infer that

   a. a causal relationship can be established between two or more events.
   *b. what is true in one case will also be true in a similar case.
   c. a general principle is validated by a question of fact.
   d. your position is true because it is demonstrated by statistical trends.
   e. a specific conclusion is true because it is verified by a general principle.

# Chapter 17 Speaking on Special Occasions

## True-False Quiz

*Indicate whether each of the following statements is true or false by <u>circling</u> the appropriate letter.*

1.   T <u>F</u>    The primary purpose of a special occasion speech is to convey information to an audience.

2.   <u>T</u> F    One major purpose of a speech of introduction is to establish a welcoming climate that will boost the credibility of the main speaker.

3.   <u>T</u> F    When giving a speech of presentation, you should usually explain why the recipient is being given his or her award.

4.   <u>T</u> F    The three major traits of a good acceptance speech are brevity, humility, and graciousness.

5.   <u>T</u> F    The fundamental purpose of a commemorative speech is to inspire your listeners.

6.   T <u>F</u>    A speech urging Congress to construct a memorial in Washington, D.C., to recognize women's contributions to the American Revolution is an example of a commemorative speech.

7.   T <u>F</u>    An after-dinner speech is best thought of as a kind of speech to inform.

8.   <u>T</u> F    "To entertain my audience by telling them about the typical mishaps that happen during family vacations" is an appropriate specific purpose statement for an after-dinner speech.

9.   T <u>F</u>    A commemorative speech paying tribute to a person is essentially a biography of that person.

10.  <u>T</u> F    The basic purpose of an acceptance speech is to give thanks for a gift or an award.

# Chapter 17  Speaking on Special Occasions

## Multiple Choice Quiz

*Indicate the best answer for each of the following questions by circling the correct letter.*

1.    One main purpose of a speech of introduction is to

    a.    explain why the person being introduced is receiving her or his award.
    b.    inspire the audience with a sense of the significance of the occasion.
   *c.    create a welcoming climate to build enthusiasm for the main speaker.
    d.    explain why listeners should pay tribute to a person, idea, or institution.
    e.    enhance the credibility of the speaker who is making the introduction.

2.    When giving a speech of presentation, you should usually

   *a.    tell why the recipient is receiving her or his award.
    b.    present the main speaker briefly and accurately.
    c.    avoid mentioning the losers of the award competition.
    d.    adapt your presentation to the main speaker.
    e.    give a brief biography of the main speaker.

3.    According to your textbook, when your fundamental purpose in a speech is to inspire the audience, you are most likely going to be giving a(n) _____ speech.

    a.    informative
    b.    persuasive
    c.    after-dinner
   *d.    commemorative
    e.    acceptance

4.    Which of the following is an appropriate specific purpose statement for an after-dinner speech?

    a.    To entertain my audience by telling them the lengths parents go to in order to get kids to eat healthy foods.
    b.    To entertain my audience by examining the lighter side of terrorism and insurgency in the Middle East.
    c.    To entertain my audience by discussing the absurd questions people ask when they call for technical support.
    d.    all of the above
   *e.    a and c only

5.  Which of the following is an example of a commemorative speech?

    a.  the President's State of the Union message
    b.  a soccer coach's pep talk
    c.  a speaker's acceptance of an award
    d.  a teacher's lecture on banking ethics
  *e.  a daughter's eulogy in honor of her father

6.  All of the following are presented in your textbook as guidelines for a speech of introduction *except*

    a.  be brief.
    b.  adapt your remarks to the occasion.
  *c.  bring the speech to life by using a hypothetical example.
    d.  try to create a sense of anticipation and drama.
    e.  make sure your remarks are completely accurate.

7.  According to your textbook, a speech in which an individual gives thanks for a gift or award is termed a(n)

    a.  speech of presentation.
    b.  commemorative speech.
    c.  after-dinner speech.
  *d.  acceptance speech.
    e.  speech of introduction.

8.  When giving a speech of presentation, you should usually

  *a.  tell why the recipient is receiving her or his award.
    b.  present the main speaker briefly and accurately.
    c.  avoid mentioning the losers of the award competition.
    d.  adapt your presentation to the main speaker.
    e.  give a brief biography of the main speaker.

9.  When delivering a commemorative speech, you should take special care to

    a.  mention all the achievements of the person being commemorated.
    b.  heighten appreciation for the person being commemorated.
    c.  use creative language to express feelings and sentiments.
    d.  all of the above.
  *e.  b and c only.

10.  Although it is always based on materials chosen for their entertainment value, the _____ speech should strive to make a thoughtful point about its theme.

  *a.  after-dinner
    b.  presentation
    c.  commemorative
    d.  acceptance
    e.  introductory

# Chapter 18 Speaking in Small Groups

## True-False Quiz

*Indicate whether each of the following statements is true or false by <u>circling</u> the appropriate letter.*

1.  <u>T</u> F    Most experts set the maximum number of members for a small group at seven or eight.

2.  T <u>F</u>    The newest or least experienced member of a small group is usually referred to as the implied leader.

3.  <u>T</u> F    The task needs of a small group include such matters as distributing the workload among group members, keeping the group on track, and helping the group reach consensus.

4.  T <u>F</u>    The procedural needs of a small group include such matters as whether members get along with each other and feel good about their roles in the group.

5.  T <u>F</u>    Collecting information about the discussion topic is an example of a maintenance need in a small group.

6.  T <u>F</u>    Hidden agendas are necessary for effective group discussion.

7.  <u>T</u> F    Disagreements in a small group should be kept at the task level rather than the interpersonal level.

8.  <u>T</u> F    "What steps should be taken to reduce gun violence in the U.S.?" is an example of a well-worded question for a problem-solving group discussion.

9.  T <u>F</u>    The best way to reach a consensus decision in a problem-solving group is to take a vote on the issue in dispute.

10. <u>T</u> F    In a symposium, each participant in turn delivers a prepared speech on a different aspect of a common topic.

# Chapter 18   Speaking in Small Groups

## Multiple Choice Quiz

*Indicate the best answer for each of the following questions by circling the correct letter.*

1.   A group member to whom other members defer because of his or her rank or expertise is called a(n)

 *a.   implied leader.
  b.   specific leader.
  c.   emergent leader.
  d.   designated leader.
  e.   appointed leader.

2.   Randall is talkative and offers his opinions freely during small group meetings. Because he participates more than the other members, he has assumed a leadership role within the group. What kind of leader is Randall?

  a.   task leader
  b.   implied leader
 *c.   emergent leader
  d.   designated leader
  e.   accidental leader

3.   According to your textbook, what are the three kinds of leadership needs faced by all problem-solving small groups?

  a.   agenda needs, task needs, and consensus needs
  b.   decision needs, maintenance needs, and personal needs
  c.   procedural needs, agenda needs, and participation needs
  d.   research needs, schedule needs, and judgment needs
 *e.   task needs, procedural needs, and maintenance needs

4.   According to your textbook, when formulating a question for discussion, a problem-solving small group should phrase the question

  a.   so the whole group can answer it.
  b.   so the group can reach a majority decision.
 *c.   so as to allow a wide variety of answers.
  d.   so as to avoid interpersonal conflict in the group.
  e.   all of the above.

5.   Which of the following is mentioned in your textbook as a responsibility of *every* member in a small group?

   a.   reach solutions swiftly
   b.   develop hidden agendas
   c.   call for a vote on major issues
   d.   avoid disagreement at all costs
   *e.  encourage full participation

6.   Once a problem-solving small group has defined the problem, what is the *next* step they should follow in the reflective-thinking method for small group discussion?

   a.   establish criteria for solutions
   b.   select the best solution
   c.   set an agenda for solving the problem
   d.   reach a consensus decision
   *e.  analyze the problem

7.   As your textbook explains, a decision that is acceptable to all members of a small group is called a _____ decision.

   a.   prudent
   *b.  consensus
   c.   deliberative
   d.   compromise
   e.   judicious

8.   If Max is designated to present the findings and recommendations of his small group's deliberations to a large group of stockholders, he will most likely need to

   *a.  prepare an oral report.
   b.   create a panel discussion.
   c.   give an impromptu presentation.
   d.   plan a town hall meeting.
   e.   moderate a symposium.

9.   Which of the following is a maintenance need of a problem-solving small group?

   *a.  easing interpersonal tensions among group members
   b.   using the Internet to research the issue under consideration
   c.   ordering lunch for the group during its scheduled break
   d.   outlining the major reason for adopting the group's policy
   e.   organizing a symposium to present the group's decision

10.  As explained in your textbook, which of the following is a defining trait of a small group?

   a.   the group assembles for a specific purpose
   b.   the group contains a minimum of three members
   c.   the group has a designated leader
   d.   all of the above
   *e.  a and b only

# Part Five

# Sample Final Exams

## Introduction to Part Five

Constructing final examinations is a perennial challenge. In addition to covering the central materials of the course in a comprehensive fashion, they must be rigorous in design yet fair in execution. They need to test the recall of key concepts without being merely an exercise in memorization. They should require judgment without being tricky or deliberately misleading. Ideally, they will challenge the best students without being unfair to the rest.

This section of the manual contains three final exams, each of which represents a different approach to testing and evaluation. The first is a one-hour exam composed entirely of multiple-choice questions (pages 431–440). The second is a two-hour exam containing a mixture of multiple-choice, short-answer, brief essay, and longer essay questions (pages 442–449). The third is a two-hour essay exam involving the analysis of a full speech (pages 451–454).

There are, of course, many other kinds of final exams that can be constructed in conjunction with *The Art of Public Speaking*. There are also many different questions that can be asked within the formats of the three exams presented here. Although some instructors may be able to use one or more of these exams exactly as they are written, the content of their questions, for purposes of this manual, is less important than their overall design. They are included here to illustrate three approaches to the final exam that individual instructors can adapt to their own classes and teaching philosophies.

An answer key follows each exam.

# Public Speaking
# Final Examination

*Indicate the best answer for each question by circling the correct answer. Each question is worth 2 points. The whole exam is worth 100 points. You have one hour to complete the exam.*

1.    The *primary* purpose of speechmaking is to

    a.    gain a desired response from listeners.
    b.    learn more about the speech topic.
    c.    gain experience as a speaker.
    d.    try out new ideas with an audience.
    e.    display the speaker's knowledge.

2.    According to your textbook, what is the *most important* early step in the process of developing a successful speech?

    a.    phrasing the general purpose
    b.    researching for speech materials
    c.    formulating the specific purpose
    d.    brainstorming for a central idea
    e.    selecting the residual message

3.    According to your textbook, a speaking outline

    a.    includes the final bibliography.
    b.    states the specific purpose at the start of the outline.
    c.    contains delivery cues for the speaker.
    d.    all of the above.
    e.    a and b only.

4.    Studies have found that public speakers will usually be more persuasive when they

    a.    use evidence that is already familiar to the audience.
    b.    present evidence in specific rather than general terms.
    c.    state evidence without drawing explicit conclusions from it.
    d.    avoid emotional appeals when seeking action from the audience.
    e.    speak slightly slower than normal when delivering the speech.

5.    As a public speaker, you face ethical issues when

    a.    selecting the topic for your speech.
    b.    researching your speech.
    c.    organizing your speech.
    d.    a and b only.
    e.    all of the above.

6.    What does your textbook say about eye contact for the public speakers who address audiences in the United States?

    a.    To appear credible and trustworthy, a speaker should gaze intently at one section of the audience.

    b.    In classroom speeches, it is most important to maintain steady eye contact with the instructor.

    c.    Speakers should look at the audience about 80 to 90 percent of the time they are talking.

    d.    Speakers who establish strong eye contact with the audience lose credibility as a result.

    e.    Even with a large audience, engaging the eyes of each person is preferable to scanning the audience in general.

7.    Language helps to shape our sense of reality by

    a.    causing events.
    b.    giving meaning to events.
    c.    communicating events.
    d.    mirroring events.
    e.    reflecting events.

8.    According to your textbook, the two most important factors affecting the credibility of a persuasive speaker are

    a.    competence and character.
    b.    prestige and charisma.
    c.    character and reputation.
    d.    popularity and intelligence.
    e.    charisma and competence.

9.    As explained in y our textbook, public speakers have an ethical obligation to avoid name-calling and other forms of abusive language because such language

    a.    is forbidden by the first amendment to the U.S. Constitution.
    b.    violates current standards of political correctness on college campuses.
    c.    changes meaning based on the frame of reference of the audience.
    d.    is used by speakers who are not fully prepared for their presentations.
    e.    demeans the personal dignity of the groups or individuals being attacked.

10.    Even when you use other interest-arousing lures in a speech introduction, you should always

    a.    startle the audience.
    b.    use a rhetorical question.
    c.    relate the topic to the audience.
    d.    tell an interesting story.
    e.    present striking statistics.

11. As your textbook explains, public speakers should strive to avoid sexist language because such language is

   a. politically incorrect.
   b. less vivid than nonsexist language.
   c. often inaccurate in portraying gender roles.
   d. unacceptable to multicultural audiences.
   e. excessively denotative.

12. As your textbook explains, if you want to persuade a skeptical audience, you need to

   a. organize the speech with Monroe's motivated sequence.
   b. urge the audience to take immediate action.
   c. circulate an audience-analysis questionnaire.
   d. answer the reasons for the audience's skepticism.
   e. focus your speech on questions of practicality.

13. According to your textbook, rather than trying to eliminate every trace of stage fright, you should aim at transforming it into

   a. controlled anxiety.
   b. visualized adrenaline.
   c. professional stage fright.
   d. positive nervousness.
   e. confident apprehension.

14. Which of the following elements usually has the greatest impact on the length a speech should be?

   a. the audience's disposition toward the topic
   b. the physical setting for the speech
   c. the audience's attitudes toward the speaker
   d. the occasion for the speech
   e. the group membership of the audience

15. Which of the following is a correctly worded main point for a speech preparation outline?

   a. Wolves.
   b. Did you know that all domestic dogs are descended from the wolf?
   c. The ancestry of the domestic dog can be directly traced to the wolf.
   d. The place of the wolf in the ancestry of the domestic dog.
   e. Wolves and the domestic dog.

16. When giving an informative speech, you should take special care to

   a. translate technical information into everyday language.
   b. state your ideas in abstract terms.
   c. establish goodwill with the audience in your introduction.
   d. avoid speaking about complex topics.
   e. prepare your introduction before the body of your speech.

17. Which of the following is one of the four major causes of poor listening discussed in your textbook?

   a. focusing on a speaker's appearance or delivery
   b. taking key-word notes during a speech
   c. suspending judgment about a speaker's ideas
   d. concentrating on a speaker's evidence and reasoning
   e. listening empathically rather than critically

18. According to your textbook, when is it appropriate to cite an abstract of a magazine or journal article in your speech rather than locating and reading the full article?

   a. never
   b. when the article is more than five years old
   c. when the article is not available on a computerized database
   d. when the only copy of the article is on the bookshelves
   e. when the article is short enough to be summarized in one paragraph

19. Which of the following statistical measures corresponds to what is popularly called "the average"?

   a. the medial
   b. the mean
   c. the medium
   d. the mode
   e. the median

20. When preparing a speech introduction, you should usually

   a. practice the introduction no more than two or three times.
   b. make sure the introduction comprises 25 percent of the speech.
   c. complete the introduction after the body of the speech.
   d. stick with the first introduction that comes to mind.
   e. use humor to gain the audience's attention and interest.

21. Which of the following does your textbook mention as an advantage of using visual aids in a public speech?

   a. Using visual aids enhances the clarity of the speaker's message.
   b. Using visual aids reduces the need for eye contact with the audience.
   c. Using visual aids can help combat the speaker's stage fright.
   d. all of the above
   e. a and c only

22. The fact that audiences are egocentric means that

   a. listeners believe their cultural group is superior to all other groups.
   b. listeners are concerned above all with how a speech will affect them.
   c. listeners will interpret the speech through the speaker's frame of reference.
   d. all of the above.
   e. a and b only.

23.    Examples are especially helpful as supporting materials because they

    a.    add human interest to a speech.
    b.    are not overly technical.
    c.    quantify a speaker's ideas.
    d.    are harder to manipulate than statistics or testimony.
    e.    enhance the speaker's credibility.

24.    Referring back to your introduction in the conclusion of your speech is recommended as a way to

    a.    secure the audience's attention.
    b.    reinforce your credibility as a speaker.
    c.    move the audience to action.
    d.    give the speech psychological unity.
    e.    develop a dissolve ending.

25.    What does your textbook say about speech dialects?

    a.    Most languages have dialects.
    b.    Dialects are usually based on regional or ethnic speech patterns.
    c.    No dialect is inherently better or worse than any other dialect.
    d.    all of the above
    e.    a and b only

26.    When reasoning analogically, you infer that

    a.    a causal relationship can be established between two or more events.
    b.    what is true in one case will also be true in a similar case.
    c.    a general principle is validated by a question of fact.
    d.    your position is true because it is demonstrated by statistical trends.
    e.    a specific conclusion is true because it is verified by a general principle.

27.    As a speaker, you would probably use more connotative words if you wanted to

    a.    arouse an emotional response.
    b.    appear as impartial as possible.
    c.    explain a technical concept.
    d.    enhance your credibility.
    e.    exploit the rhythm of language.

28.    What does your textbook recommend regarding the *last* step of practicing delivery for a speech?

    a.    Listen to a tape of the speech and make last-minute changes in it.
    b.    Practice the speech in front of a mirror to check your body language.
    c.    Prepare your speaking outline so it is brief and easy to read at a glance.
    d.    Rehearse under conditions as close as possible to the actual speech situation.
    e.    Time yourself as you practice the speech out loud and as you use visual aids.

29.    According to your textbook, emotional appeal is

   a.    inappropriate in a persuasive speech on a question of policy.
   b.    often necessary when a speaker is trying to move an audience to action.
   c.    most effectively generated by using emotionally charged words.
   d.    unethical unless the emotional appeal is combined with causal reasoning.
   e.    seldom used by public speakers in support of honorable causes.

30.    When making a multimedia presentation, you should

   a.    limit yourself to showing charts, graphs, photographs, and drawings.
   b.    be prepared to give your speech even if the equipment malfunctions.
   c.    use a different set of fonts for each chart to keep the audience interested.
   d.    reduce the number of main points to make sure you do not run out of time.
   e.    tell your audience which software program you are using for the speech.

31.    According to your textbook, when selecting fonts for a visual aid you should usually use

   a.    a wide variety of fonts.
   b.    decorative fonts.
   c.    a different font for each line.
   d.    italicized fonts.
   e.    no more than two fonts.

32.    When taking research notes, you should

   a.    take only a few notes so you do not get too much information.
   b.    put all the notes from each source on a single index card or sheet of paper.
   c.    distinguish among quotations, paraphrases, and your own ideas.
   d.    record notes only when you're sure you'll use the information in your speech.
   e.    all of the above.

33.    What are the three criteria discussed in your textbook for assessing the soundness of documents found on the World Wide Web?

   a.    length, accuracy, and graphics
   b.    interactivity, objectivity, and authorship
   c.    graphics, sponsorship, and accuracy
   d.    creativity, reliability, and length
   e.    authorship, sponsorship, and recency

34.    Rosalie will be giving a persuasive speech on organ donation and wants to distribute organ-donor cards to her listeners. When should she distribute the cards?

   a.    before she starts the speech
   b.    after she reveals her topic in the introduction
   c.    while telling how organ-donor cards work during the body of the speech
   d.    while urging her audience to take action during the conclusion of the speech
   e.    after she has finished speaking

35.    If you were giving a speech and needed to know the number of people who die each year in the United States from accidental drowning, which of the following would be the best source to consult?

    a.   *Current Biography*
    b.   *Reader's Guide to Periodical Literature*
    c.   *Statistical Abstract of the United States*
    d.   *Webster's Geographical Dictionary*
    e.   *Encyclopaedia Britannica*

36.    Research indicates that the impact of examples is greatly enhanced when they are followed by _____ that show the examples to be typical.

    a.   analogies
    b.   syllogisms
    c.   credibility statements
    d.   emotional appeals
    e.   statistics

37.    Which organizational pattern would probably be most effective for arranging the main points of a speech with the specific purpose, "To inform my audience how to set up an online business"?

    a.   chronological
    b.   problem-solution
    c.   spatial
    d.   causal
    e.   comparative-advantage

38.    What organizational pattern would probably be most effective for arranging the main points of a speech with the central idea "There are five major categories of dog breeds"?

    a.   visual
    b.   chronological
    c.   problem-solution
    d.   causal
    e.   topical

39.    "To inform my audience how to make genuine French croissants" is a specific purpose statement for a speech about a(n)

    a.   object.
    b.   process.
    c.   function.
    d.   event.
    e.   concept.

40.    "A dream deferred dries up like a raisin in the sun" is an example of

a.    simile.
b.    metaphor.
c.    alliteration.
d.    all of the above.
e.    a and c only.

41.    If Bruce Willis were to deliver a speech about the future of medical care in the United States, his *main* task in the introduction of his speech would probably be to

a.    gain attention.
b.    reveal the topic.
c.    establish credibility.
d.    preview the body.
e.    define key terms.

42.    "To persuade my audience that there should be tougher enforcement of laws to protect the victims of domestic abuse" is a specific purpose statement for a persuasive speech on a question of

a.    value.
b.    attitude.
c.    policy.
d.    opinion.
e.    judgment.

43.    As Christopher delivered his speech, he noticed that some members of his audience looked confused as he explained one of his main points. As a result, he slowed down and explained the point again. In this case, Christopher was

a.    dealing with external interference.
b.    adjusting the channel of communication.
c.    interpreting the audience's frame of reference.
d.    compensating for the situation.
e.    adapting to audience feedback.

44.    If the following transition were used in a persuasive speech, the speech would most likely be organized in _____ order:

Now that I've told you about declining voter involvement in this country, let's look at what we can do about it.

a.    causal
b.    spatial
c.    comparative-advantages
d.    problem-solution
e.    topical

45.  Arranged in random order below are a main point, two subpoints, and two sub-subpoints from a speech preparation outline. Which is the main point?

a.  The largest members of the hawk family are Old World vultures.
b.  Raptors are powerful birds of prey with hooked beaks and sharp talons.
c.  Among Falconiformes, the hawk family is the largest and most diverse.
d.  The hawk family includes eagles, hawks, kites, harriers, and vultures.
e.  There are two orders of Raptors—Falconiformes and Strigiformes.

46.  Michael is preparing a persuasive speech for class in opposition to gun control. The most important factor for Michael to consider when analyzing his audience is probably is

a.  knowledge of the topic.
b.  disposition toward the speaker.
c.  cultural background.
d.  religious beliefs.
e.  attitude toward the topic.

47.  According to your textbook, the following statement is an example of what type of fallacy?

Why should we be concerned about Siberian tigers becoming extinct when there are more and more homeless people who need our support?

a.  red herring
b.  *ad hominem*
c.  hasty generalization
d.  slippery slope
e.  either-or

48.  When conducting a question-and-answer session, you should

a.  allow each questioner to ask as many follow-up questions as they wish.
b.  try to bluff your way through when faced with a question you can't answer.
c.  direct your answers primarily to the audience as a whole.
d.  all of the above.
e.  a and b only.

49.  What error in reasoning is exemplified by the following statement?

French movies are all dull. I saw three of them last semester in my film class and couldn't stay awake through a single one.

a.  false cause
b.  faulty deduction
c.  invalid analogy
d.  hasty generalization
e.  circular thinking

50.    Ryan began his speech by saying:

Imagine that you are on a deserted island—palm trees sway in the breeze, the warm sun is on your face, and the smell of tropical flowers is in the air. Suddenly, the sound of distant drums breaks your euphoria. What do you do—panic? What would you do if you found yourself in such a situation?

What kind of supporting material did Ryan use in his introduction?

a.    peer testimony
b.    extended metaphor
c.    synthetic example
d.    artificial simile
e.    hypothetical example

# Answers to First Sample
# Final Exam

| 1. | a | (Chapter 5) | 26. | b | (Chapter 16) |
|----|---|-------------|-----|---|--------------|
| 2. | c | (Chapter 4) | 27. | a | (Chapter 11) |
| 3. | c | (Chapter 10) | 28. | d | (Chapter 12) |
| 4. | b | (Chapter 16) | 29. | b | (Chapter 16) |
| 5. | e | (Chapter 2) | 30. | b | (Chapter 13) |
| 6. | c | (Chapter 12) | 31. | e | (Chapter 13) |
| 7. | b | (Chapter 11) | 32. | c | (Chapter 6) |
| 8. | a | (Chapter 16) | 33. | e | (Chapter 6) |
| 9. | e | (Chapter 2) | 34. | e | (Chapter 13) |
| 10. | c | (Chapter 9) | 35. | c | (Chapter 6) |
| 11. | c | (Chapter 11) | 36. | e | (Chapter 7) |
| 12. | d | (Chapter 15) | 37. | a | (Chapter 8) |
| 13. | d | (Chapter 1) | 38. | e | (Chapter 8) |
| 14. | d | (Chapter 5) | 39. | b | (Chapter 14) |
| 15. | c | (Chapter 10) | 40. | e | (Chapter 11) |
| 16. | a | (Chapter 14) | 41. | c | (Chapter 9) |
| 17. | a | (Chapter 3) | 42. | c | (Chapter 15) |
| 18. | a | (Chapter 6) | 43. | e | (Chapter 1) |
| 19. | b | (Chapter 7) | 44. | d | (Chapter 8) |
| 20. | c | (Chapter 9) | 45. | b | (Chapter 10) |
| 21. | e | (Chapter 13) | 46. | e | (Chapter 5) |
| 22. | b | (Chapter 5) | 47. | a | (Chapter 16) |
| 23. | a | (Chapter 7) | 48. | c | (Chapter 12) |
| 24. | d | (Chapter 9) | 49. | d | (Chapter 16) |
| 25. | d | (Chapter 12) | 50. | e | (Chapter 7) |

# Public Speaking
# Final Examination

There are four parts to this exam. Parts I and II are to be answered directly on the exam pages. Parts III and IV are to be answered in your blue book. You have two hours to complete the exam.

## Part I    Multiple-Choice    (20 points)

*Indicate the <u>best</u> answer for each question by circling the correct letter.*

1.    As your textbook explains, if you want to persuade a skeptical audience, you need to

    a.    organize the speech with Monroe's motivated sequence.
    b.    urge the audience to take immediate action.
    c.    circulate an audience-analysis questionnaire.
    d.    answer the reasons for the audience's skepticism.
    e.    focus your speech on questions of practicality.

2.    According to your textbook, rather than trying to eliminate every trace of stage fright, you should aim at transforming it into

    a.    controlled anxiety.
    b.    visualized adrenaline.
    c.    professional stage fright.
    d.    positive nervousness.
    e.    confident apprehension.

3.    When taking research notes, you should

    a.    take only a few notes so you do not get too much information.
    b.    put all the notes from each source on a single index card or sheet of paper.
    c.    distinguish among quotations, paraphrases, and your own ideas.
    d.    record notes only when you're sure you'll use the information in your speech.
    e.    all of the above.

4.    According to your textbook, emotional appeal is

    a.    inappropriate in a persuasive speech on a question of policy.
    b.    often necessary when a speaker is trying to move an audience to action.
    c.    most effectively generated by using emotionally charged words.
    d.    unethical unless the emotional appeal is combined with causal reasoning.
    e.    seldom used by public speakers in support of honorable causes.

5.    As a speaker, you would probably use more connotative words if you wanted to

    a.    arouse an emotional response.
    b.    appear as impartial as possible.
    c.    explain a technical concept.
    d.    enhance your credibility.
    e.    exploit the rhythm of language.

6. If the following transition were used in a persuasive speech, the speech would most likely be organized in _____ order.

> Now that I've told you about declining voter involvement in this country, let's look at what we can do about it.

   a. causal
   b. spatial
   c. comparative-advantages
   d. problem-solution
   e. topical

7. As explained in your textbook, public speakers have an ethical obligation to avoid name-calling and other forms of abusive language because such language

   a. is forbidden by the first amendment to the U.S. Constitution.
   b. violates current standards of political correctness on college campuses.
   c. changes meaning based on the frame of reference of the audience.
   d. is used by speakers who are not fully prepared for their presentations.
   e. demeans the personal dignity of the groups or individuals being attacked.

8. If your specific purpose statement were "To inform my audience about the major archaeological sites in Central America," you would probably organize your speech in _____ order.

   a. topical or causal
   b. spatial or comparative
   c. comparative or chronological
   d. chronological or causal
   e. spatial or topical

9. Michael is preparing a persuasive speech for class in opposition to gun control. The most important factor for Michael to consider when analyzing his audience is probably its

   a. knowledge of the topic.
   b. disposition toward the speaker.
   c. cultural background.
   d. religious beliefs.
   e. attitude toward the topic.

10. Studies have found that public speakers will usually be more persuasive when they

   a. use evidence that is already familiar to the audience.
   b. present evidence in specific rather than general terms.
   c. state evidence without drawing explicit conclusions from it.
   d. avoid emotional appeals when seeking action from the audience.
   e. speak slightly slower than normal when delivering the speech.

11.   Referring back to your introduction in the conclusion of your speech is recommended as a way to

    a.   secure the audience's attention.
    b.   reinforce your credibility as a speaker.
    c.   move the audience to action.
    d.   give the speech psychological unity.
    e.   develop a dissolve ending.

12.   What are the three criteria discussed in your textbook for assessing the soundness of documents found on the Internet?

    a.   length, accuracy, and graphics
    b.   interactivity, objectivity, and authorship
    c.   graphics, sponsorship, and accuracy
    d.   creativity, reliability, and length
    e.   authorship, sponsorship, and recency

13.   What does your textbook say about eye contact for public speakers who address audiences in the United States?

    a.   To appear credible and trustworthy, a speaker should gaze intently at one section of the audience.
    b.   In classroom speeches, it is most important to maintain steady eye contact with the instructor.
    c.   Speakers should look at the audience about 80 to 90 percent of the time they are talking.
    d.   Speakers who establish strong eye contact with the audience lose credibility as a result.
    e.   Even with a large audience, engaging the eyes of each person is preferable to scanning the audience in general.

14.   Rosalie will be giving a persuasive speech on organ donation and wants to distribute organ-donor cards to her listeners. When should she distribute the cards?

    a.   before she starts the speech
    b.   after she reveals the topic in her introduction
    c.   while telling how organ-donor cards work during the body of the speech
    d.   while urging her audience to take action during the conclusion of the speech
    e.   after she has finished speaking

15.   According to your textbook, _____ plagiarism occurs when the speech as a whole is ethical but the speaker fails to give credit for particular quotations and paraphrases.

    a.   incidental
    b.   informative
    c.   inferential
    d.   invalid
    e.   incremental

16. Research indicates that the impact of examples is greatly enhanced when they are followed by _____ that show the examples to be typical.

    a. analogies
    b. syllogisms
    c. credibility statements
    d. emotional appeals
    e. statistics

17. What error in reasoning is exemplified by the following statement?

    French movies are all dull. I saw three of them last semester in my film class and couldn't stay awake through a single one.

    a. false cause
    b. faulty deduction
    c. invalid analogy
    d. hasty generalization
    e. circular thinking

18. According to your textbook, when selecting fonts for a visual aid you should usually use

    a. a wide variety of fonts.
    b. decorative fonts.
    c. a different font for each line.
    d. italicized fonts.
    e. no more than two fonts.

19. Arranged in random order below are a main point, two subpoints, and two sub-subpoints from a speech preparation outline. Which is the main point?

    a. The largest members of the hawk family are Old World vultures.
    b. Raptors are powerful birds of prey with hooked beaks and sharp talons.
    c. Among Falconiformes, the hawk family is the largest and most diverse.
    d. The hawk family includes eagles, hawks, kites, harriers, and vultures.
    e. There are two orders of Raptors—Falconiformes and Strigiformes.

20. Because it follows the process of human thinking, _____ is particularly useful for organizing persuasive speeches that seek immediate action.

    a. Mitchell's strategic progression
    b. comparative advantages order
    c. Monroe's motivated sequence
    d. problem-cause-solution order
    e. Morgan's psychological series

## Part II   Short Answer   (10 points)

*Answer each of the following questions in the space provided.*

21.    The following main points are arranged in _____ order.

    I.   The raised right arm and torch of the Statue of Liberty symbolize America's role as a beacon light of liberty to people the world over.

    II.  The body of the Statue of Liberty is lined with staircases, which give a good view of the inside contours.

    III. The base of the Statue of Liberty contains a plaque with the poignant lines beginning "Give me your tired, your poor . . . ."

22.    "To persuade my audience that our state should impose stricter regulations governing the safety of amusement park rides" is a specific purpose statement for a persuasive speech on a question of _____.

23.    Mental imaging in which a speaker vividly pictures himself or herself giving a successful presentation is called _____.

24.    According to your textbook, when is it appropriate to cite an abstract of a magazine or journal article in your speech rather than locating and reading the full article?

_____

25.    According to your textbook, the following statement is an example of the _____ fallacy

    I think the governor has excellent ideas for prison reform. After all, polls show that 70 percent of the state supports his position.

26.    The belief that one's own group or culture is superior to all other groups or cultures is termed _____.

27.    What is wrong with the following specific purpose statement for an informative speech? Rewrite the statement to conform with the criteria given in your textbook for effective specific purpose statements.

Ineffective
   Specific Purpose:                    The major beliefs of the Baha'i religion.

Error:

More Effective
   Specific Purpose:

28.   The similar arrangement of a pair or series of related words is a language device called _____.

29.   The following main points are arranged in _____ order.

     I.    The first major type of environmental pollution is land pollution.
    II.   The second major type of environmental pollution is air pollution.
   III.  The third major type of environmental pollution is water pollution.

30.   State the specific purpose for the speech on environmental pollution whose main points are expressed in question 29:

    _____

    _____

## Part III   Short Essay   (30 points)

*Answer <u>five</u> of the following in your blue book. Each answer should take no more than a page. Be sure, in each case, to illustrate your answer with an example.*

31.   What does it mean to say that people are egocentric? What implications does the egocentrism of audiences have for you as a speaker?

32.   If a picture is worth a thousand words, why should a speaker worry about explaining visual aids to the audience?

33.   Explain the following statement: "When you present a persuasive speech, you should think of yourself as engaged in a mental dialogue with the audience."

34.   Why is determining the specific purpose such a vital step in the process of preparing a speech?

35.    Briefly explain the following statement: "Public speaking is a form of power and therefore carries with it heavy ethical responsibilities."

36.    Explain the following statement: "On most occasions when we are looking for 'just the right word,' what we are really looking for is just the right idea."

## Part IV   Long Essay   (40 points)

*Answer <u>both</u> of the following questions in your blue book.*

37.    What are the three major kinds of supporting materials used in public speeches? Evaluate the use of supporting materials in the following speech excerpt. Be sure to deal with *all* the supporting materials in each paragraph, and *be specific* in assessing their strengths and weaknesses.

> Wetlands include swamps, marshes, lakes, any area that is full of water. In addition to providing habitat for thousands of different animals, wetlands are a major barrier to the damage caused by the flooding of lakes and rivers. According to William Niering, "Because they hold water like sponges, wetlands prolong and moderate runoff after heavy precipitation or snow melt. Without wetlands, floods would ravage the American landscape."

> Wetlands also help protect the quality of America's water supply. Mark Christianson, a lobbyist for environmental issues, stated in the *Nebraska Law Review* that "Filtration of pollution is one of the most valuable functions of wetlands. Wetlands can recycle amazing amounts of polluted water."

> Yet despite their many benefits, America's wetlands are being destroyed by business interests and urban sprawl. Imagine a canteen full of water. This canteen could provide almost a week's worth of refreshment in a hot desert. But what if there was a small hole in the canteen? Then the water might last just five days, or four, or maybe just two. This is what is happening to America's wetlands. More than 11 million acres of American wetlands—an expanse twice the size of New Jersey—have been drained in the past three decades. Ten times that amount have been lost since the Pilgrims arrived. Environmentalists report that today we are losing wetlands at an average rate of 458,246 acres each year. The hole in the canteen is dripping.

38. What are the requirements of a good speech introduction?  Evaluate the following complete introduction to a classroom speech in light of those requirements.  Be specific in your answer.

> Remember the opening scene in *Raiders of the Lost Ark*? Indiana Jones enters an ancient cave, hidden deep within the jungle. After facing deadly traps of all kinds and spiders as big as your fist, he emerges from the cave with a solid gold idol of a human head.
>
> Last year a golden head similar to that one was actually found in South America. Of course, there were no traps, no spiders, and certainly no Indiana Jones. But to its discoverers, this find was more exciting than any movie because this golden head was no film prop. It was the genuine article.
>
> This object of pure gold was only one of many treasures found during last year's archaeological excavation of an ancient tomb of the long-vanished Moche civilization of ancient Peru. Today, based on my research, I would like to tell you what is known about the history of the Moche civilization. Then I want to explain how recent excavations have made the Moche a hot topic for today's anthropologists.

---

# Answers to Parts I and II of
# Second Sample Final Exam

## Part I

| | | | | | | |
|---|---|---|---|---|---|---|
| 1. | d | (Chapter 15) | 11. | d | (Chapter 9) |
| 2. | d | (Chapter 1) | 12. | e | (Chapter 6) |
| 3. | c | (Chapter 6) | 13. | c | (Chapter 12) |
| 4. | b | (Chapter 16) | 14. | e | (Chapter 13) |
| 5. | a | (Chapter 11) | 15. | e | (Chapter 2) |
| 6. | d | (Chapter 8) | 16. | e | (Chapter 7) |
| 7. | e | (Chapter 2) | 17. | d | (Chapter 16) |
| 8. | e | (Chapter 14) | 18. | e | (Chapter 13) |
| 9. | e | (Chapter 5) | 19. | b | (Chapter 10) |
| 10. | b | (Chapter 16) | 20. | c | (Chapter 15) |

## Part II

21. spatial   (Chapter 8)

22. policy   (Chapter 15)

23. visualization   (Chapter 1)

24. One should never cite an article in a speech on the basis of the abstract alone.   (Chapter 6)

25. bandwagon   (Chapter 16)

26. ethnocentrism   (Chapter 1)

27. Error:  Written as a fragment, not as a full sentence.

    Specific Purpose:     To inform my audience about the major beliefs of the Baha'i religion.   (Chapter 4)

28. parallelism   (Chapter 11)

29. topical   (Chapter 8)

30. To inform my audience about the three major types of environmental pollution. (Chapter 8)

# Public Speaking
# Final Examination

Your assignment is to analyze the accompanying speech and to answer a series of questions about it.

The speech was presented by a student at the University of Wisconsin to her public speaking class.

In analyzing the speech, you should draw upon any appropriate materials read or discussed in your class this term.

Answer *all* the questions about the speech clearly, concisely, and in full sentences. Your answers should be precise, specific, and supported with appropriate quotations from the speech or by reference to line number.

The most effective way to use your time is probably to spend roughly the first half of the exam period analyzing the speech and working out preliminary answers to the questions, and to spend the second half entering final answers in your blue book. But however you divide your time, you should be sure to analyze the *whole* speech carefully and thoroughly in light of *all* the examination questions *before* you attempt to fill in your blue book.

The examination questions are on the other side of this sheet.

When you have completed the examination, give to your instructor your blue book, the speech, the examination instructions, and your scratch paper.

## Examination Questions

1.    Following the guidelines given in the textbook, state the specific purpose of "The Dangers of Chewing Tobacco." Also following the guidelines in the textbook, state the central idea of "The Dangers of Chewing Tobacco." Identify the method of organization used in the speech. Write in full sentences the main points in the body of the speech. (10 points)

2.    What are the objectives of a good speech introduction? Identify by line number where the introduction of "The Dangers of Chewing Tobacco" begins and ends. How well does it fulfill the objectives of a good speech introduction? Support your answer by referring to specific passages of the introduction. (15 points)

3.    What are the three basic types of supporting materials used in public speaking? Evaluate the speaker's use of *all three* kinds of supporting materials in lines 23–60 of "The Dangers of Chewing Tobacco." Support your answer by reference to specific passages in the speech. (30 points)

4.    What is the need issue in a persuasive speech on a question of policy? What is the plan issue? What is the practicality issue? Why is it important for a speaker to deal with all three in a persuasive speech on a question of policy? Which issues does the speaker deal with in lines 61–85? Assess how effectively the speaker deals with these issues. Be specific and support your answer by reference to specific line numbers and/or passages in lines 61–85. (20 points)

5.    What is a transition? What is a signpost? Why is the skillful use of these and other connectives important to effective public speaking? Identify by line number *two* places where the speaker uses a transition in the body of "The Dangers of Chewing Tobacco." Identify by line number *two* places in the body where she uses signposts. (10 points)

6.    Explain why audience analysis and adaptation are so important to effective public speaking. How well does the speaker relate "The Dangers of Chewing Tobacco" to the attitudes and experiences of her listeners? Illustrate your answer by reference to specific passages in the speech. (15 points)

# The Dangers of Chewing Tobacco

1  On March 30, Tom, a 23-year-old man from northern Wisconsin, went in for his yearly
2  dental checkup. As far as he could tell, there were no real problems except maybe the one or
3  two usual cavities that the dentist always seems to find. The dentist began poking around at
4  Tom's teeth, but soon became more interested in Tom's lower lip and gums. The dentist
5  noticed an unusual growth on Tom's lower lip and asked if Tom was a regular user of
6  chewing tobacco. Tom answered yes.

7      After a series of tests, Tom was diagnosed as having a deadly type of oral cancer. Just one
8  week after Tom's dental checkup, he had surgery to remove the cancer. This photograph
9  shows Tom after his surgery. [At this point, the speaker displayed an enlarged color
10  photograph showing what Tom looked like after surgery.] As you can see, a large portion of
11  Tom's lower lip was removed and the area was drawn together by stitches. The surgery left
12  Tom disfigured and looking quite grotesque, but it was not the worst part. Tom died just one
13  month later. Chewing tobacco caused Tom's death.

14      Due to the fact that I am currently studying to be a dentist, and because my father is a
15  dentist and I have worked for him as an assistant for over four years, I have actually seen
16  cases similar to Tom's which result from chewing tobacco. I have also attended a number of
17  seminars on this topic, and today I'd like to persuade each of you to feel as strongly as I do
18  about the dangers of chewing tobacco.

19      In my speech, I'd like to show you the many problems that can result from chewing
20  tobacco. Then I'd like to persuade each of you to take action and help change the lenient laws
21  governing the use of chewing tobacco in our society. Let's begin by looking at how
22  widespread the problem of chewing tobacco really is.

23      Chewing tobacco is more common than you may think. According to the American Cancer
24  Society, one in every twelve Americans is a regular user of chewing tobacco. The average
25  age of first use is just ten years old, which means that many children are chewing tobacco
26  when they are in fourth grade. The American Cancer Society also reports that 40 percent of
27  high school boys have tried chewing tobacco—and, what's worse, 21 percent of kinder-
28  gartners have tried it. Children are using chewing tobacco before they can even read the
29  warning labels!

30      Now you know that chewing tobacco is widespread, but you may wonder what could
31  possibly happen when a person uses chewing tobacco. Well, smokeless tobacco has multiple
32  dangers according to the American Dental Association and the American Cancer Society.
33  First, tooth decay and tooth loss can occur. Chewing tobacco contains grit and sand, which
34  wear away at the teeth. It also contains added sugars to improve the taste—but they also wear
35  away at the teeth, leading to cavities and tooth loss.

36      Another effect of chewing tobacco is gum disease. Regular use of chewing tobacco causes
37  visual gum damage in less than two to three months. According to the American Dental
38  Association, about half of all teenage users have some type of gum problem. But what's
39  wrong with gum disease? Well, it causes the gums to pull away from the teeth, which further
40  increases the risk of tooth decay and loss.

41      Gum disease and tooth loss are serious enough, but as we saw at the beginning in the story
42  about Tom, chewing tobacco can have most serious consequences. According to the American
43  Dental Association, those who use chewing tobacco just once in a while have four times the

44  risk of developing oral cancer than do nonusers. And if that isn't bad enough, those who use
45  chewing tobacco three or more times a week for over a year have fifty times the risk of
46  developing cancer than do nonusers. This risk is even greater than that of smoking cigarettes.
47  But unlike smoking cigarettes, where cancer develops slowly over time, chewing tobacco can
48  cause cancer in teens and young adults.

49  For example, Sean Marsee, a 19-year-old high school student from Oklahoma, was one of
50  the most well-liked students in his senior class. Sean used chewing tobacco from age 12 to age
51  18, when he was diagnosed as having oral cancer during his senior year in high school. As a
52  result, Sean had to have a series of disfiguring operations. First three-fourths of his tongue
53  was removed. Then all the muscles and lymph nodes on the right side of Sean's face and neck
54  were removed. And lastly his jawbone was removed from her to here. As you can imagine,
55  Sean was left looking quite grotesque. But this was not the worst part. As extreme as the
56  surgery was, it could not stop Sean's cancer from spreading, and he died just one year later.
57  There can be no doubt that chewing tobacco caused Sean's death.

58  I know this is a terrible thought, but the point I'm trying to make is an important one. You
59  must be aware of the terrible consequences of chewing tobacco because next time it could
60  happen to you or to someone you love.

61  Let's look, then, at what can be done to diminish the use of chewing tobacco. First, the
62  laws in Wisconsin pertaining to the age at which chewing tobacco can be bought must be
63  strengthened. The law in Wisconsin states that chewing tobacco can be purchased at age
64  eighteen, but according to the Department of Law Enforcement, the laws on chewing tobacco
65  sales have been ineffective. To be effective, the laws must be enforced and have adequate
66  penalties.

67  A number of other states, including California, set the fine for selling chewing tobacco to
68  minors at $1,500 for the first offense and $6,000 for the second offense. According to the
69  American Dental Association, this law has cut the use of chewing tobacco by minors by
70  almost 60 percent. I would like you to help pass a law resembling this in Wisconsin. You
71  must help stop people from selling cancer to our children. You can make a difference. You
72  can write to our legislators urging that a bill like this be created here in Wisconsin.

73  Second, use of chewing tobacco during all professional sporting events should be banned.
74  According to the American Dental Association, the primary reason children develop an
75  interest in chewing tobacco is because they see their role models doing it. These role models
76  include parents, relatives, and friends, but more importantly, they include sports stars.
77  Children see athletes as role models. Children think if it's all right for athletes to use chewing
78  tobacco, it must be all right for me to do it too. If these role models would stand up and say
79  chewing is wrong, many of our children would change their minds about the drug.

80  What we need, then, is a ban on chewing tobacco use during professional sporting events.
81  You may think this is impractical, but already one baseball team, the Kansas City Royals, has
82  taken a stand. They have switched from chewing tobacco to bubble gum. You can help
83  influence other teams to do the same. I urge you to write to your favorite team or to your
84  favorite athlete urging them, individually or as a team, to take a stand against chewing
85  tobacco as the Royals did.

86  In conclusion, then, I am pleading with each of you to take action against the use of
87  chewing tobacco. When you think of this subject, remember the problems of chewing
88  tobacco. Remember Tom—and remember Sean. By adopting the measures I have discussed
89  today, you can help stop what happened to Tom and Sean from happening to others.

## Notes on Third Sample Final Exam

The speech used for this exam—"The Dangers of Chewing Tobacco"—is also available in Part V of the *Instructor's Manual*. I have used it here to show how the speeches in Part V of the manual can be adapted for use with this exam format. A different speech would require some changes in the exam questions.

Regardless of which speech you use for this exam, it is important to provide line numbers that students can refer to in their answers. It is also less cumbersome if you print the speech so it will fit on both sides of a single page.

Because the exam contains six questions, I have assigned each question a different number of points depending on the difficulty of the question and the amount of time it should take students to answer. When administering the exam, be sure to point this out to students so they can apportion their time accordingly.

For full discussion of "The Dangers of Chewing Tobacco," see the commentary that follows the speech in Part V of the *Instructor's Manual*.

# – NOTES –

# – NOTES –

# – NOTES –

– NOTES –